On the Rugged Plains of North Dakota They Have Always Had To Grow Their Own Doctors

North Dakota, Heal Thyself

The story of The First Hundred Years at
The School of Medicine and Health Sciences,
The University of North Dakota

1905-2005

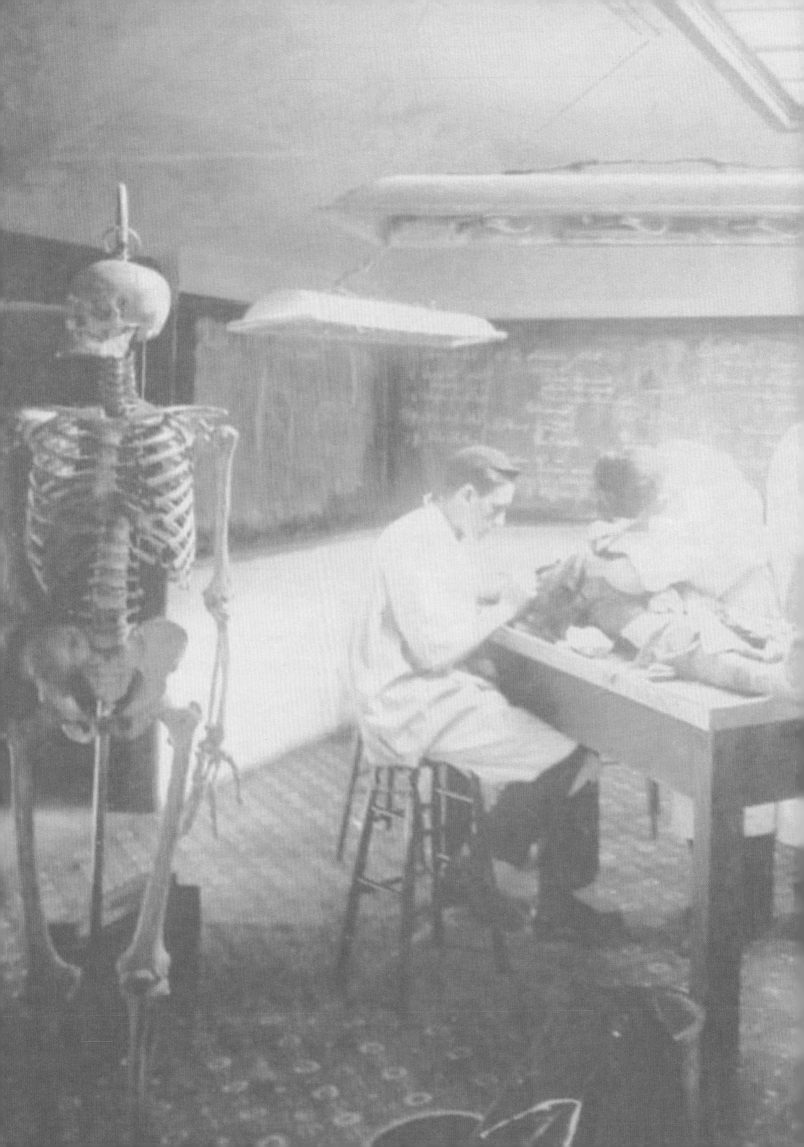

On the Rugged Plains of North Dakota They Have Always Had To Grow Their Own Doctors

North Dakota, Heal Thyself

The story of The First Hundred Years at
The School of Medicine and Health Sciences,
The University of North Dakota

1905-2005

By John W. Vennes, Ph.D. & Patrick A. McGuire

Library of Congress Cataloging in Publication Data
has been applied for.

ISBN 0-9769614-0-7

Printed in the United States of America.

CONTENTS

Everywhere the old order changes
and happy are they who can change with it.

Sir William Osler, 1895,
"Father of American Medicine"

This book is dedicated to all past and present deans, faculty, staff and students who contributed measurably to the mission of the School of Medicine and Health Sciences and to those university administrators who acted on behalf of the school. A special recognition is given to the physician faculty and hospitals in the state who made the training of medical students and residents a reality. The book is also dedicated to the many legislators and citizens of North Dakota who vigorously supported the school over the past 100 years.

Shortly after I was appointed dean in 1995, I met with local news reporters to outline my goals and hopes for the School of Medicine. I remember emphasizing the credo behind the founding of this school in 1905 — the long venerated truth I had become familiar with during my interviews and research.

If the citizens of the state wanted doctors to settle here, went this maxim, they pretty much had to grow their own. That was a mission, I told the press, that I believed in and intended to carry out with vigor. I was a bit taken aback, though, when I saw the headline above the story about my remarks in the next day's *Grand Forks Herald*:

North Dakota, Heal Thyself

Of course, that play on the Biblical "Physician, Heal Thyself" sums up beautifully the philosophy behind this unique medical school. One hundred years ago it was difficult, at best, to recruit doctors — qualified or not — to what was unfairly judged a remote and undesirable outpost without much of a future. The movement that led to the founding of this school recognized that even a two-year medical school would shift the odds dramatically in favor of getting more doctors to settle in North Dakota and guarantee a future worth working toward.

Reading that headline my second morning on the job, I realized I had issued myself a challenge from which there was no backing away. I had spoken the sacred words and the headline writer was going to hold me to it. Fair enough, for I have never considered straying from that most worthy mission. The graduation and retention of qualified doctors from this medical school to serve the citizens of this state is the reason this institution was started one hundred years ago. Today, it remains the primary mission of the School of Medicine and Health Sciences at the University of North Dakota. Further, I can report with pride that nearly half of all doctors practicing in the state today are graduates of this school.

Pride, by the way, is awfully easy to develop here, for in spite of having the smallest full-time faculty of all one-hundred-twenty-five medical schools in the United States, our dedicated professors and staff manage to turn out bright, humane doctors whose scores rank in the top quarter of the scores of all of those schools. I'm extremely proud of our faculty, students and staff who make this such a special place. Ours is a remarkable family of educators, including renowned scientists and researchers, clinical experts in all major disciplines, and a large number of dedicated North Dakota physicians who volunteer to take our students into their practices and share their patients and their skills.

I'm truly honored to be the dean of this "gem" of a medical school and, like all the deans before me, I hope to leave it stronger for the next leader to build upon. Yet, often I sense that our inspiring story — full of characters, drama, risks taken and ground gained over a century of sacrifice and hard-fought progress — is only partially understood by North Dakotans.

With our centennial observance on the horizon, I thought it a wholly fitting time to help our citizens recall and celebrate the deeds of those who went before us and who laid the groundwork for our ability today to send excellent medical professionals out into our daily lives.

About four years ago I asked Dr. John Vennes, Ph.D., my good friend, colleague and hunting partner, to begin work on a history of the School of Medicine and Health Sciences. Dr. Vennes, a dedicated scientist and a man who has shown great skill and compassion as an administrator here over a most distinguished career, was the perfect choice. Since coming to the university just after World War II, Dr. Vennes has maintained a professional relationship with almost every person of note across the decades of this medical school's existence.

He knew and worked with the great Dr. Harley French, whose tenure as perhaps the most important dean in the school's history began in 1911, six years after the school was founded. Dr. Vennes also developed a close relationship with Dr. Art Saiki, M.D., an early UND grad hired by

Harley French and beloved by his students and colleagues. He knew him well enough to deliver the eulogy at his funeral.

There are many other important names associated with this school's impressive past and present — Tom Johnson, Gene Cornatzer, Ed James, Tom Clifford, Sharon Wilsnack, Bob Nordlie, Judy DeMers, Randy Eken, Lee Christoferson, Sr., Mary Wakefield, Manuchair Ebadi, to name a few — with whom Dr. Vennes has worked and shared counsel. In fact, of the twelve deans who have served this school on a full-time or an interim basis in the past century, John Vennes has known and served nine of them. Technically it's ten, because for two years, he served as interim dean himself. For his unselfish loyalty and commitment, he was honored by the university with its highest tributes, the Sioux Award, an honorary degree, and the President's Medal.

Over the past four years, John has been busy interviewing scores of luminaries who have graced our medical school — past and present faculty, alumni, administrators, community leaders — and has amassed a library of nearly one hundred videotaped conversations. In recent years his enthusiasm for this project has made him a familiar face in our community with his fascinating PowerPoint history of the medical school, "Some Light on the Past."

Of course, a centennial celebration is an ideal and obvious time to summon up fond memories of the past. But it is also an essential exercise that light be shed on the people and events that helped to make us what and who we are today. Every citizen of this state deserves to know and appreciate the full story of what our medical pioneers and their successors have accomplished. Their story inspires and reaffirms our values as citizens of the great Northern Plains and caring members of the human family.

At the same time, all North Dakotans deserve to experience a measure of pride at what they have achieved through their hard-earned tax dollars, their political sensitivity to healthcare issues, and their faith in the system. Perhaps the most gratifying act of faith undertaken in the last hundred years by our visionary citizens was the overwhelming voter approval in 1947 of a separate mill levy whose proceeds go directly to support of the School of Medicine. Those funds, which have assisted the school for more than fifty years, represent the renewal of the vow of 1905 that, indeed, North Dakotans must heal themselves through their own medical school.

After John had finished his work, we discussed what to call this book. It seemed to both of us that the title should reflect as much of that courage and spirit and indomitable will of our ancestors as possible. At the same time, we wanted to get across to those unfamiliar with our story the nature of the challenge faced by all in making North Dakota a healthy place to raise a family.

I recounted for John the story of that first press conference, and within moments we were both in agreement that we'd found the title: challenge stated, challenge met. Welcome to "North Dakota, Heal Thyself."

That this School of Medicine has lived up to its historical mandate and social challenge will be apparent to any who venture between the covers of this lively narrative of the past hundred years. No academic treatise, this, but a story accessible to all — including myself. Imagine my surprise when I read that the very first dean of this school, Dr. Brannon, and I graduated from the same small, but outstanding, college in Indiana — Wabash College in Crawfordsville — he in 1889 and I, seventy-eight years later, in 1961.

So, I invite you to read on and to celebrate with all of us at the School of Medicine and Health Sciences of the University of North Dakota not only our hard-earned past but also the bright future those dusty days of healing have earned for us all.

H. David Wilson, M.D.
Grand Forks, 2005

I came to the University of North Dakota as a young man from the rural northwestern corner of the state. Largely by chance I chose microbiology to become my life's work.

My greatest enjoyment in the early years as a graduate student learning new science information was working with professors who were dedicated to the success of all students. There is little doubt that this school's faculty always has focused on the needs of students, yet demanded excellence, as in: "If you don't do the work, you don't get the grade."

Reflecting on students I've seen since joining the faculty in 1952, I think of a combination of things. Those who came here had the ability to complete a basic science course and do well at any medical school in the country. However, often they wouldn't have had the opportunity to enroll elsewhere because of the stiff competition at other medical schools and other state's residency requirements. In case after case, if it hadn't been for this medical school (a two-year program from 1905-1975; four years with residency training ever since) those students wouldn't have become doctors at all.

Additionally, the students brought with them a particular work ethic. They took it for granted that transferring after two years meant they'd better achieve. A common statement I heard after completing their medical degree elsewhere was, "I was surprised when our professor of neuroscience asked, 'Where did you learn your anatomy?'" It became a standard compliment.

The need to compete at a four-year school and the culture shock of going from rural North Dakota, say, to Boston and Harvard was all they needed to make damn sure they did well. And they did.

I attended the University of Michigan in 1954 since UND's medical school had no Ph.D. program at that time. I had won their graduate research award and was presenting my first research paper in Houston, Texas, when a number of people asked where I planned to go after I finished my degree. I said I was going back to North Dakota — it was a given. It never crossed my mind that I would do otherwise.

Not only was this my home, but the state and the University had served me well by providing me with a high-quality, low-cost education. At the time I went to Michigan, the dean of the UND medical school, Dr. Ted Harwood, was interested enough in my career that he scrounged together some funds to help pay my tuition. I returned to North Dakota not because I felt I owed him something — which I surely did feel — but because of that faith he had placed in me. In this brief life, it's not enough to simply go where the opportunities are; one must go where the faith is strong and the light is bright.

It's good, of course, to occasionally shine some of that light into areas that don't get enough of it. Over the years I've spent at the University I've learned that the citizens of this state yearn for opportunities to invest their taxes in public institutions we can all be proud of. Our frugality might be legend, but I believe that people in North Dakota are always ready to support works that truly benefit the state, and it has long occurred to me that our medical school is certainly one of those. It is an institution that impacts just about everyone and therefore one with which everyone tends to identify. It is also an institution, unfortunately, that doesn't always get enough light.

I suspect I had such thoughts on my mind when David Wilson asked to see me. He'd just been appointed dean of the medical school in 1995 and perhaps he felt: "Here's this old guy who's been around. He must have some information." We struck up a relationship and over the years have become good friends, sharing regular morning coffee and yearly wild turkey hunts.

His suggestion that I work on a one-hundred-year history of the School of Medicine and Health Sciences to coincide with our centennial celebration resonated with me. I've long been a student of our local history and feel it is important that the stories and issues facing our leaders of yesterday not be forgotten. Clearly, evidence of our past is useful information. It can inspire, surprise and serve as a model for what or what not to do in the future.

Fortunately, the story of this school of medicine has many positive lessons whose undeniable truths still point the way into our next century. The most obvious lesson is the determination of our predecessors to stay the course in the face of upheaval and, even more important, to persevere in spite of myriad difficulties that so often disrupted their personal and professional lives.

Rather surprisingly, another lesson came to light during my research. In the first ninety years of this medical school, we had essentially a Flexnerion curriculum. This is a system based on the tried and true (but sometimes boring) method of two solid years of static lecturing to students before they engage in clinical studies. In those same ninety years there existed two cultures at the medical school. One was that of the basic scientists (including myself) who were not always mentors for medical students, even though they taught them. The second was that of the clinical faculty, the medical doctors who were obviously mentors.

David Wilson not only modernized the curriculum — turning it into a dynamic hands-on experience that leaves little room for boredom — but he has brought those two often disparate cultures together. Our new system depends on spirited team cooperation of scientists, clinicians and students — one culture with one mission — and it's working extremely well. One might even say it's making history here. David has not only attracted people to the school who have created basic science departments as good as they ever have been, he's also tried — and it's not easy — to attract research activity in the clinical departments. He's an extraordinary academic, a pragmatic intellectual who knows how to make things happen. He's been a winner.

His story and the stories of dozens of other selfless teachers, doctors, professors, scientists, students and citizens of North Dakota make up this history that most certainly deserves celebration.

A word about the writing style of this book: David and I thought that the best way to shine light on the coming of age of our wonderful institution was to present it in a highly readable, accessible format and to avoid a more formal academic approach or a dry recitation of names and dates and tenures. That's why we enlisted the help of Patrick McGuire, a long-time newspaper journalist with strong ties to the medical school and North Dakota. The arrangement Pat and I worked out was that he would create the narrative based on our interviews and tell the story in the third person, using a reportorial style. It gives the story a more "objective" feel and spares me (and you) an awkward litany of my own exploits, such as they were, from days gone by.

John W. Vennes, Ph.D.
Grand Forks, 2005

Chapter 1

CHAPTER ONE

The Trail Blazer

The sun had just gone down that April evening in 1894 when a train from Minneapolis rolled into a tiny matchbox of a station two miles west of the city of Grand Forks. The sign on the red wooden shed read simply, "University."

A prim, Victorian bachelor with starched collar, neatly trimmed Vandyke and the haunted eyes of a teacher of the Greek classics watched as the train slid to a stop. His name was Webster Merrifield, a Yale man who for the past three years had held the office of president of the University of North Dakota. It was not an enviable job.

The entire university consisted of three buildings — one of them a barn where the janitor kept his horse and cow and where the biology department raised frogs. All three buildings stood in a field directly behind Merrifield, reachable by negotiating a series of planks laid across the mud. You couldn't see anything in the gathering dusk, only the faint glow of kerosene lamps in the distance.

Indeed, dark was an appropriate mood that evening. In the bitter competition for public funding since statehood four years earlier, Merrifield's university was dead last behind a pair of normal schools in Mayville and Valley City and, the darling of the legislature, the agricultural school in Fargo. The country, meanwhile, was in the middle of a depression caused by the Panic of 1893. Money was scarce and drought on the Northern Plains had kept wheat production below average for

Previous page:

The future dean
Melvin A. Brannon leads a science class at the University of North Dakota in 1903, two years before he founded the School of Medicine and became its first dean.

some time. State warrants paying the faculty at the university could not be cashed without the bearer accepting a ten to fifteen percent gouge. In less than a year, the legislature would cut off all funds for the university. In his darkest moments, Merrifield wondered if the ten-year-old institution was not doomed. Many fully expected it to simply dry up and blow away.

Perhaps, though, he had an inkling that night of better things to come. Not that the man he was waiting to welcome to North Dakota — an unheralded high school teacher of natural science from Fort Wayne, Indiana — looked or sounded to most people like anything special. But Merrifield was a shrewd judge of character, and when the head of his biology department resigned, it was to this young man now stepping off the train that he had reached out.

"Brannon," said the young man, grasping the hand extended to him.

"Merrifield," replied the president, eyeing him carefully. He looked hungry and Merrifield liked that. He was an unusually farseeing man, but could even he have suspected that in only nine years this young scientist would become the founding dean of the University's School of Medicine?

Years later, Brannon would record his first impressions of the university as he walked the planks into darkness behind Merrifield. When he awoke the next morning and had a chance to study his surroundings more closely, he discovered that he was standing in the center of a twenty- acre plot of ground bordered by wooden fences that held off the encroachment of wheat in all directions. The university itself he described as "possessing only an apology of a physical plant.... A few promising toothpick-like cottonwood and elm trees had been encouraged to grow on either side of a curving drive. This barren and almost treeless campus was separated from the city of Grand Forks by two miles of open country." He hadn't yet heard about the little problem of getting his paycheck cashed, but when he did, he recalled, "The net result of those operating factors was tremendously depressing."

If these were second thoughts about his career shift west, they did not show in the energy and enterprise he immediately displayed in his work. Almost from the moment he stepped off that train, Brannon immersed himself in a series of public health crises. His solutions would not only save many lives, they would prove the university to be indispensable, and endow Merrifield with enough political capital to get things done.

Brannon was not simply a teacher of natural science. His specialty was bacteriology whose modern-day equivalent is the exacting science of microbiology. Not only was Brannon good at what he did, he also was a visionary. He embraced the very latest theories from Europe that linked microorganisms or germs to disease. He also believed in the necessity of sanitation and was a strong supporter of public health measures.

To many citizens in the last decade of the Nineteenth century, the idea of germs and bacteriology was a newfangled concept. A lackluster American scientific community and a dangerously incompetent medical-education system had choked off the growth of hard sciences. An inordinate amount of the history of American medical thought throughout the century records the cross-pollination of bad science and quackery.

In fact, it was a time when rational thought — literally, Rationalism — had been supplanted by the philosophy of Romanticism, which suggested that the arbiters of life's mysteries should be the spirit and emotions rather than the mind and logical thought. These conflicting philosophies might simply have been topics for an existential debate if it had not been for their influence on medicine.

During this Romantic age in the first part of the Nineteenth century, homeopathic treatments had become very popular, based on the notion that what ailed you was what also would cure you. By ingesting watered-down portions of certain natural substances, a patient could somehow counteract the poisonous effect of already having ingested too much of the same substance. Disease, under this philosophy, was caused by spiritual weaknesses and affected the emotions while showing itself through physical symptoms. Homeopathy was just one of many unconventional approaches to healing that sprang up, along with faith healing, phrenology, osteopathy and mechanical manipulation of the body.

Ironically, the conventional approaches that rational medical people had produced up until then, while grounded in the best intellectual thought of the day, were just as bizarre by today's standard. For instance, Benjamin Rush, who is thought by most medical historians to have been the nation's leading doctor in the late Eighteenth century, was a proponent of something known as heroic medicine. An aggressive form of treatment, it held that illness was caused by an overabundance of liquids within the body. The best way to alleviate symptoms was to get rid of the excess. Its two most common forms were the draining of blood and the use of chemicals to purge the digestive system.

That is what Rush advocated during the awful outbreak of yellow

Melvin A. Brannon

Brannon, a pioneer in bacteriology, resolved several local health crises in North Dakota involving contaminated public water supplies.

fever in Philadelphia in 1793. Some claim that when George Washington died five years later at Mount Vernon, it was because the loss of blood during one of those heroic healing procedures sent his body into catastrophic shock. Even so, it was not long afterward that Meriwether Lewis and William Clark were carefully instructed in similar methods before embarking on their epic adventure through the unexplored lands of the Louisiana Purchase. In 1805, for example, Clark noted in his journal "Sah-cah-gah-wea our Indian woman is very sick this evening. I blead her." (Sakakawea, as she is remembered today, was the teenage Shoshone woman captured by the Hidatsa and later given to a French explorer named Charbonneau. He was hired as an interpreter by Lewis and Clark at Fort Mandan, in present-day North Dakota. They asked that Sakakawea accompany them on their exploration.)

The public eventually grew tired of the aggression enacted on their bodies and longed for a less heroic, gentler form of medical treatment. The new ideas of Romanticism were taking shape when the pugnacious and under-educated Andrew Jackson became president; he seemed to embody a desire for a wilder, freer, more sensation-based approach to life. Homeopathic medicine was the perfect companion to the times, as were cures based on religion or electricity or the manipulation of bones in the head and spine. Though they often were branded as fakery, these treatments appealed to many. Oddly enough, scientists began to borrow bits and pieces of these alternative approaches, and the holistic practitioners borrowed from science or made claims that science backed their approach. The result was a mishmash that rendered the quality of medicine in the first half of the Nineteenth century extremely low or, at the very least, dangerously inconsistent.

While scores of medical schools opened for business in the middle of the century — some even affiliated with universities — their standards were all over the map. Most medical schools were proprietary, meaning they were primarily set up to make money. In many of them, attendance at medical lectures was open to whoever could pay the price of a ticket. Thus, association with a university was not necessarily a guarantee of credibility. Rarely was there a requirement that medical students need have any education prior to admission — even the ability to read or write. The idea of enforcing a set of educational standards was unpopular because it was feared that students who found one school too difficult would drop out and pay their money to an easier school.

Many schools had no laboratories. Often they were simply

rented halls taken over temporarily by local doctors who may or may not have had a practice. Students had little if any clinical experience in these early medical schools, as most states refused to allow dissection of human cadavers. Few of them required graduates of medical schools to be licensed in order to become doctors. In fact, many students never actually graduated; they simply attended a series of lectures over a period of a few months and were granted their diplomas even before they took any examination — and exams were not always required.

Not until the formation of the American Medical Association in 1847 did the idea of requiring basic standards of admission and curriculum in medical schools gain currency. North Dakota became one of the first states to set standards on the licensing of doctors. Perhaps because the first governor of the Dakota Territory was a practicing physician — William Jayne of Illinois — the territorial legislature enacted in 1869 a code that required a doctor to show evidence of having studied two full courses of instruction, plus graduation "from some school of medicine."

It was a modest requirement that would evolve over the next twenty-five years into one of the strictest such laws in the nation. It demonstrated that the notion of safeguarding public health was gaining ground. In fact, in the mid-Nineteenth century, theories about the cause of disease, most originating in Europe, had begun to attract American scientific interest — even as low-quality medical schools proliferated. One theory held that disease simply occurred spontaneously in the blood, thus ruling out the notion that a disease could be spread. During the American Civil War, a more logical theory took hold. Doctors saw such a high rate of non-battle deaths in filthy, overflowing military hospitals that they began to connect disease with unsanitary conditions. Many subscribed to the noxious-odor or miasma theory, which suggested that disease was caused essentially by bad air associated with waste, decomposition and unsanitary conditions. Although the theory was missing an important link, it did motivate many medical people to advocate cleanliness and the sterilization of medical instruments and bandages.

During this time, at the beginning of the 1860s, the germ theory of disease was beginning to be discussed in Europe. Scientists such as Louis Pasteur, Joseph Lister and Robert Koch made breakthrough advances in connecting bacteria to specific diseases. Still, although large cities in the eastern United States had witnessed epidemic outbreaks of cholera and smallpox in the early Nineteenth century, most settlements in America were not densely populated and therefore huge outbreaks of disease, on the scale of those that had ravaged Europe, were uncommon.

Among white pioneers on the wide-open, sparsely populated high Northern Plains, epidemic was a particularly foreign idea. Not so for the American Indian, however. Living in close-knit villages, they were completely vulnerable to "white man's diseases." In 1780, the Mandan tribe, which had settled along the upper Missouri River in present-day North Dakota, was hard hit by smallpox brought in by French traders. The disease wiped out two-thirds of the tribe's population of 3,600. Fifty years later, in 1837, a steamboat carrying trappers and settlers took the Missouri up to Fort Clark, about sixty miles north of the present site of Bismarck. On board was at least one white traveler with smallpox. The ensuing epidemic nearly wiped out the entire Mandan tribe, reducing their number from about 1,200 to a little more than one hundred. Among the dead was Four Bears, the Mandan chief. The epidemic also devastated the Hidatsa and Arikira tribes.

A doctor at Fort Clark attempted to halt the spread of the disease by vaccinating several Mandan women. But most of the Indian population had built up no immunity to fight off even the smallest portion of the smallpox introduced through vaccination. Most of those Indian women died.

Tragedies such as these — combined with what Indians viewed as wanton trespass on lands given to them via treaties with the United States government — hardened their hearts toward white settlers. Massacres of settlements were becoming common when gold was discovered in Montana and Utah in 1862. "Men and women smitten with the lure of the yellow dust," wrote historian Dr. James Grassick, "were willing to brave any danger and endure any hardship if only they could get there....In addition to rough roads or no roads at all, the hazards of wind and weather and at times the scarcity of food and water for man and beast, there was the added danger of attack from the Plains' tribes who at this time were anything but friendly to the whites whom they blamed for breaking promises, for destroying and scattering the buffalo and for preempting their native haunts."

The gold rush brought thousands of pioneers west, many cutting straight across the Indian lands of the new Dakota Territory, which had been created in March 1861. Because of the threat of Indian raids, the U.S. Army began sending mounted escorts of cavalry with wagon trains that crossed the Great Plains. Those escorts included military doctors, the first practicing physicians to appear in the Dakotas. In 1862, Capt. James Fisk led the initial escort accompanied by the first of those Army doctors, William Dibbs. Fisk and Dibbs made four trips west from Fort Abercrombie on the Red River of the North south of present-day Fargo, to Fort Walla Walla in present-day Washington state.

Grassick, a long-time North Dakota physician, wrote a book in 1925 called "North Dakota Medicine." He includes an excerpt from Dr. Dibbs' records of one of those trips: "On July 28, 1864, a little son was born to Mrs. Murphy. Capt. Fisk halted the wagons for the day and gave up his tent for the use of the sick woman." That wagon train later was attacked by Indians near the Bad Lands. Several pioneers were killed; Dr. Dibbs treated the wounded. Grassick cites an article about the raid in the St. Cloud Democrat in the fall of 1864. Written by a survivor of the attack, it might be the first reference to a white woman's giving medical aid in the Dakotas. "Mrs. W.K. Leonard of Anoka," it said, "deserves great credit for services rendered in attending to our wounded. She is a truly noble woman."

Weiser volunteered to negotiate with an advance group of the Indians to avoid an all-out battle. But shortly after the parley began, the doctor was shot dead, very likely becoming the first medical man to die in the Dakotas.

A more dubious first may belong to Dr. Josiah H. Weiser, a member of the Minnesota Mounted Rangers. His unit joined the force of Gen. Henry Hastings Sibley, which had been sent into the Dakota Territory in 1863. They were looking for a band of Santee Sioux accused of killing settlers in the Minnesota River Valley the previous year. The Army found the Santee near the present-day town of Tappen in Kidder County. Weiser volunteered to negotiate with an advance group of the Indians to avoid an all-out battle. But shortly after the parley began, the doctor was shot dead, very likely becoming the first medical man to die in the Dakotas.

Generally, though, the typical work of an Army doctor in the Dakota Territory was much more prosaic than tending to battle wounds. Dr. William. B. Davis, the post surgeon at Fort Totten near Devils Lake, wrote that only two of his patients had died in his seven years of duty: an old cavalryman who had fallen and an infant suffering from dysentery. "Please note," he wrote, "I attribute this remarkably small mortality to the bracing climate and physically picked personnel and not to personal skill."

The long gray line
UND students at the turn of the Twentieth Century often participated in military drills on campus.

Davis noted that tonsillitis always followed a thaw and that venereal disease "was almost a negligible quantity." There were numerous surgical cases for fractures and horse kicks, he said, and several cases of frostbite and snow blindness.

"On one occasion a ranchman was brought to me with the most intense photophobia (snow blindness) I have ever seen following long trips on snow covered prairie. It occurred to me to try to anesthetize the eyes.... I cupped my hand and poured into the hollow of it about a teaspoonful of sulphuric ether and then had the patient bend over the hand, which resting on his temple, forehead, side of nose and cheek, entirely prevented the escape of the ether vapor (volatized by the heat of my hand) and confined it around the spasmodically contracted lids. In about a minute or less I removed my hand and told the patient to open his eye, which he did without the slightest difficulty or pain. The eye remained opened long enough to make the appropriate local applications to the conjunctiva. I have used this method in every type of photophobia with unvarying success and can heartily recommend it to you."

Another Fort Totten doctor, James B. Ferguson, recalled when an epidemic of the "grippe" struck the post. "We had the wards full of the elder men, most of them belonging to the band. When I found them collapsing under it, I did not scruple to dose them with the old fashioned stimulant — whiskey — and I am under the impression that some of their lives were saved that way."

Ferguson adds to the impression that life for an Army doctor was quiet. "As far as medical history," he wrote, "there was none. It used to be said of the West that you had to shoot a man to start a graveyard. At Fort Totten you had to freeze him to death. The Fort was established in 1867. The first three graves contained men who were frozen...."

But there were other challenges for a post doctor, such as the time a supply of animal vaccine arrived with orders from on high to vaccinate everybody.

"The results of the vaccination filled the hospital with sore armed men," he wrote. "It was a sight to see. One night I awakened by a great noise and when I reached the ward I found a man standing on his mattress and bedding breaking the glass out of one of the windows with his bare hands. He was bloody from head to foot. I saw he was asleep and slapped his face and awakened him. Some of my sore-armed men thought he had gone insane and were hiding under their beds."

Meanwhile, another type of physician had begun to appear in the Dakotas — the railroad doctor. As the Great Northern and Northern Pacific railroads crossed the Red River from Minnesota in the early 1870s, they sent doctors along with their work crews. While these physicians willingly treated settlers and other non-railroad employees, they were necessarily a transient breed, moving on with the progress of the track. But because of the railroad, a more permanent brand of doctor was about to find its way to the Dakotas. For in addition to the acreage beneath their tracks, the railroads had been given huge tracts of land by the federal government. They lost no time in selling that land to eager pioneers, recruiting them in entire colonies based on ethnic origin or religious background. They plunked them down along the railway at regular intervals in ready made settlements. Gold was no longer the lure, but instead, something beyond price beckoned: the chance to own your own farm and live on your own terms.

Thus was begun the great Dakota population boom. In 1877, there were about 16,000 people living in what is now North Dakota. By 1889, the year of statehood, that number had exploded by almost a dozen-fold to 190,000. The doctors who headed west along with the emigrants came in all varieties, from reputable men with solid educations to those with suspect credentials and homemade remedies.

Into Grand Forks, for example, came a homeopath named Dr. May, who dispensed something called "Dakota ozone." According to Grassick, he got drunk at a July Fourth event and passed out just as he was about to deliver an oration. He left town under cover of darkness.

The first real doctor to settle in Grand Forks was even less fortunate. Dr. George A. Haxton of Randolph, Minnesota, arrived in 1877, opened an office, ordered up a $100 shipment of drugs, and died of smallpox before they arrived. A freight agent named D.M. Holmes took possession of the drugs and began selling them. He later went into business as the region's first pharmacist.

Himself an immigrant to the West from his native Scotland, Grassick couldn't resist characterizing these pioneering medical men.

"It was not considered good ethics to inquire too closely into a man's past or to inspect too critically the trail over which he had come," he wrote. "Into this world in the making, with its atmosphere of action came the Doctor because he wanted to come. It may have been that he felt the restraints of the East too exacting, the freedom of the West too enticing, the desire for adventure too alluring or what was most often the case the longing for opportunities of service which a new country affords too appealing. At any rate he was here and no man was his master."

The Dakota doctor of the late Nineteenth century, he said, was

Wheeler's office
Many of the original furnishings from Henry Wheeler's Grand Forks medical office are on display today in a local museum.

Photo courtesy of Gerald Groenwold

High plains doctor
One of the first and most prominent physicians in Grand Forks, Henry Wheeler, almost larger than life, exuded the independent spirit of the high plains.

a versatile man who could "adapt himself to conditions and mingle freely with men of various stations and conditions of life... it made him a power to be reckoned with in molding community spirit... although he was greeted by his associates familiarly as "Doc" he was held by them in a sort of venerated esteem, an individual to whom they went for counsel and advice, not only on professional subjects but on matters pertaining to their everyday life."

That is a fairly accurate description of a young doctor named Henry M. Wheeler, who moved to Grand Forks in 1881. Born in New Hampshire in 1853, he was two years old when his parents moved to Northfield, Minnesota, south of St. Paul. The town is known today for St. Olaf College, Carleton College and the 1876 bank robbery by the notorious outlaw gangs of Cole Younger and Jesse James. (See story on next page.)

Just how Henry M. Wheeler managed to get through medical school at the University of Michigan is a yarn that has made him a legend in at least three states.

On September 7, 1876, Wheeler was home in Northfield, Minnesota, getting ready to return to Michigan for his final year of medical school. A group of eight riders, all wearing long linen dusters, rode into town that day and pulled up at the First National Bank of Northfield. No one knew it at the time, but they were Cole Younger, his brother Bob Younger, Frank and Jesse James and four other desperadoes — the most notorious outlaws of their day. They'd been drinking hard liquor all day and were drunk and mean. They dismounted, entered the bank and proceeded to rob it. The teller, Joseph Heywood, refused to open the safe and was shot dead. Outside, a Swedish immigrant named Nicholas Gustafson who didn't speak English, was caught up in the gunplay and also was killed.

Two of the citizens of Northfield who heard the commotion went into immediate action. One of them was the owner of a hardware store, Anselm Manning, who ducked into his shop and came out with a rifle. The other was the young medical student, Henry Wheeler. When he heard the shots coming from the bank, Wheeler ran into the Dampier Hotel and grabbed the house rifle. He scurried to a second floor window just as the robbers were coming out of the bank and mounting their horses.

As they made their getaway down the main street of Northfield, they passed right below the hotel window. Wheeler, who would later earn the reputation as the most prolific big game hunter in North Dakota, took aim and shot the outlaw Clel Miller out of his saddle.

He was dead on the ground. A second shot from Wheeler smashed the elbow of Bob Younger. The hardware merchant, Manning, shooting from the front of his store, killed gang member Bill Stiles and wounded Cole Younger.

A posse went out after the remains of the gang and eventually rounded up the Younger boys, ending their criminal careers. Both of the James boys got away. The story might have ended there if hadn't been for the peculiar requirement in those days of certain medical schools. While some states had a law against the dissecting of human corpses, Michigan allowed it, but required its medical students to supply their own cadavers.

One begins to wonder what young Wheeler would have done had not the James-Younger gang come to town that day. As it was, he asked the sheriff if he could have the bodies of the two dead outlaws, but the sheriff said no. He did hint, however, that the outlaws were to be buried right away and in shallow graves.

That night, according to "Robber and Hero, the story of the Northfield Bank Raid" by George Huntington, (MHS Press, St Paul 1986), Wheeler did a little grave robbing. He dug up the two corpses and packed them in barrels marked "Fresh Paint." They were shipped via train, along with the future surgeon, Dr. Wheeler, to Ann Arbor. The story doesn't even end there. It is said that when Wheeler arrived in Grand Forks in 1881 and set up his practice, the human skeleton he kept on display in his office was that of Clel Miller. It was apparently lost in a fire during the 1920s.

Wheeler graduated from Carleton and was admitted to the reputable school of medicine at the University of Michigan. He graduated in 1877, practiced for a time in Northfield, and then took a year of post-graduate training at the College of Physicians and Surgeons in New York City, which later became associated with Columbia Presbyterian Hospital. He came back west and settled in Grand Forks, where he blossomed almost immediately as one of Grassick's "powers to be reckoned with," becoming the first doctor in North Dakota to establish a group practice. He flourished as a well-known character during his forty-plus years as, perhaps, the city's best-known physician.

Wheeler was a big man, "brave and reckless," according to one account, clearly larger than life. For years his was the most prominent medical practice in town. He helped organize the state medical society and served as its president. He held the position of surgeon for the Northern Pacific and Great Northern railroads and was elected to two terms as mayor of Grand Forks. He also was behind the building of St. Michael's Hospital and persuaded the Catholic Order of Sisters of St. Joseph to staff the facility.

Many still accord Wheeler the honor of being the very first dean of the School of Medicine at the University of North Dakota. Technically that is correct, for in 1886 Wheeler was elected dean by the university's Board of Regents. One small problem: No medical school existed and wouldn't exist for another nineteen years. The election later was deemed to be illegal and Wheeler "resigned." The next year, in 1887, the territorial legislature did approve a $1,000 set-aside for establishing a chair of medicine, but by then a new president had taken over the university and all bets were off.

The move to establish a medical school only three years after the founding of the university proper in 1883 again underscored the growing perception of the public that their health was at risk without more legitimate doctors. The tens of thousands of population boomers who immigrated to the territory in such a short period had made heavy demands on insufficient public health capabilities. Diseases caused by unclean drinking water, poor sanitation facilities and contaminated milk began to claim large numbers of victims. Childhood illness was especially rampant in the early 1880s. A couple could almost count on losing two out of every three children to tuberculosis, cholera, smallpox, typhoid fever, diarrhea infantum, tetanus and diphtheria. Too often the source of those diseases wasn't understood. The science of bacteriology, though developing rapidly, was still largely an Eastern or European idea.

Things began to change with the push for statehood. In 1885, the territorial legislature amended its code of 1869. Doctors who wanted to practice in the territory still needed to prove they had graduated from a medical college. If they hadn't gone to college, they needed to pass an exam given under the direction of a superintendent of public health and also to show that they had been in practice for ten years. Whether a college man or not, a doctor was required under the new law to be of good moral character and not be a drunkard. Finally, it cost $2 for a license. That year, 739 of them were granted.

In 1889, when North Dakota was granted statehood, the legislature enacted the Medical Practice Act, setting even tougher standards for licensure. The heart of the act was the establishment of a State Board of Medical Examiners. The board was to be composed of eight doctors and one civilian – who had to be a lawyer. This board was empowered to administer exams to those wishing to practice medicine in the state. But not just anyone could take the exam. Candidates were required to have attended three courses of lectures of at least six months each. The act was later amended to require full graduation from a medical college that included attendance at four courses of lectures of eight months each.

At the first meeting of this board, two classifications of licensed doctors were established. The "Old Practitioner" license was granted to anyone five years out of medical school. Those with less than five years were licensed as a "Recent Graduate." The difference? Both Old Practitioners and Recent Graduates needed only a sixty-five percent score on the exam in the subjects of Practice of Medicine, Surgery, Materia Medica (Drugs), Obstetrics and Diseases of Women and Children. But while Old Practitioners needed only a thirty-five percent score in Anatomy, Chemistry, Physiology, Pathology, Histology, Preventive Medicine, Diseases of the Eye and Ear, Medical Jurisprudence and Diseases of the Nervous System, Recent Graduates had to score fifty percent in those subject fields.

The inequity of that system didn't last long. By 1896, everyone who took the exam for licensure was required to score no less than sixty-five percent on every subject, with an average of seventy-five percent.

The creation of the Board of Medical Examiners came as a result of increased levels of public concern about ill-trained doctors and quacks practicing medicine in the state. Even so, the law required that two of the eight doctors named to the board by the governor be homeopaths. Thus, by April 1894, when a certain train from Minneapolis stopped just west of Grand Forks and discharged Melvin A. Brannon, the state of North Dakota had demonstrated it was willing to license older doctors who didn't have to know very much about the basics of medicine. In turn, they were overseen by a board partially consisting of doctors whose practice was not based on science.

Only a month before Melvin Brannon stepped off his train, Grand Forks had suffered through what was called one of worst epidemics of typhoid fever known in the history of epidemiology. As many as five hundred people had become infected; 150 died. Outbreaks such as this had happened before in Grand Forks as the population continued to grow, but medical practitioners of the day had been almost helpless. This time, in desperation, local merchants appealed to the university for help, and when they did, Webster Merrifield had just the man for the job.

Brannon went right to work on the problem. His investigation showed that raw sewage from nearby Crookston, Minnesota, was being dumped into the Red Lake River — the main source of potable water for Grand Forks. Brannon was aware of the work of German scientist

When boxes of Cream of Wheat were shipped to warmer climates of the country, those (beetle) eggs were hatching and customers were finding bugs in their cereal. Brannon studied the situation and devised a way to kill the eggs by increasing temperatures at a certain point in the process.

Robert Koch, who, in 1884, had isolated the bacteria that caused cholera. Only two years earlier in Hamburg, Koch had discovered that cholera bacteria could be filtered from a city's water supply by passing it first through sand. Brannon suggested Grand Forks try a sand filtration system. The city fathers agreed, and Brannon and his colleague, Earle Babcock of the UND department of chemistry, supervised the construction. Brannon then conducted bacteria studies of the water at regular intervals for the next twelve years. The result: typhoid outbreaks ceased.

That was only the beginning. The Grand Forks Chamber of Commerce asked Brannon to provide a bacteriological survey of dairies in the area and of the milk they supplied to the city. Dairy farms never before had fallen under any hygienic inspection. Brannon found the tuberculosis organism in bacteria in several milk supplies. According to Dr. Grassick, "This resulted in securing the passage of the first milk ordinance northwest of the Twin Cities. Its observance under guidance of (Brannon)...saved the lives of over 40 children...."

Soon Brannon was using his meager scientific facilities at the university to assist local doctors in diagnosing diphtheria, typhoid fever,

On Being a Young Prairie Doctor

It was the most wonderful feeling in the world to start my own practice in a small town. My patients were all my friends and my guinea pigs. I studied a lot and they were very patient with me. I remember when I first came to town, I was very young for a practicing physician and I looked even younger, more like a high school kid to some of my patients. There were three ladies in town who started off being friends and we have always been friends. They were all pregnant and they were waiting for this young doctor to come to town so they could have him deliver their babies.

We had a maternity home in the town of Mott for five to ten years. It was the last one in the state that was licensed, because the health department said they would continue to license that maternity home as long as I took full responsibility for it. The nearest hospital was Elgin, twenty-four miles away, so the maternity home was great for the people who lived there. In fact, when I first moved there we didn't have any paved highways, so we

(continued on next page)

tuberculosis and various kinds of cancer. Perhaps his most famous consultation came when the makers of Cream of Wheat, developed in Grand Forks, approached him with a potentially ruinous problem. It seems that beetles had been getting into the flour in the local mills and had infested the wheat grits with their eggs. When boxes of Cream of Wheat were shipped to warmer climates of the country, those eggs were hatching and customers were finding bugs in their cereal. Brannon studied the situation and devised a way to kill the eggs by increasing temperatures at a certain point in the process. The company soon was capitalizing on Brannon's idea, selling its product with the label "Sterilized Breakfast Food."

In 1896, the federal government had heard of Brannon and asked him to conduct a survey of all the grasses and forage plants native to North and South Dakota. It took him the better part of two years to collect samples of each, but he did it. As for the department of biology itself, Brannon found very few students interested in the subject when he first arrived. That changed quickly. Because of the excitement he generated by solving one crisis after another, more than half of those enrolled at UND just one year later were biology students.

His courses became so popular that the university even erected a new building — although not without prodding. In urging construction, Brannon wrote to the Board of Trustees: "The urgent need of a science hall has become so obvious that the most casual visitor to the university remarks, 'Has this state no interest in her chief educational institution and its scientific work? If so why are you not provided rooms commensurate with attendance?'" In many ways, the venerable Science Hall, which opened in 1902 and has since disappeared, was very much the house that Brannon built.

Merrifield, in the meantime, hadn't been idle. With the help of a wealthy UND trustee named William Budge, he led a fundraising drive that brought in $30,000 — enough to keep the university afloat until the depression had faded. It's interesting to note that even though their salaries had been suspended, the university faculty contributed $1,000 to that fund drive.

That combination of needed cash along with Brannon's dramatic successes created a favorable political atmosphere for reconsidering the creation of a medical school. Brannon, more than anyone else, championed the idea, believing that the most natural evolvement of a department of biology in a university setting would be to establish a school of medicine. He argued his case before two key constituencies — state legislators and doctors. He was a persuasive man and won support by asserting a premise that has been part of the rationale for a school of medicine at the university ever since: If our children can't attend medical school in North Dakota, they will go elsewhere to become doctors and very likely not come back. He backed it up with statistics showing that more than fifty young men and women had left North Dakota thus far to attend medical school elsewhere.

This occurred as reputable medical schools across the country had begun standardizing the education of doctors, hoping to separate themselves from the fly-by-night organizations. A course of forty-five months generally was agreed on as the new standard. The first twenty-four months would be devoted to basic laboratory sciences and the remaining years given over to clinical work.

Because of that breakdown, there arose nationally at the start of the Twentieth century the idea of creating "half schools." These would allow states that could not afford a full-fledged four-year school to train students in the basics for two years and then have them transfer to a four-year school to complete their medical degree. The idea was immediately popular with rural states that had neither the money nor large hospitals to establish full medical schools.

Pushed by Brannon — and his enthusiastic biology students — a study was authorized by the university to examine the possibility of establishing a two-year school of medicine. Brannon sought the advice of the leading medical schools at the time, asking questions about curriculum, recruiting of faculty, sources and cost of equipment, and how much it all would cost. One of the important results of that study was Brannon's insistence not only on a curriculum for medical students, but also a two-year course of liberal studies and science that prospective students would need to complete before they could be accepted into the medical school. Among the requirements his faculty committee agreed on: English literature, rhetoric, algebra, geometry, history, Latin — through Cicero — German, a semester of Greek, botany, zoology and physics.

In 1902, this course of study was offered by the university as part of the curriculum for a new school of pharmacy. Three years later in 1905, the university's Board of Trustees authorized Brannon to bring it all together by organizing a two-year school of medicine. The faculty added its support and, unlike in 1887, the legislature quickly followed. On September 26, 1905, the School of Medicine at the University of North Dakota opened its doors and accepted its first students.

In those first years, the school allowed some students to enroll in a "short course," skipping over the preparatory work and taking only

On Being a Young Prairie Doctor

(continued)

had to drive over gravel roads to Elgin, Richardton or Hettinger to a hospital. They were pretty happy, especially in the wintertime, to have a maternity home and a doctor who would serve there.

The maternity home was Mrs. Grass's home. She was married and her husband was old. She was a good old German lady who'd had this home for Dr. Mercline and other doctors over the years. She must have had some training, but her experience was such that she could sit with these ladies in labor and she could encourage them; and at the time they were due to deliver, she could tell exactly what stage they were in. I don't think she ever did a rectal or vaginal examination, but she could tell by timing, feeling the belly and the attitude, and she could always get me there in time for a delivery. I don't think we ever had a precipitate delivery at her place. Never did.

Bob Hankins, class of 1948, earned a doctor of medicine degree from Loyola University, Chicago. He practiced for twenty-two years in Mott, N.D. and was the first head of the family practice center in Minot.

the science courses. That was quickly done away with so that most of the early students followed a four-year course of study — two years of prep work and two years in the laboratory sciences. Those students who completed all four years received a bachelor of arts degree and a certificate in medicine. By sticking to that standard, North Dakota became one of the first medical schools in the country to require a two-year pre-med course for its students. Yale, for example, didn't require that until 1909.

In his initial call for students in the university bulletin, Brannon's enthusiasm was palpable. "Beginning with the school year 1905-06, the University will offer the first two years of a regular four year's course in medicine. It is expected that students who complete this course will be admitted to all reputable medical colleges and given full credit for two years of work."

The new School of Medicine was to occupy space on the third floor of the new Science Hall, now one of eight buildings on campus, all heated by steam and lighted by electricity. Brannon seemed pleased with the arrangement, noting, "The facilities of the university for offering the first two years of a standard medical course are unsurpassed."

He may have exaggerated just a bit. "The school began," writes Louis G. Geiger, in his University of the Northern Plains, "by any modern standard, with practically no equipment, laboratories or faculty. It shared the top floor of the science building with the department of biology and the museum."

But it was there. And in January 1906, the state's Board of Medical Examiners unanimously approved the two-year entrance requirements for the new medical school as well as the basic science curriculum. One of the signatories to this vote was none other than the so-called first dean of the medical school, Dr. Henry M. Wheeler, now secretary of the Board of Medical Examiners. Wheeler was already giving lectures in surgery at the new medical school, which suggests he may have ignored a conflict of interest by participating in the vote of approval. In any case, he became, in essence, the first chair of the department of surgery.

The first student to complete the official Brannon program was Sverre Oftedahl, who graduated in 1909. He transferred to Rush Medical College in Chicago, where he earned a doctor of medicine degree in 1911. Oftedahl went on to a successful practice in Fargo, becoming not only the first graduate of the School of Medicine, but also the first student to return to his home state to practice medicine — just as the doctor had ordered.

In 1905, when the medical school opened, medicine was still in the dark about the electrical and chemical dynamics of most of the body's organs. Not surprisingly, Brannon's first basic science curriculum was heavily weighted toward anatomy.

It included courses in histology (the study of microscopic structure of tissue), chemistry, anatomy, physics, embryology (the study of formation and early development of living organisms), physiology (the study of the characteristics of life and living matter), bacteriology, hygiene, pathology, preparatory surgery, morbid anatomy (the study of diseased organs) and physical diagnosis. Seventy-five percent of students' time was devoted to work in the low-ceilinged rooms of the science building, now fitted out with benches, dissecting tables, microscopes, microtomes, staining and embedding apparatus, models of organs and charts of the body. There was a small medical library and an even smaller museum of skeletons, stuffed deer and buffalo, and a few embalmed cadavers. The state legislature had passed a law that sent unclaimed corpses to the medical school and allowed their dissection.

The costs for each student were $145 a year, including $50 for lab fees; $1.35 each week for thirty-five weeks for a room, and $3 each week for boarding and use of a bathroom and laundry facilities. There was no actual tuition charge in those early years, while medical schools outside North Dakota were charging students anywhere from $200 to $500.

Aside from Wheeler and Brannon, the faculty of the new medical school included two local physicians, August Eggers, and a UND grad named Archie L. McDonald. The latter had earned a medical degree from prestigious Johns Hopkins University Medical School, and as will be seen, his presence may have helped the school a few years later at a crucial moment. The faculty also included the first woman to teach in the medical school, a Miss Kildahl who instructed in histology.

Brannon also had retained the services of two of the state's leading bacteriologists. Dr. H.H. Healy was the superintendent of the State Board of Health, and Gustav Ruediger, an M.D and a Ph.D., was the state bacteriologist and pathologist. Those positions had been created by the legislature through the work of Brannon and his faculty colleague, Dr. John Taylor. It was Taylor, a state senator, who championed medical school issues in Bismarck. He introduced the bills that created a Division of Medicine, designed to include a public health laboratory within the medical school. The director of this lab was to be the ex-officio state bacteriologist and professor of

Johanna Kildahl
Kildahl, who taught histology, was the first woman to teach in the medical school.

The class of 1906
Science Hall served as a perfect backdrop for a photograph of the university's entire senior class.

bacteriology and pathology in the medical school. This relationship continued until 1949, when the departments of bacteriology and pathology and the State Public Health Department became separate entities with separate staff.

In a measure of their respect for Brannon and his work as a bacteriologist, the legislature appropriated $5,000 for the maintenance of the state lab and $2,000 for equipment. Ruediger, its first director, was a graduate of Rush Medical College. "He possessed vigor and imagination," according to Geiger, "and the lab developed rapidly in the seven years he was at the university."

One of Ruediger's tasks was to create a bureau of vital statistics, calling for the immediate registration of all births and deaths in the state. It was also the director's job to "make bacteriological examinations of bodily excretions and secretions, water and food and make preparations and examinations of pathological tissues submitted by the state superintendent of public health or any licensed doctor in North Dakota."

In his first year as director, Ruediger conducted more than 1,800 examinations, finding that one out of every six samples contained bacteria from diphtheria, tuberculosis or typhoid fever. In a very short time, he became the new Brannon, the recognized authority on sanitation and public health in the state. In 1909, he organized the Public Health League, which brought together citizens and professionals for the first time. Within ten years the lab was processing 20,000 samples annually; it practically invented the sanitary outhouse by publishing plans and standards for privy hygiene.

Though it would be another sixty-three years before a Department of Community Medicine was established in the School of Medicine, the founding of the state laboratory marked the formal beginning of officially coordinated public health efforts in North Dakota.

Brannon, by the way, managed to keep his own research going while he was dean, founding a public biology lab in Devils Lake in 1908. His writings on his discoveries there were supposed to be published in the annual reports of the North Dakota Hydrobiological Station in Devils Lake. But, according to a 1947 article in the UND Alumni Review, "The most important and dramatic work was never published because the state was too poor to print the reports. The manuscripts were lost somewhere with the state printer." They were never recovered.

That's fairly typical of the way Brannon has been treated by history. While other, better-known figures populate the story of this medical school — godsends such as Harley French, Art Saiki, Gene Cornatzer, Tom Johnson — Brannon's name is usually left off that honor roll.

Brannon wasn't a doctor and he left Grand Forks after twenty years to become president of the University of Idaho and later chancellor of the University of Montana. Though twice he was asked to return and become president of the entire University of North Dakota, he said no. A final indignity to his memory was not discovered until Brannon's granddaughter, Eleanor Woodason of Foxboro, Massachusetts, paid a visit to the modern School of Medicine and Health Sciences early in 2000. While reviewing the impressive gallery of photographs of former deans of the school in the new Harwood Building foyer, she came to the picture of Melvin A. Brannon. But, she frowned, that isn't Grandfather at all. Indeed, Brannon's features were quite similar to those of several of his colleagues of the time. The slight has since been corrected.

But it does prompt the question: "Exactly who was he?" For that, his granddaughter might express it best: "He stood six feet tall and you felt every inch of his height. He was a proud, strong and moral person who really cared about people and educational freedom."

Eleanor's mother often told of how she and her sister would go with their father on Saturdays to the lecture halls of the School Of Medicine. They would play contentedly while Dean Brannon caught up on some unfinished business. "One particular day," she recalls, "they missed the last street car and had to walk to 207 Chestnut Street. It was snowing hard and Grandpa blazed the trail, followed by my aunt and mother. When they reached home it was 26 below."

After all, blazing trails was what Brannon did. That his trail in North Dakota was sufficiently cleared for those who would follow became evident in 1909.

Not only was 1909 the year of the School of Medicine's first graduation, it was also the year that the prestigious Carnegie Foundation embarked on an ambitious survey of all medical schools in the United States and Canada. The study was prompted by the American Medical Association, which had been decrying the poor quality of medical education by citing the large number of proprietary schools that had poor facilities and were employing unsound methods.

To conduct the survey, the foundation turned to a most unlikely source. Abraham Flexner was not a doctor and, indeed, had seen only one medical school in his life — the Johns Hopkins School of Medicine in Baltimore, where his brother had graduated. Abraham Flexner was a high school teacher by training and had been a principal. He also had just completed a lengthy study of the colleges of America. Based on the recommendation of his well-connected brother, the Carnegie Foundation gave Abraham the job.

Flexner took four weeks to think about the situation and then set off on an inspection tour of 167 medical schools. Mentally he would compare each with the Johns Hopkins School of Medicine, using a five-point rating system to guide his critiques.

1 What kind of standards regulated admission to the school?
2 How large was the faculty and what kind of training did it have?
3 How much money is in the school's budget and in its endowments?
4 Were there proper facilities such as labs and qualified lab instructors?
5 Did the school have a useful association with neighboring hospitals?

Abraham Flexner came to Grand Forks roughly in the middle of his tour, in May of 1909. The school had only nine students, but listed nine faculty members and seven other instructors.

And although the school's budget was only $6,500, Flexner was favorably impressed by the credentials of the faculty members and the teaching methods he observed. Again, according to Louis

Gustav Ruediger

A medical school faculty member, Ruediger was the first director of the state's public health lab. He led the fight against bacteria that caused diphtheria, tuberculosis and typhoid fever.

Louis Geiger

A UND historian, Geiger chronicled the early years of the medical school in his 1958 work *The University of the Northern Plains: A History of the University of North Dakota 1893-1958.*

Geiger's history, the size of the faculty as presented to Flexner was something of an exaggeration. There really was just one full-time medical professor — but it was Dr. Archie McDonald, who had trained at the same medical school as Flexner's brother — Johns Hopkins. Just how much that connection affected Flexner's report is unknown, but it surely didn't hurt. The rest of the faculty, Geiger notes, were part-time teachers and full-time physicians practicing in Grand Forks.

Even so, Flexner found a positive match in Grand Forks against his five-point checklist, with one extra mark in UND's favor: Flexner was very keen on the need for doctors in rural areas, and was critical of states and schools that ignored such needs. Thus, he wrote, "...Before any vested proprietary interest could be created, they have fixed the state practice requirement at two years of college work. The state though thinly settled is prosperous, and no anxiety is felt that the high standard will deplete the medical profession of the state."

Flexner also agreed more with Brannon than Geiger years later on the quality of facilities at the school. "The laboratory of bacteriology, being at the same time the public health laboratory of the state, is well equipped and very active. Subjects given in the regular university laboratories are likewise well provided for. For the specifically medical subject — physiology, pathology, anatomy — the provision is slighter. The students are, of course, few. A library and museum have been started."

Winning the blessing of Flexner was crucial for two reasons. First, most schools — including some very large ones — didn't fare as well. Almost all of the proprietary schools faded away after being blistered by Flexner. For example, he told of visiting one such school where he had been met by the dean at the local train station. He was taken to a restaurant, wined and dined and returned to the train station in the dean's horse and buggy without ever seeing the school. Flexner got on the train but immediately hopped off after the dean had waved him goodbye. He then went to the school, where he bribed a janitor to let him in. He found deplorable conditions — no lab facilities, no books, no benches, no cadavers, no skeletons.

Second, the Flexner report was a groundbreaking point in American medicine and gained a measure of fame as time went by. A school that stood up to his withering scrutiny was a school worth watching. Flexner himself became a well-known educational reformer.

In the meantime, in 1907 the Association of American Medical Colleges granted the fledgling School of Medicine its first accreditation. Later that year, the State Board of Medical Examiners

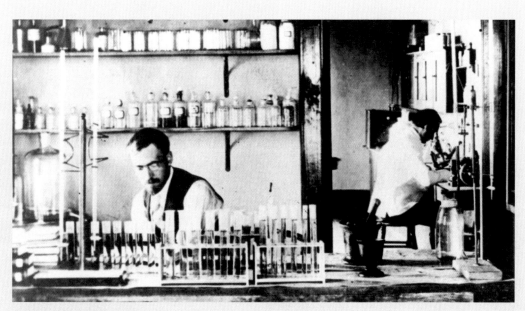

Public health lab
Dr. Gustav Ruediger, the state's first bacteriologist, analyzed tissue samples sent to him by doctors across North Dakota. One in six samples contained the deadly bacteria of diphtheria, tuberculosis or typhoid fever.

ruled that the state could refuse an application for a medical license if the doctor in question had attended a school "defective in teaching facilities." Specifically, it said, "All applicants must present evidence...of having graduated from, a reputable medical college and having attended the lectures...not less than four years of eight months each." The following year it simply required that all applicants show proof of an education equal to that at the University of North Dakota.

Shortly after Flexner's report was released, Melvin Brannon was eased out as dean of the School of Medicine. Much had been made in those early years of accreditation that Brannon was not a doctor. So he became, instead, the dean of the university's College of Liberal Arts — he had, after all, devised an effective pre-medical curriculum heavily focused on the humanities. A year later, Brannon earned a Ph.D. from the University of Chicago, becoming, at last, Dr. Brannon. Two years later he departed the university to blaze new trails elsewhere. But he left behind quite a mark.

His replacement as dean at the School of Medicine arrived with as little fanfare as Brannon had received seventeen years earlier. His name was Harley E. French and all agreed that he had a tough act to follow.

Chapter 2

CHAPTER TWO

Harley and Tuck
Save the Day

Harley French was only four years out of Northwestern Medical School in 1911 when he was hired as professor of anatomy and dean of the School of Medicine at the University of North Dakota.

He was, however, a very mature thirty-eight years of age, having entered college late in life due to difficult financial circumstances. Those circumstances would turn out to be the ideal training for the job he now assumed.

He was born in rural Delphi, Indiana, in 1873, the oldest of seven children. His father, David Scott French, was a carpenter and a sometime farmer, although prosperous at neither. He was a man who liked to raise vegetables, fruit trees and the occasional steer. Harley's daughter, Mary Margaret Frank, later would recall that her grandfather "was not an educated man, but a thinking, questioning one." Though he was an agnostic, his wife, Mina, was a deeply religious member of the Campbellite Christian Church.

The family moved to Kearney, Nebraska, when Harley was seven and lived on a 160-acre homestead farm far from the local school. "My father used to tell of a terrible windstorm through which he and his brother Burton made their way one cold day from school, looking forward to the warmth and comfort of the kitchen," Mary Margaret recalls. "But when they reached the house, their mother would not open the door. She only signaled to the little boys to go to the other side of

Previous page:

Gross Lab
At the start of 20th century, states such as North Dakota began to allow the dissection of cadavers. At UND, the Gross Anatomy Lab became the centerpiece of early medical student training.

the house and wait. If she had opened the door, she was sure that the whole house would have blown down."

The family moved again when Harley was nine, this time to the small town of Palouse near Walla Walla, Washington. Some years later he recounted that trip in the fall of 1882. "We had come west to San Francisco by train, from there to Portland by boat, from Portland to Walla Walla by boat and train. From Walla Walla to someplace on the Snake River by train, from there to Almota by boat and from Almota to Palouse by wagon." Ever after, he considered Palouse his hometown.

He attended high school there and earned money for a year's worth of college at Spokane by sawing wood. When he was only seventeen, says Mary Margaret, "just beginning to shave," he became a schoolteacher at the Paradise Prairie School in the little town of Johnson, near Palouse. He then fell into a pattern that would continue for years. He would teach for one or two semesters until he had enough money to put himself through another year of college. He studied off and on at the University of Idaho and the State College of Washington, supplementing his income by selling books and doing farm work. His brother Burton was doing the same thing and though they had their hopes set on careers in medicine and law, they channeled most of the income from their odd jobs to their family.

Burton made it through college before Harley and found a career not only in law but also in politics. He served as a United States Congressman from Idaho for twenty-eight years. "All this time I had been expecting to study medicine," wrote French years later, "but in 1900 I despaired of that ambition." Finally, his brother Burton relieved him of the burden of supporting the family so that he could finish his college education. Harley not only excelled at academics — he was elected to Phi Beta Kappa — but was editor of the student newspaper at the College of Washington in Pullman and president of the student assembly. At Northwestern Medical School in Chicago, French found it his duty, says his daughter, not only to study medicine, "but also to see plays and hear concerts and visit exhibits." He even thought it would be good for him to join a fraternity, so he became a Nu Sigma Nu man.

His goal, says Mary Margaret, was to return to the hills of Walla Walla and become a country doctor. But the University of South Dakota at Vermillion lured him into the academic world. There he met Mabel Townsley, the daughter of the family that ran the local boarding home where Harley took many of his meals. Mabel was the university's registrar and taught English. She did not particularly care

for South Dakota and would spend her days wishing for grander surroundings and fighting off the disappointment of an ordinary life. She and Harley French married in 1910 and a year later were bound for the big city of Grand Forks. Things looked very promising there. Her husband was to become dean of the School of Medicine and she was promised a brand-new house.

In retrospect, if Melvin Brannon's departure had set off a nationwide search for the best possible replacement as dean, the University of North Dakota could not have done better than to hire the somewhat severe, strait-laced Harley French. More likely, however, French got the job because he was nearby in South Dakota and had just earned his master's degree from the University of Chicago, giving him more degrees than Brannon had.

UND had just graduated five students from its School of Medicine when he arrived in Grand Forks in 1911. That left twelve medical students and another twenty pre-medical students, including Solveig Sigrid Gislason, who, in 1914, became the first woman to graduate from the program. She went on to practice in Edina, Minnesota.

According to French's notes, he found "small but possible quarters assigned the school in Old Science Hall, with laboratories and classrooms in proportion. Laboratory equipment and library showed intelligent and thoughtful care. There was a small but good faculty, and there were about a dozen medical students and perhaps twenty students in the premedical years. In short, the school was a going concern."

French brought to the job two distinct talents: He was an excellent teacher and he was thoroughly organized, sometimes to the point of obsession. He was a man who answered every piece of

Dr. Harley French
Arguably the most important dean in the history of the medical school, Harley French kept the two-year program together during The Great Depression, even when it lost its accreditation.

The medical school, 1910

The students and faculty who gathered for this striking photograph in 1910 included some of the medical school's early luminaries. In the front row, from left to right: Dr. A.H. Caldwell; Dr. R.T. Young; University president Webster Merrifield; Dean Melvin Brannon; Dr. A.L. McDonald and Dr. Gustav Ruediger. Fourth from the left in second row is Sverre Oftedal, who, in 1909 became the first graduate of the medical school.

mail he ever received, including junk mail and advertising fliers. If his daughter wanted him to read to her from Rudyard Kipling's "Just So" stories, French would spend time pre-reading the story to himself, and making small pencil checks at certain words to be sure he used the right inflection when it came time for the actual reading. "He was very proud," says Mary Margaret, "and glad to be reading to me, but he wanted to do it well."

In the classroom, those talents translated to a demanding teacher sometimes described as a taskmaster by his former students. But, apparently, he never was a taskmaster with a mean streak.

"He was very nice but very strict and very methodical," recalls Dr. Eva Gilbertson, a graduate of the class of 1939 and one of the first women medical students at the school. "He always had a twinkle in his eye, especially if he asked you a question and thought he had you cornered."

Slowly, French began to refine and expand the School of

Medicine. Where Brannon's hallmark had been in his research, French preferred instead to focus everything on teaching, at which he was a natural. He had an ability to convince students that his own favorite discipline — anatomy — was essential to their future careers as doctors.

In only a handful of years he had placed such a stamp of quality on his graduates that four-year schools would gladly accept UND transfers on his recommendation alone. Harvard University became one of the top five medical schools to which North Dakota graduates transferred. About half of the students transferred to one of the Chicago-area medical schools such as Rush or Northwestern, and in subsequent years, other transfer favorites included Colorado, Indiana, Kansas, Louisville, Johns Hopkins, Tufts, Minnesota, St. Louis, Creighton, Nebraska, Oregon, Pennsylvania, Jefferson, and Vanderbilt.

French busied himself in his spare time by playing key roles in

Dapper Doctor
James Golseth, M.D, 1939, strikes a natty pose early in his medical career. He later established the Gustav Golseth and Wesley Morrish Medical School Endowment at UND to provide scholarships for exceptional medical students.

local organizations. He was president of the Grand Forks District Medical Society in 1913 and 1914, and was elected president of the North Dakota Medical Association in 1921. In his private life he was a member of the Kem Temple of the Masonic Lodge, or Shrine, in Grand Forks, but, according to Mary Margaret, "I cannot remember that he was ever an active or enthusiastic member."

Not so with the Lions Club. "He was a good Lion," says his daughter, "His enjoyment of the fun and frivolity that went on in the Lions Club was a pleasure to watch." French was also an active member of the Plymouth Congregational Church and later the Federated Church, where he was a trustee and a deacon.

"He seldom missed a Playmakers play or a faculty lecture or recital or a Phi Beta Kappa or Sigma Xi initiation," says Mary Margaret. "He always had a ticket for the Artist Series and never failed to attend a program unless he was out of town."

He liked to garden and tended a small vegetable patch in the back yard of the family home on Hamline Street.

About that house: When he came to Grand Forks in 1911, French and a friend built a small home on Hamline next to the Sigma Alpha Epsilon fraternity house.

"My mother was terribly disappointed in the house," says Mary Margaret. "She saw this plain, brown house. That wasn't what she wanted at all. She wanted a really nice house. She'd say, 'Oh, Daddy and the carpenter just threw up that house.' The idea was we'd get a better house after awhile. But then came the First World War and then came the Depression. We always lived in that house. I didn't see anything wrong with it. I looked at it as home. My mother made a lovely thing of it inside. She was a lovely hostess and I don't think she suffered all the time. But it was a bitter disappointment."

French faced a series of thorny challenges in his first ten years in Grand Forks, not all of them having to do with the School of Medicine.

When Brannon was still dean, UND's hands-on president, Frank McVey, had him start a preparatory nursing program, adding a trained nurse to the faculty. Then in 1915, with French as dean, McVey insisted that the medical school add a course in embalming — a play for support from the North Dakota Funeral Association. In Geiger's spare language, however, "Neither nursing nor embalming proved successful."

Apparently the nursing program drew few students, while the embalming course raised eyebrows. It was not exactly the kind of thing French wanted the medical school to be connected with. Both programs fizzled in 1917, although today the very successful College of Nursing at UND is a separate program from the medical school.

If the embalming course bothered French, he seized the opportunity to keep presidential interference at a minimum by heading the committee that wrote a new constitution for the university. The new document created the Deans' Advisory Committee and the Administrative Committee, which gave a louder voice to faculty in daily operations of the university. From that point on, the president had to consult with the faculty before appointing, promoting or firing faculty members or reorganizing university departments.

French even played a role in picking McVey's successor as president, serving as chair of the committee that hired his replacement.

One of his most difficult challenges, however, came in 1918. With the First World War under way, French volunteered for the Army. He was forty-four years old, however, and the government told him he could best serve the country by staying where he was and teaching future doctors. At that time, in the fall of 1918, the Student Army Training Corps formed to train students on college campuses across the country as future officers. French organized local doctors to help administer examinations to recruits being inducted into the SATC camp on campus.

One of those volunteers was Dr. James Grassick, the transplanted Scotsman. "On assuming duties at the camp," he later wrote, "there was little sickness of any kind, but in a few days the influenza struck and it spread like wildfire. In an exceedingly short time there were over three hundred fine fellows flat on their backs."

This was the great influenza epidemic of 1918 that swept the nation, killing hundreds of thousands. Classes and student drills were suspended and the university was quarantined. With almost all of the 473 students becoming ill — twenty-nine would die — fraternity houses and Budge Hall became makeshift hospitals and quickly filled to overflowing. Another 3,000 cases of the flu were reported in the city of Grand Forks. Adding to the difficulty, more than half the state's doctors and a quarter of the nurses were abroad on the battlefields of France.

One who remained, however, impressed many with his dedication. "Dr. French was onto his job late and early," wrote Grassick. "He did valiant service for his country; not only in educational and administrative lines but in caring for the ailing at a time when help was so much needed, and so hard to procure. His

Mary Margaret Frank

Harley French's only daughter, Mary Margaret, remembers her father as fun loving at home, but strict and methodical about the medical school.

Solveig Sigred Gislason

In 1914 she became the first woman to graduate from the UND medical school. She was one of many committed women over the years who paved the way to modern times at the medical school. Today half of all graduates are women.

services were eagerly sought for and as cheerfully given. Off the campus as well as on it, in visiting the sick, in attending to details, in advising, and counseling with those in authority, and in guarding the interests of the University, he did a work that was very commendable; and all so quietly and so unostentatiously that few recognized its real worth."

Doing service on the front lines of a public health crisis was perfectly in line with French's philosophy. Other than his love for teaching, he had developed a true affinity for public health, and after the war played a major role in transforming public policy in North Dakota. Public health law had not been dealt with comprehensively in the state since 1890, the year after North Dakota was admitted to the Union. The legislature passed that year the Medical Practice Act. While the law was revolutionary for its day, the advance of medicine and the fuller understanding of the germ theory of disease had rendered it weak and irrelevant.

"Nearly every legislature until 1923 added something," says Grassick. "As a consequence the various enactments defied the skill of our best legal talent to interpret or to harmonize. They were conflicting, ambiguous and unworkable."

Much of the code in the early decades of the Twentieth century came under the administration of the state's Superintendent of Public Health. In 1921, the superintendent's salary was $100 a month. It was reduced by legislative fiat that year to zero. Who could operate a public health entity on zero? Harley French could and did. In 1921 when he was appointed superintendent of public health, he began an aggressive campaign to reorganize the state's public health machinery and to educate citizens and legislators on the importance of safeguarding the public's health. He proposed the creation of a state health department that would coordinate the dozens of official and quasi-official public health agencies and bring a new emphasis in towns across the state to establishing sanitary water and milk supplies and monitoring sewage disposal and disease eradication. The surgeon general of the United States was impressed enough to assign Dr. Robert E. Olsen of the U.S. Public Health Service to assist French.

In 1923, the legislature bowed to pressure mounted by the state's doctors — spearheaded by French — and passed a law creating a North Dakota Department of Health. It was composed of a public health advisory council with a state health officer as its director. In the same year that Henry Wheeler's booming private practice in Grand Forks took on its first female partner, the new state law called for the advisory council to include at least one woman among its members.

Harley French also succeeded in boosting the salary of the public health officer from zero to $3,600 a year. He would not be around to collect it, however, as his term expired in 1923.

Enrollment in the School of Medicine fell off slightly during the war years, but more than doubled in the years after. In 1916, the school counted twenty-three students and graduated eight. By 1922 that had risen to forty-two total medical students with eighteen graduates. It peaked in 1930 with a total enrollment of sixty, half that number graduating. In fact, by 1925, the school was such a going concern that French was limiting admissions to thirty students a year because of the shortage of space. By then, the School of Medicine had spilled out of its third-floor home — in what was now called the "Old Science" building — to rooms on its second floor, and some space in the Chemistry building. The small medical library had moved to the university's main library. With or without the room, however, French turned away up to four hundred admissions a year from out-of-state students, attracted by the low costs of North Dakota's tuition.

But if times were promising for the School of Medicine during the 1920s, they became absolutely desperate in the 1930s during the Great Depression. While the country struggled with a bottomed-out economy, people in North Dakota felt the double calamity of a seemingly endless drought that ruined crops, brought plagues of grasshoppers and turned much of the Midwest into a dust bowl.

Elwyn Robinson, the UND professor whose History of North Dakota remains a classic, estimated that over a ten-year period, the drought cost farmers in North Dakota more than $1 billion in lost revenue. Per capita income in the state was only forty-seven percent of the national average, which was itself at an all-time low. At the end of 1936, three out of four taxpayers in the southwestern counties of the state were delinquent. One in every three farmers lost their farm. From 1932 to 1937, unpaid property taxes cost the state coffers $34 million.

At the university, the impact of these hard times was deeply felt. Salaries for faculty and administrators were cut by more than half, and Harley French saw his meager salary of $4,800 reduced to $1,920. Dutifully, each year he would present a strong case for increased funding for the School of Medicine. Things had gotten bad enough that more than a dozen faculty members ("well trained, and faithful men...who had given from one to several years of

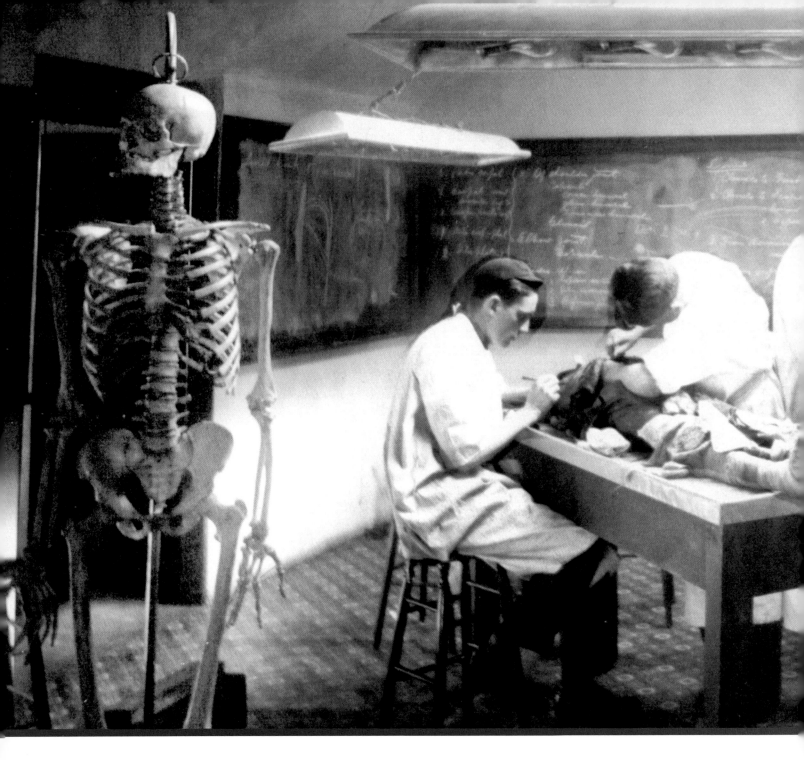

Early dissecting lab
Medical School Dean Harley French (third from right) was known as an excellent teacher of human anatomy and for starting impromptu lectures on philosophy or religion while dissecting cadavers.

faithful service here....") left for better jobs elsewhere. French even canceled subscriptions to medical journals to cut corners. But each year the legislature turned down his request for new funds and whittled away at what it had already given him.

"Unlike many of the medical schools of the country, North Dakota has not shared in the generous, almost extravagant expenditures for buildings and equipment that have been so common," French wrote some years later. "It is one of the schools that has had to carry on with very modest provisions in every way. Its support has been from the state which has had many calls for every dollar it had to spend...."

The crisis got much worse. Gone were the heady days when Flexner patted the School of Medicine on the back and said, "Well done." The next critics to arrive at the university were less disposed

to give points for good intentions. In 1936, the Association of American Medical Colleges withdrew its accreditation of the School of Medicine in a scathing report that essentially said the school had ceased to exist as a recognizable medical college: The faculty was too small, their salaries were impossibly low and the budgets for supplies and equipment were minimal.

It even criticized the library, "located in two or three stacks in the basement of the University Library building...the alcove between the stacks provides reading space to accommodate five or six students." It seemed to doubt claims that the library had 3,000 books, saying perhaps they were scattered through several departments and perhaps found on shelves in the students' coatroom. In a near pathetic response, French said, "But this basement is all above ground and is well lighted and there is plenty

A Man of Few Words

Perhaps the ultimate testimony of Harley French's dedication to his work comes from Grand Forks physician Rodney Clark, class of 1946. Clark was one of dozens of military men who were put through medical school by the armed forces during World War II. It was the only time that the University of North Dakota had a student body in its medical school made up almost entirely of non-residents. The Army would assign students to the medical school closest to their home, which is how Clark, a western Minnesota native, wound up in a Grand Forks classroom on that memorable day of May 6, 1945.

"We were in anatomy class," Clark recalls, "doing a section on cadavers, with three or four students to each one. The dean was at the blackboard, lecturing about the pararectal fossa, which we were dissecting. It was kind of a warm day. No air

(continued on next page)

of room in the general reading room." He even said that the committee had missed the several books he kept in his own office, but it was to no avail. The School of Medicine was placed on probation.

Even for Harley French, who was well acquainted with getting by on zero, these were distressing times. Not that it ever showed on his face — which was usually a mask of ambiguous propriety — or that he ever let on at home that things were difficult.

"I thought we were fine," recalls Mary Margaret Frank. "My mother and Daddy never talked about finances. I didn't know we were in any way handicapped. We didn't go out and spend a lot of money, but we didn't suffer, or at least I didn't. I think my mother was humiliated. But Daddy never said very much about it. My mother and I used to say Old Science Hall could burn down and we wouldn't know about it 'til we read it in the paper."

She does recall, however, her father putting a brave front on things.

"It was hard to get faculty to stay in North Dakota, because they weren't paid very much," she says. "They'd come for a year or two and then they'd go to a bigger and better job. Daddy took that very well. He'd say the institution is bigger and stronger than an individual. An individual has to take what opportunity he gets. And the institution can somehow manage in another way.

"But I know he was very much upset. After his death, I was looking through his papers. One letter I found nearly broke my heart. It was a letter to a big medical school asking if there might be a place for him to teach. It just looked as if there wasn't going to be anything more in North Dakota. It was that horrible. Nothing ever came of that, because I think he felt he needed to stay here or the school would go to pieces."

Today, many believe it would have. "I have little doubt that without Harley French, the school would have vanished," says John Vennes, a former student of French's and a man who has served in practically every administrative and faculty position at the school, including a stint as interim dean. "Getting French to come to North Dakota was a strange quirk of fate for this medical school. They couldn't have chosen better if they'd tried and I'm not sure how they tried. But he was the glue that held this place together for so many years."

If so, what was it that held Harley French together through difficult years until after World War II when the belt began to loosen just a bit? His daughter, Mary Margaret, credits the three loves of his life: his family, his students and his colleagues.

Family life at 316 Hamline Street with Mabel and their two children, Mary Margaret and Townsley, was quiet but normal. "He wasn't a terribly social person," says Mary Margaret. "He liked to garden and he played bridge. He was good at that. He was a quiet, gentle person. He attracted children, dogs and cats, who followed him around like the Pied Piper. He wasn't bossy at all. But he could take charge when he had to."

Above the fireplace Harley hung an oil painting of Gloucester Harbor, Massachusetts, done by Paul Barr, the head of UND's art department. "It was the one and only piece of art my parents bought. They both liked it very much, enough to spend some money on art."

For years the family had no automobile and French became a familiar sight bicycling around town. Mary Margaret remembers going to public school on the streetcar. French had a special saddle built for his bike so that his daughter could ride with him. "I thought that was just great to ride with my Daddy."

In the mid-1920s, before the Great Depression set in, French came close to leaving the university. He took a year's leave of absence and moved his family to Philadelphia, where he taught at the University of Pennsylvania Medical School and did some research. For his wife, Mabel, the grandeur of Philadelphia was finally what she had wanted and hoped for all her life. The family lived in a Philadelphia suburb and the children attended private schools. Mary Margaret longed for Grand Forks; Mabel did not.

"My mother thought it was just wonderful being in Philadelphia. She hoped maybe Daddy would get a job there. And I guess he thought about it. And it seems I heard him say this one time, that he'd rather be a big frog in a little puddle than a little frog in a big puddle. So he came back, much to my delight and much to my mother's sorrow."

Far from being a brooding recluse, however, Mabel French became a well-known hostess, arranging frequent get-togethers at her modest little home for new faculty members and their wives. She also began inviting students to an annual party at their home — an event that later became formalized as The French Tea.

"They loved to come to our house," recalls Mary Margaret. "It wasn't a palatial house but it was a house. It wasn't an institution. It was always hard on me because I was shy. I didn't know how to talk with the boys. I always wished I were older."

Faculty wives would pitch in and provide coffee and cookies

Dr. Art Saiki

A most unusual man, Saiki complemented French's somewhat stiff "Herr Professor" style with an informality and joviality that made him one of the best loved teachers in the history of the medical school.

while Mary Margaret and her brother watched from the shadows.

"We had a big stairway as you came into the house. In the winter the students had to go upstairs and leave their coats on the bed. One time one of boys slipped on the steps and fell down the stairs. And the kids thought that was wonderful. It was so funny. After that, they'd watch everyone coming in, hoping they'd fall."

Mabel French died of cancer of the lymph glands in 1945. She had been ill and confined to bed for several years, but every year she managed to rally to be able to host her annual student teas. Only a few weeks before she died she hosted a party at her homemade house on Hamline Street.

Though he never admitted it, French was partial to the family pet, a wirehaired terrier named Tuck. "We just loved him," says Mary Margaret. "We loved every cubic inch of him. Theoretically, he was my brother's dog. But as my mother said, 'We all used the same dog.'"

Tuck liked to follow French on his daily walk to the campus. "Daddy didn't really want him to do that. But Tuck would sneak along where he couldn't be seen and then when he got to the door he'd say, 'Hi, here I am. I want to be with you.' Daddy was so kind and gentle. He thought, 'Well, he isn't doing any harm. Okay, come on.'"

Understandably, several of French's students have fond memories of Tuck.

"Dean French was an unusual man," remembers Clay Klakeg, class of 1943. "He was a little man with a little dog that would parade through the classrooms and check on everybody."

"Our lab was on the second floor," recalls Eva Gilbertson, class of 1939, "and we would see Dr. French coming across the campus. We always knew when he was coming into the room, because he always had his dog with him. It was a terrier of some sort. There was a blackboard Dr. French used as a screen across the doorway so that the lab wasn't visible from the hallway. And the dog would come in and run underneath the blackboard, so we knew that a couple of seconds later Dean French would come through the door."

His students remember him as much for his quirks as for his mastery of the material. A man who loved language, he would sprinkle his lectures with asides on the Greek origins of certain medical terms. While lecturing on anatomy, he would casually swing his leg up onto the top of his desk and point out the tibia, the fibula, the anklebones and so on, individually.

"He chewed tobacco, but he didn't want us to realize that he chewed tobacco," recalls Dr. Dean Strinden, class of 1950.

"Periodically, he would wipe his pen across his mouth and walk back and forth in front of the class with his arms behind him and gently scatter his chewing tobacco on the floor to get rid of it."

Others remember him chewing cloves as he went from table to table in the gross anatomy lab. Sometimes, on those visits, French would surprise his students by starting a discussion on philosophy or religion as they dissected their cadavers. Or he would suddenly point out that a particular blood vessel in a cadaver looked a lot like the road to Crookston.

"He was a very intelligent, excellent teacher," recalls Dr. Edward Hagan, class of 1940. "Everybody's attention was focused on him. He was very calm, and about the worst that he might say to you while you were working on a cadaver would be a little mumbling under his breath or a shake of his head if you were wrong."

Often he would read aloud from the textbook as students followed along. More than once, his students would turn a page and look up to see Dr. French still on the original page, but reciting the text from memory.

At the end of class he would almost always say, "Well...there's lots to read and think about now. Keep working."

While he is remembered as a largely sedate man, he was not without a sense of humor. Dr. James Mahoney, class of 1941, recalls how some years after he had graduated and gone into practice, he met French at a meeting. "He came up to me and tapped me on the chest and said, "Yes, yes, on the whole now, I have not really made up my mind yet whether I should have admitted you or not."

Dr. Dean Strinden recalls a more elaborate display of his humor. "As our examination he'd have us face away from him and put our hands behind our back. He would walk around with a small sack of bones. He would put one in your hand and you were to identify the bone, tell all the muscles attached to it and tell what the muscles were supposed to do. In that bag he had an ossified penis from a dog. Once in a while he would drop that into somebody's hand and, of course, it was a totally foreign bone and you would fumble around trying to figure out what in heaven's name is this bone from and then you would try to make up some story. He was standing back there with a big smile on his face because he knew it had nothing to do with human anatomy."

His students remember that he knew every one of them by their first names and would never pass up an opportunity to greet them or strike up a conversation. Sometimes the close interest he took in his students drove them a little crazy.

"You weren't supposed to date and you weren't supposed to drink when you went into medical school," says Mahoney. "This business of not having a girlfriend, once in a while, for Saturday night was not so good. I had a friend, Ruth, who was a drum majorette and a very lovely gal. She used to lead the band at all the activities and she didn't like the no-dating policy either. The dean had a pattern every morning of walking from his home to the medical school and he always had his favorite dog with him. The first semester, Ruth began walking behind the dean every morning on her way to class. Then she enticed his little dog to get interested in her and pretty soon the dean got interested in her because of the little dog, and then pretty soon they were walking on the campus together. By the end of that first semester, I could go back to dating again because she had some nice conversations with the dean as to how normal life ought to be lived."

When students finished their studies of the skeleton, French would announce that he was having his annual weekend picnic and that they should come to the campus that Saturday with their old clothes on. It was not your average picnic, not a picnic at all to some, for this was the meeting where he assigned specific cadavers to groups of students. The bodies — either donations noted in a will or unclaimed corpses that by law were sent to the medical school — were stored in a large vat of formalin. Students were required to dip down into the vat and catch the end of a pole to which a cadaver was attached by hands and feet. Students brought their cadavers up, cleaned them and rubbed them down with Vaseline.

"Some of us, of course, had been through some rather difficult times, so it didn't particularly bother us as we had seen a lot worse over in wartime," says Strinden. "The younger folks who had never, ever experienced having any contact with a dead person, well, it was a very traumatic experience. I suspect Dr. French was using this as kind of a washout time. If you couldn't take this, you couldn't take the rest of it, either."

In his off hours, French spent a good bit of time with Dr. Grassick, whom he considered his closest friend. Grassick, a Grand Forks physician, shared French's interest in public health and served as superintendent of public health for six years. He headed the influential North Dakota Anti-Tuberculosis Association for many years and founded Camp Grassick between Jamestown and Bismarck as a summer retreat for children with tuberculosis. In 1917, French made him a "special lecturer" at the School of Medicine. During the

Grassick's bones

Dr. James Grassick, historian and close friend of Harley French, purchased the skeleton of the Highgate Mastodon (named after the town where it was found, Highgate, Ontario) in 1898. He donated it to UND in 1902 where it remained in pieces in storage until 1947 when it was transferred the State Historical Society in Bismarck It was assembled in 1992 with help from the North Dakota Geological Survey. The skeleton is on permanent display at the North Dakota Heritage Center in Bismarck.

George Talbert

Hired by Harley French, George Talbert chaired the department of physiology and pharmacology from 1924 to 1944. He was one of a nucleus of outstanding scientists who stuck it out with French during the lean years.

influenza outbreak, Grassick was named surgeon for the Student Army Training Corps. He helped organize emergency efforts. He was elected president of the state medical association in 1923.

By his own claim, Grassick owned the finest private collection of American pre-historic and modern relics of anyone in North Dakota. In 1925, he donated to the university a skeleton of a mastodon, which he described as "the most perfect ever discovered." Supposedly, the bones were kept in a box at the university museum, to be assembled as soon as an appropriate building was erected to house it.

"He was a very special kind of person," says Mary Margaret Frank. "He wrote a small quote book every Christmas. And whenever Daddy would go downtown to a Lions Club meeting, he would always call on Dr. Grassick. My father liked him very much. He was such a dear, special friend. When he died it was really quite a blow to Daddy."

Besides Grassick, French counted two of his colleagues as close friends. He and Mabel socialized frequently with George Addison Talbert and his wife and children. Talbert was the head of the physiology and pharmacology department from 1924 until his retirement in 1944. He was one of a nucleus of outstanding scientists who stuck it out with French during the lean years. During his two decades, Talbert taught all or parts of every course offered in his department and instituted graduate courses in physiology and pharmacology, leading to a master of science degree.

In those days, research played only a very small role at the School of Medicine. Brannon, of course, was the original researcher. But in those days, experiments were virtually limited to guinea pigs, rabbits and dogs. Talbert, however, pushed research further. He was keenly interested in heat adaptation and the human body's process of sweating. He jury-rigged a vest with test tubes that collected sweat from the chest, and then analyzed it for salt and other chemicals. He would measure blood and urine for similar chemicals, using students and even the janitor, Fred Campos, as his subjects. He had several papers published in national journals.

The other stalwart on the faculty was Art Saiki. A most unusual man, he complemented French's somewhat stiff "Herr Professor" style with an informality and joviality that made him, perhaps, the most beloved teacher in the history of the medical school.

Saiki was born on the Hawaiian island of Kauai in 1899 to uneducated Japanese parents. The island had no high school and at

fifteen, Saiki was doing what his parents had done — cutting sugar cane. But the principal of what passed as a grade school on the island, was so convinced that Saiki was a smart boy who needed more education that he gave him $40 so he could travel to the big city of Honolulu. There Saiki worked in a soy sauce plant and a pineapple-processing factory and put himself through high school and the University of Hawaii.

After graduating in 1924, Saiki accompanied some classmates to the mainland. One of them had been accepted at the University of North Dakota's medical school. Saiki's plan was to become an electrical engineer, but by the time he and his friend arrived in Grand Forks, he had changed his mind and thought perhaps he would be a doctor. He met Harley French and asked him if there might be a place for another student in the School of Medicine. In those days very few non-residents were admitted to the School of Medicine, but Harley French saw the same something in Saiki as that principal on Kauai and he made an exception.

Medical brain trust

The circumstances behind this photo are unknown, but most likely it is a group from the North Dakota State Public Health Department, circa 1941. From left, top row: Walter H. Moran, H.V. Werner, Art Saiki, Richard J. Maginn; middle row: C.L. Nutzman, Lenier A. Lodmell, M.G. Westmoreland; front row: G.A. Talbert, Elizabeth Smith, Ruth Davies, Della Mathys, Delores Dawn, Harley E. French.

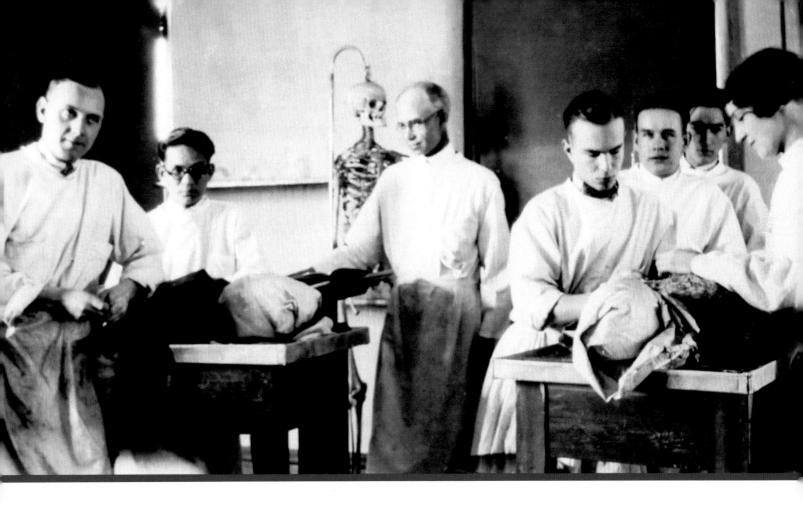

Student and mentor

Art Saiki, (second from left in this Gross Anatomy lab photo) showed up unannounced at UND in 1923 with a friend who had been admitted to the medical school. French (center) liked him right away and accepted him into the medical school.

Saiki rented a room with Mr. and Mrs. Paul Dorscher at 1510 Second Avenue North. Dorscher, a German immigrant, was an engineer for the Great Northern Railroad. His wife was a Russian who had spent time in a convent. They treated Saiki like a member of their family. In the meantime, Saiki found a part-time job working for Dr. George Arthur Henry, a silver-haired Ph.D. and theologian who taught at the University. Henry and his wife had just moved into a new home and needed help finishing the work on the house. Henry was impressed with Saiki's character and the quality of his work. When Saiki graduated from the School of Medicine and prepared to leave for the University of Nebraska in Omaha for his final two years, Henry arranged with local businessmen to help with Saiki's finances.

After earning a medical degree in Omaha, Saiki went to work there for an ophthalmologist. He made house calls and enjoyed the work, thinking he would become an eye doctor. But then George Talbert sent him a note inviting him to return to UND to teach physiology. Saiki moved back in with the Dorschers and re-established his friendship with Dr. Henry.

While teaching physiology, Saiki drifted into doing some work with the pathology department. In the fall, about a year after Saiki returned to Grand Forks, the head of the pathology department left. It was too late for French to do any recruiting, so he asked Saiki if he minded giving lectures in pathology. Both French and Saiki thought the job would be temporary. But at the end of that academic year, the dean asked Saiki to stay on as a permanent pathologist. A year after that, French promoted Saiki to full professor and chair of the department.

The move relieved French of an extra duty that he had taken on intermittently since 1914 when Gustave Ruediger left his position as the first director of the public health laboratory. Other men had filled that job over the years, but whenever they left, French would have to assume the responsibility in the interim. In Saiki, he found the perfect man to handle the duties required as the state's bacteriologist and director of the public health lab.

Although Saiki had never completed a formal residency in pathology, he became over the next forty-three years one of the best-known men in his field. "Art Saiki was one of the most profound micro-pathologists in the world," says Mahoney, one of his former students. "He was one of the most dedicated people I've ever met."

Dedicated enough that he spent his summers, when students were gone, voluntarily working alongside top pathologists in Chicago, including the legendary George Papanicolaou, who introduced the "Pap" smear. Back at UND, Saiki would offer post-doctoral training in pathology to local doctors who wanted to learn more. He did this on his own time at nights, in his lab at the school. In the meantime, he accepted tissue samples sent to him by physicians across the state and in a short time earned a reputation for his careful and accurate work. Because he was humble enough to acknowledge what he did not know, Saiki often would send difficult tissue samples to top pathologists around the country for a second opinion.

Colleagues say it wasn't unusual for him to receive a note from those experts that said something like, "Dear Dr. Saiki, I reviewed your slides and I can understand why you thought it was such and such, but in one corner of the slide there's a cluster of cells that makes me think it's this kind of sarcoma and not that kind." Meanwhile, a different expert would have examined the same slide and dashed off a gruff response saying it was obviously such and such, all the while implying it had been a waste of his time to look at it. But with each slide, Saiki's knowledge increased. When the American Board of Pathology was created some years later, it exempted Saiki from taking an exam and certified him on the spot.

Saiki's demeanor was much like that of Harley French. Both were quiet men who seldom got excited. Students revered both men.

He seemed always to be comfortable and informal, with his flowing white pompadour, his shirts with hacked-off sleeves and the ever-present glass canister of whiskey-flavored cigars on his desk.

French, on the other hand, could be distant and somewhat stiff, his answers to questions usually brief and to the point. Not Saiki.

"I could go in and talk to him anytime I wanted," recalls Dr. Robert Fischer, a former chair of the microbiology department. "You could ask him a question, but you could also talk about what your feelings were about a certain issue."

"Dr. Saiki was an unusual person," adds Dr. Clay Klakeg. "He took everybody under his wing. You couldn't help but like him. He didn't have a mean bone in his body."

James Barger, class of 1939, remembers the day in the laboratory when a fellow student who had been out celebrating the night before was having difficulty concentrating. The routine in those days was for Saiki to deliver a lecture in the morning, after which everyone would adjourn to the laboratory on the third floor. Saiki would walk around to each cluster of students gathered round their microscopes and hand out tissue samples that he had made up on glass slides.

When Saiki got around to Barger's hung-over classmate, he could see the difficulty. He said, "Do you want a slide this morning, or are you too tired?" As Barger remembers it, the student slipped off his stool and went down on his hands and knees groping around on the floor, muttering 'Slide, slide, I had one right here, just now.'

"Saiki just looked at him and smiled," recalls Barger, a far cry from the reaction Dean French might have had — especially since he disapproved of medical students drinking or even dating. Yet, different as the two men were, they became bound by ties of the strongest affection.

"Dr. Saiki became a really good friend of ours," says Mary Margaret. "He was very kind and generous. He's the one who taught me how to drive. Daddy thought somebody else should teach me rather than him. Dr. Saiki was a very good teacher. I remember one time when I was in high school I went down to a church camp in Valley City for a week or so. Art Saiki drove me down and picked me up again. It just shows how much Daddy trusted him."

French thought enough of Saiki to place him on the medical school's admissions committee. The two men often had differing opinions about the criteria for admission, but Saiki ultimately convinced French that factors other than academic prowess be considered in selecting students.

"Superior intelligence," he once told a reporter for the university's alumni magazine, "is not a prerequisite for becoming a good doctor and may even be a detriment because a bright student tends not to work hard enough."

The corollary to this philosophy was Saiki's lifelong belief: "Teachers should teach, not judge." This disregard for one of the most traditional aspects of teaching — assessing a student's worth in terms of a grade — confounded many of his colleagues, but endeared him further to students. Saiki often would stand up for a student whose low grade, he felt, did not reflect that person's total worth. He would address such an issue in terms of the student's being "unfairly judged." He would insist that the qualities most important to a doctor were measured by: being careful in making a diagnosis, being honest enough to admit to mistakes and to being humble enough to know your own limitations.

Almost certainly, his railing against being judged was connected to his experience at being discriminated against because of his Japanese heritage. He often told stories of the prejudice he had experienced. He attended a conference in Winnipeg in the 1940s during World War II. When he got to his hotel where he had reserved a room, he was told none was available. He recalled trying to rent an apartment in Grand Forks after seeing a vacancy sign in a window. When he knocked on the door, the owner told him the apartment had just been rented and proceeded to remove the vacancy card from the window. Five minutes later, after Saiki drove around the block, the vacancy card was back in the window.

Certainly the ugliest form of that discrimination occurred in the 1930s. In those years, St. Michael's Hospital had a school of nursing and Saiki was one of the teachers. He fell in love with one of his students, a woman of Finnish-Swedish heritage named Lydia Knoppala. In 1934, they wanted to get married, but could not find any church or justice of the peace who would marry a Japanese man and a white woman. They went out of state, several states away, in fact, but could find no one to marry them. When they came back to North Dakota, Saiki spoke to an attorney friend. The lawyer told him if he and Lydia lived together for a year, they would legally become common-law husband and wife — as married as anyone else.

So that's what they did. They never formally married, but moved in with the Dorschers. They had two sons, Henry — named for Dr. Henry — and Jack. After four years of marriage, however, tragedy struck. Lydia developed a rare form of deadly meningitis that causes adrenal hemorrhaging. She died within three days of falling ill. She was just twenty-eight. Henry was three and Jack was only eighteen months old.

Such was his relationship with the Dorschers that Mrs. Dorscher

Rising from the Dead

The custodian in the anatomy department, Fred Campos, became known for a very unusual practice. After cleaning the anatomy labs at night he would occasionally like to take a rest. So he would lie on an empty cadaver table in the gross dissection lab. Although we had heard this story before, we thought it was just somebody telling stories. Then one night we were going through the gross lab to get to the room where we would be dissecting cadavers the next day. There was some light coming in the windows from the outside, so we didn't bother to put on the ceiling lights. As I started into the room, one of the cadavers started to rise from the table. I would have turned and run across campus, but one of my classmates flipped on the light and there was Fred getting up off the table.

Richard Olafson, M.D., class of 1957, is a native of Drayton. He practiced neurosurgery for years at the Neuropsychiatric Institute in Fargo and later served as associate dean of the medical school's Fargo campus for more than two decades.

offered to raise the two boys while Saiki was at work at the university. "She was a great woman," says Jack Saiki today. "I called her Mom." For several years, he says, the three of them, father and two boys, lived in the upstairs bedroom, sharing the same bed.

Saiki never remarried. He later told his son that whenever he broached the subject of remarrying, Jack and Henry would become very upset. At the same time, Saiki had a very close friend at UND who was chair of the department of mechanical engineering. He was a Russian who had once been head of the Russian Navy's Baltic Sea fleet. (Only in North Dakota!) He had been married to an East Indian physician who died in childbirth. Because both he and Saiki had gone through the same trauma, they had something in common. Both men, as they talked about their experiences, felt particularly bad about the long hours they had spent at work and not at home with their wives. That, says Jack Saiki, might have been the key reason his father never remarried.

"In my younger years," he recalls, "I said he married medicine when he lost my mother."

Jack Saiki went on to become a doctor, graduating from UND in 1959 and spending most of his career as a respected oncologist at the University of New Mexico's school of medicine. He became interested in medicine very early in life, he remembers. In the close quarters of the Dorscher's upstairs room, he would browse through his father's medical books with fascination.

"I essentially grew up in the medical school," he says. "My father took my brother and me to his office in the Old Science Hall, which was the old medical school building. I remember as a kid walking all the way to medical school. We saw the frogs they were doing experiments on. And the turtles. Also, I can remember where they kept the cadavers. We were not told what they really were. Most often it was in the evenings, usually on Saturdays, we were the only ones there. My father would look through his microscope, "reading" the pathology slides of the surgical biopsies from not only Grand Forks but around the state. Simultaneously, he would be typing the report. My brother and I would fold the reports, place them in an envelope and stamp them. We then would drive late in the evening from the school to the post office to mail those reports. I think my brother and I knew more about that building than even the faculty."

His father, he says, was soft spoken. "When he said something you believed it. You listened to it. He never got angry — if he did it was rare. If he got upset, it was not in front of me. But if he told you to do something...you didn't dare not do it."

Jack and his brother lived with the Dorschers until he was in the third grade. Eventually they moved to an apartment near Central Park and later to a rented duplex.

"I find it very interesting, in retrospect," says Jack, "that my father had the ability to survive with nobody to talk to. It amazes me that he left Hawaii — in those days, travel didn't exist. To have the courage to leave his family and end up in North Dakota, it requires some sort of adventuresome trait. He had it. I don't know that I could have done that. To live his life alone."

Except that, he loved teaching. "I suspect his students meant a tremendous amount to him," says Jack. "Without a family — except me and my brother — those relationships became very special."

Jack Saiki had his father as a teacher when he was in medical school. "I discovered him as a shy person," he says. "I'd never noticed that before. He would always bring something in that he had read. When talking about typhoid — he brought in an article on Typhoid Mary. When he did that, he'd stand in the center of the hall and stand a little bit sideways reading it. Something I wouldn't have known about him."

In those classes, Jack Saiki learned why his father enjoyed the study of pathology. "My father used to say that pathology was a great field to learn about human behavior," he says. "I couldn't see the connection. He said you do an autopsy and you find something that the surgeon or doctor didn't know about. Some of them get very upset. Some find it interesting. Some of them find it as a terrific learning experience."

Even as a pathologist assigned to perform an autopsy, Art Saiki treated his patients and their families with respect. "Early in my career at UNM," says Jack, "a student from Grand Forks came to me and said her grandfather had become ill and died. After my father did the autopsy, he went to their home to sit down with the family to tell them about what his findings were. That would never occur in this day and age.

"Relating to what my father was like, the one value that stands above all others is integrity, something that played a dominant role in my life, because of how much he stressed the importance of this value. Another characteristic that he stressed, not by word but by example, is 'doing right.' I think this incorporates excellence and quality. It didn't matter what kind of work you did. It reminds me of a wonderful quote by John Gardner: 'The society which scorns excellence in plumbing because plumbing is a humble activity, and tolerates shoddiness in philosophy because philosophy is an exalted activity, will have neither good plumbing nor good philosophy. Neither its pipes nor its theories will hold water.'"

After World War II, when his boys were in their early teens, Saiki sent them to Hawaii to live with his brother. They lived there until 1950, when they got word that their father had become ill. He was diagnosed with a thoracic malignancy and was scheduled for surgery at the Mayo Clinic. The boys got on a flight back to the mainland. But by the time they arrived, doctors had changed their mind. It was not cancer, but tuberculosis, a disease he also had suffered from as a boy.

In those days, a diagnosis of TB meant a patient had to spend time in a sanatorium. Saiki spent nearly a year at Sunny Rest sanatorium in Crookston, while Jack and Henry started high school in Grand Forks, living in Saiki's Alpha Avenue home near Riverside Park. Essentially, they took care of themselves.

Saiki began to notice a ringing in his ears. He thought he was losing his hearing because he could not hear his watch ticking. His doctors seemed deaf to his concerns...

In Crookston, doctors treated Saiki with streptomycin, one of the new drugs developed since the war. But the doctors treating him did not know enough about it. Saiki began to notice a ringing in his ears. He thought he was losing his hearing because he could not hear his watch ticking. His doctors seemed deaf to his concerns, maintaining him on the drug until he was profoundly deaf. By the time he came home from Crookston at the age of 50, he needed a hearing aid.

"He was not a happy person after that," says Jack. "I wouldn't see him smile. I'd see him angry. I'd never seen that in him before. Now, looking back, it's clear he was depressed. He was worried about his career, his ability to teach, to enjoy music and go to a movie. He had no sense of direction. You lose that ability. The human ear has the ability to filter out sound. When he had the hearing aid, he heard everything. He heard dishes rattle in the kitchen. It would make it difficult to hear someone he was talking to."

The adjustment period lasted about six months, after which Saiki adapted, finding he could still teach.

"It was a bitter thing for him," says Dr. Rodney Clark, a retired

Grand Forks physician, class of 1946. "He wasn't stone deaf, but you had to talk very loud. You could see he was just a little more into his own world."

Saiki's well-known sense of humor still bubbled up occasionally. Colleagues would chuckle, noting that when certain loquacious staffers began to annoy Saiki, he would simply turn down his hearing aid. One dean later told him, "I sometimes think your deafness insulates you from a lot of the petty discussion and enables you to focus your attention on the heart of the matter."

Even so, Saiki's deafness did not lessen his energy for work. In 1955, his department of pathology started a residency program. John Vennes recalls "evening seminars in which Dr. Saiki would pass around tissue slides, smoke his cigar, and patiently wait for the residents to arrive at a conclusion on their diagnosis."

A man who worked as hard as he did had to be organized. Saiki regularly sent away to dozens of medical journals for reprints of articles that may or may not have had something to do with pathology. His faculty colleagues came to rely on him whenever a topic came up that they needed to bone up on. Before going to the library or starting their own research, they would call Saiki and, chances were, he had several reprinted articles in his collection covering the topic.

"I appreciate the long hours, the self-sacrifice and the hard work which you have given your profession," Dean Theodore Harwood wrote to him once. "Heaven knows you did not do it for the money. You have not done it for personal ambition. My feeling is that it has been because you love your fellow man."

When he died in 1980, Saiki was buried beside his common-law wife, Lydia, on a hill surrounded by wheat fields in the Finnish-Lutheran cemetery in Michigan, North Dakota.

"I have often thought of what one good deed can mean," says Earl Strinden, the former head of the UND Alumni Association, which honored Saiki with its coveted Sioux Award before his death. "We don't know the name of that teacher or principal back on that little island in Hawaii, but we do know the impact Dr. Saiki had on so many generations of students at the University of North Dakota."

Chapter 3

CHAPTER THREE

Vote Yes for More Doctors

In 1932, as the hard times caused by an international economic depression were setting in, Harley French wrote an article for the regional medical journal Lancet. In it he raised for the first time in public the concept that the two-year School of Medicine at North Dakota might one day become a four-year, degree-granting institution.

"What of the future of the school?" he asked. "Will there continue to be a place for any two-year school? Will it ever be a complete school?"

The practical minded French put his finger on three things that needed to happen to keep the school, as presently configured, alive.

First and most obvious: The state needed to support the medical school with adequate funding levels. In 1932, funds were so far from adequate the situation was eating away at the solid reputation the medical school had built in its first twenty-five years. "It would seem," French wrote hopefully, "that the work is so important that the state would not let it cease."

Second, the school itself had to keep turning out graduates of such high quality that any four-year medical school would be proud to have them. With selfless teachers such as French, Art Saiki and George Talbert, this probably was the one factor about which no one had to worry. As historian Louis Geiger put it some years

Previous page:

Uncle Sam in scrubs
Facing a doctor shortage in the military during World War II, the government paid medical schools such as UND's to train new doctors. It was the first time that a majority of medical school classes at UND were comprised of out of state students.

Dozens of Medical School graduates
served in combat during World War II and
came back changed men. Included in these
sidebars are some of their recollections.

Sherman vs. Palm

I was in the V12 program of the Navy and sent out to a naval hospital in Bremerton, Washington. Upon completion of that, I was asked if I would like to have destroyer duty or the Marines. I had always been impressed with the Marine's so I told them I would like to join the Marines. On September 21, 1943, we sailed over to New Caledonia. I disembarked and went to an officers' camp awaiting transportation out to my assignment, which was the 1st Marine Division. While I was at this transient camp, I saw some Marines and I asked them if they had known a Tom Clifford. They said, "Well, yes, he is a tank commander." Tom and I had quite a background. In 1938, Tom enrolled in economics when I was in my first year of medical school. We were both Kappa Sigs and played all different sports, but we did have an especially good touch football team. Tom was a huge man and was great on a team like that. We were very close and I think we won the championship that first year. We parted when I left for Rush in 1940 and I believe he had a couple of years left at the university.

On meeting Tom over at New Caledonia, he wanted me to have lunch with him in one of these permanent camps overseas at that time. They were almost luxurious compared to what a transient officer was getting. I went out there for a meal about 4 p.m. One of the privileges the permanent camp in the Marine Corps had at that time was that the officers could have a beer ration. I had a couple of cans of beer and we ate a fine meal, and Tom said, "Have you ever been in a tank?" I said, "No, I never have." And Tom said, "Come on and I'll show you how it is."

We get into this Sherman tank, which is a thirty-four-ton tank. It was a huge thing. Then we looked at the 75mm gun on it and we got in there, and Tom said, "Now watch." The thing roared and started up. Tom had the controls and he would lightly pull one control and the tank would swerve to the right and knock down a huge palm tree. Then he would use the other control and he would pull it back and the tank would swerve around again and hit another palm tree and knock it down. We had a great time knocking down ten or twelve palm trees with this huge tank.

Later, on New Britain, we were training for another invasion and one evening I was sitting down when some Marines came by and just out of curiosity, I asked if they happened to know of Tom Clifford. And the guy said, "Yes, we know Tom — a big fellow? As they hit the shore on Saipan, he was blown out of the hatch by Japanese gunfire and was evacuated." I had heard a lot of bad things about Saipan and I really felt sorry about this happening to Tom. I started to laugh to myself at the vision of this big, healthy fellow getting blown out of a tank on landing in Saipan. It wasn't until years later that I was able to talk with Tom and ask him how he got on there. It wasn't a serious enough injury to put him out of the war, but he was out a few weeks and returned in time to go in with the 1st Marine Tank Battalion on landing on Iwo Jima.

Edward Hagan, class of 1940, earned a medical degree in 1942 from Rush Medical College. He served his internship in the Navy during World War II, and while serving with the 1st Marines, was awarded a Silver Star and two Bronze Stars for bravery in action, as well as a Purple Heart. Clifford, by the way, also earned Silver and Bronze Stars and three Purple Hearts, and he was ordered to pay for the palm trees he had damaged.

later, French was "the father of medical education in North Dakota.... His single-minded dedication to his profession provided a living example of the meaning of the Hippocratic Oath."

The third condition was perhaps the most prescient, and the one item on French's list that no one in the state could really control. Simply put, the medical schools to which North Dakota hoped to keep transferring its students needed to have the continuing ability to accept transfer students.

"The conditions seem to be as favorable now as they have ever been," wrote French. "In fact, they are better than has been feared at various times. Just what future developments may be cannot be foretold."

Not for another forty years would those "future developments" materialize, causing most of the nation's four-year medical schools to stop accepting two-year transfer students, and creating a crisis that threatened the existence of UND's School of Medicine. In the meantime, French seemed resigned to more realistic expectations for his little medical school.

"It may be that so far as we can now foresee the future of the state, North Dakota should not look forward to having a complete medical school. Possibly the work of the first two years, well provided for, is the reasonable share to expect from a state of the wealth, population, and social conditions of North Dakota."

If that was the gauntlet of pride thrown down at the feet of North Dakota budgeters, it lay untouched in the dust for years. Between 1932 and the end of World War II, it certainly seemed as if the state did not see the work of the medical school as important at all, so stingy were its financial outlays. Not only were depression and drought complicating the scenery, but also politics in North Dakota had taken a decidedly bizarre turn.

This was the time when the old Nonpartisan League reinvented itself, in 1933 electing the controversial William Langer as governor. While he instituted a popular moratorium on foreclosures in the state and made it illegal to ship grain out of North Dakota, he also cut state spending to almost nothing. Ultimately, he was removed from office for violating campaign laws. His lieutenant governor, Ole Olson, took over and served a few months until 1934, when voters elected Democrat Thomas Moodie to replace him. Moodie was abruptly removed from office, however, when an investigation revealed he had not lived in North Dakota for the full five years before his election — as required by law. When his lieutenant governor, Walter Welford, assumed the reins of power, he became

On Campus During the War Years

It was a unique situation at UND during the war. Almost all the people in our class were military. Normally, a class would have all North Dakota guys. But these guys were from all over the country. We became a very close-knit class. There weren't that many other men on campus. So we made our own fun. We've had regular reunions every five years.

Rodney Clark, M.D., class of 1946, was a long-time OB-GYN specialist in Grand Forks and a member of the UND faculty.

My Heart Sank into My Stomach

My father-in-law was Dr. Lohman, a physician in Fordville, North Dakota. I had some time before I was going to be called to active duty, so I went to Fordville, where I took over his practice for a few weeks when he went out to vacation on the West Coast. Dr. Lohman did a fair amount of obstetrics and most of those deliveries were in the home. Because of the stability of chloroform over ether, he used chloroform for its pain relieving effect. I can remember when I was in med school they told us, 'Do not use chloroform.' But I didn't have anything else. I was in this home and the bedroom was connected to the living and dining rooms with an open archway and, of course, they just had a curtain across this. The lady was in labor behind the curtain and I had one of her sisters to help pour the chloroform while I was delivering the baby. During this process, I looked up and the lady wasn't breathing. This chloroform was coming out of the container at a rapid clip. My heart just sank right into my stomach, but fortunately when the sister stopped pouring chloroform onto her mask, the lady's natural instincts to start to breathe came back and she did. I remembered that for years, and wondered what in the world would have happened if I had gotten into a more difficult situation.

Donald Skjei, M.D., class of 1944.

the fourth governor in a span of only seven months. Further roiling the waters, the unpredictable Langer bounced back and won the governorship again in 1936.

With such inconstancy at the highest levels of state government, the medical school stood little chance of a financial turnaround. French, however, was cut from hard wood and by the sheer force of his will the school survived the hardship of trading accreditation for probation. According to the North Dakota Centennial Blue Book, he was doing essentially what many in the state did at that time to survive. "Most North Dakotans stubbornly held on, husbanding their resources and spending carefully. Even during the hard times, for example, drought-stricken counties and cities rarely missed bond payments, and indeed the public debt in the state was substantially reduced during the Depression years."

Thus, almost as if nothing had happened at all, French continued to graduate students and to find them places to which they could transfer to earn a medical degree. And those schools continued to praise the quality of the students they got, accreditation or not.

A dozen years after subtly hinting that North Dakota did not have what it took to develop a full-fledged medical school, French spoke at the Governor's Conference on Medical Care and Health Service in Bismarck. He was nearing retirement that July of 1944. He had been dean of the School of Medicine for thirty-three years, devoting every bit of his energy to the nearly impossible task of keeping it all together. That spring his wife, Mabel, died of cancer. She never had the wonderful house she always wanted and, perhaps, French at this meeting felt that he would put up with too little for too long.

"I have never been very hopeful that the state would ever be willing or able to support what is necessary for a complete medical school," he said. "Nor can I say that I am developing any sudden hopes at this time."

Nevertheless, he proceeded to lay out a rationale for a "complete" four-year medical school at the university and to challenge once more those in charge of the state's funds to rise to the challenge.

He based the need for a four-year school on the simple fact that there were only 368 physicians in a state of about 640,000 people — and many of those doctors had been called into military service. In 1942, for example, only 161 towns and villages in the state had at least one of those 368 doctors — a far cry from the peak year of 1918 when the state had 604 doctors in 268 localities. (It would get worse. By 1960, fewer than one hundred towns in North Dakota had a doctor.) French also noted that only one out of every four graduates of the School of Medicine who left North Dakota to complete a medical degree returned to practice in the state. (That, too, would worsen, falling to one in six within fifteen years).

"If we could give a larger part of the medical training in North Dakota," French suggested, "I think we could be sure that half of our graduates instead of a fourth, would remain in this state for a reasonable life of practice. One way to interest more doctors in coming to the state would be to increase the facilities for medical training in our own state."

To make the School of Medicine a "complete school," he said, would require a clinical facility that would supply student doctors with enough patients for study. His suggestion: Build a charity hospital of 250 beds and make it part of the medical school.

In those days the standard model of a "complete" medical school such as those urban schools to which North Dakota students transferred — was based on training young doctors in large, publicly funded county or municipal hospitals. Such facilities traditionally drew their patients from low-income and indigent populations in the immediate area. At these "teaching hospitals," medical students were sure to come across samples of most medical conditions they would need to understand to become competent doctors.

That same year, other voices in North Dakota began to echo similar ideas. One was Dr. Ralph E. Leigh, a prominent Grand Forks physician and a 1922 graduate of Harley French's medical school. Actually, the word "prominent" does not do Leigh justice. In the early 1930s, Leigh became the medical school's very first teacher of obstetrics and gynecology, delivering a one-hour weekly lecture to second-year students. Also, during the Depression, when the university did not have funds to pay for architectural plans for the "Winter Sports Building," Leigh picked up the tab himself. He went on to promote skating and hockey and brought traveling ice shows to Grand Forks. He also became physician for the university's hockey team. Ralph Leigh's father, Henry James Leigh was an Illinois doctor who had settled in North Dakota in the late Nineteenth century. Three of Ralph Leigh's sons, two grandchildren and a great-grandchild also would go on to become doctors in coming years.

As the first director of alumni at UND, Leigh took up the cause

Ralph E. Leigh

After World War II, Dr. Leigh (Class of '22) used his position as the first director of the UND Alumni Association to push for a four year medical school.

Alfred Lawton

The man who succeeded Harley French as dean in 1947 had excellent credentials: an M.D., and a Ph.D. But after only a year on the job, he left to take a position in the Veterans Administration.

for a four-year school, equating low funding with the low number of doctors in North Dakota. In an address before the alumni, Leigh complained of "half spending in our medical training and getting one-fourth returns." He called for the development of a medical center at the university, the construction of new buildings, including a university hospital for the indigent, and the use of existing hospitals in the state as training sites for medical students.

Another supportive voice was that of John A. Page, a UND professor of education elected president of the Alumni Association in the mid 1940s. He wasted no time in raising the consciousness of the state legislature to the plight of the medical school — still underfunded by the state and under probation by the Association of American Medical Colleges. Page declared that "the salvation of the medical school" was the legislature's challenge.

Suddenly people were talking about the need for more doctors and translating that to a need for an enlarged medical school. That would mean spending money, but with the war in its final months, prosperity seemed finally at hand. Prices for crops had risen and farm debt was falling. Within a year, a post-war construction boom would further boost the economy.

Harley French could smell that prosperity like his morning coffee.

"In my mind," he argued at that Bismarck meeting, "there is no doubt that such a plan could be worked out and that it would be both possible and desirable. If we wish to go a step further, we could do something more for medical education and at the same time take the best step that I know of to insure that a reasonable number of desirable doctors and nurses locate and remain in the state."

But French also knew it never paid to count your chickens before checking in with the hen. He therefore tempered his optimism with his usual grain of salt.

"What will be done? I am not so sure. There will be so many other plans clamoring for attention, all the way from temporary and disjointed patchwork to Utopian dreams that we cannot know."

Clearly, however, a fresh breeze of hope was blowing across the prairies. With the winning of the war came the defeat of hard times, budgetary stalemates, belt tightening and fear. Optimism replaced pessimism as sailors, soldiers and marines came home to start families and make good on long-held dreams. Change became the order of the day.

Much of that change occurred in medicine, partly owing to several advances developed under the pressure of war. During most of the fighting, the only medications available to treat combat infection were sulfa drugs. Late in the war years, penicillin came into use in limited applications. Doctors would dissolve penicillin powder in water and use it to bathe open wounds. Just as the war ended, an injectable form of penicillin became available. Meanwhile, vaccines for common diseases had been improved, especially one for influenza. Plasma had been developed to save the lives of soldiers who had lost blood, and morphine was introduced as a painkiller. The synthetic drug Atabrine was developed, replacing quinine tablets as the main treatment for malaria.

Such changes fired up a new sense of excitement and possibility nationwide regarding health care. But as the end of the war promised prosperity, it presented the School of Medicine with yet another serious financial problem. During the war, the government had paid the university to educate doctors for the military. With the war over, government funding was coming to an end and the probationary accreditation granted by the Association of American Medical Colleges was in jeopardy once more. Hence, alumni president John Page's perceived need for salvation.

The state legislature felt the heat. In 1945, it gave in and approved Page's plan to establish a State Medical Center and advisory council. This was not to be an actual building, but a bureaucratic structure designed to oversee medical spending, operations and planning. In the same session, the legislature also approved funds for a new science building at the medical school. Construction would not begin for another two years, owing to a shortage of manpower and materials caused by the war. By the time it began, the legislature had approved even more money for the building — $400,000.

But even more dramatic than a paper bureaucracy and a new building was the willingness by the state legislature to commit for the long haul. Post-war prosperity meant an expanding population and even greater demands on the diminishing number of doctors in the state. Prodded by Leigh and Page, legislators began to agree with the idea that a four-year medical school could change that. It approved a ballot measure in its 1947 session to amend the State Constitution to establish a one-mill levy on all property in North Dakota — said revenues earmarked strictly for the School of Medicine. Voters never had approved such a levy for any particular issue, let alone a particular institution such as a school of medicine.

The campaign to approve that mill levy couched the issue in the simplest of terms: "Vote Yes for More Doctors." In 1948, North Dakota voters did just that, approving a constitutional amendment

A Dollar a Day

I was totally awed, and still am, that I was accepted into medical school. My parents never really went along with the idea. They said we can't afford to send you to medical school and I said, well, let me go anyway. Let me try. I worked hard one summer out in Idaho and one summer in the shipyards in Washington State and many times on the farm. Thirty-five cents an hour was a good wage then. I calculated that if I could eat on a dollar a day, I could make it. The lunch at the Commons was thirty-five cents and dinner was sixty-five cents. That's how I made it through.

Clay Klakeg, class of 1943, practiced for nearly forty years in Santa Barbara, California.

that called for a one-mill levy — which at that time amounted to about $500,000 a year. Their approval was a de facto endorsement of the university's expansion to a four-year medical school. In fact, the passage of the mill levy put in motion a series of events that changed the fortune of the school. In 1949, the brand-new science building opened and the regional medical journal Lancet endorsed the idea of a four-year medical school in North Dakota.

Harley French, in the meantime, retired as dean of the School of Medicine in 1947, though he continued to teach for several years. Some of his students joked that, wizened and rail-thin, he looked as if he had been around the formalin so long that he was preserved. Though he still taught his anatomy course, he developed a noticeable tremor in his hand.

"We'd spend several hours dissecting some small nerve," recalls Dr. Ralph Dunnigan, class of 1953. "He would come along and pick up the tweezers and his tremor was such that by the time he was done with the nerve, it was shattered."

Alfred Lawton was his immediate successor as dean in 1947. A man with an M.D. and a Ph.D., he was a teacher and researcher at Northwestern University Medical School. At UND, he became both dean and chair of the department of physiology and pharmacology. After only a year on the job, however, he left to take a position in the Veterans Administration.

The university turned then to Wilbur Potter, a quiet Mississippian with a soft drawl and another combination M.D. and Ph.D. Potter also had a master's degree in engineering and had done some of the original research in artificial hearts. Like Lawton, he became dean and chair of physiology and pharmacology.

While Potter's tenure lasted only five years, several key changes occurred on his watch, helped considerably by the mill levy. He oversaw the construction and completion of the new medical science building and saw to it that the School of Medicine won back its official accreditation by the Association of American Medical Colleges. He also became the first dean to tap into clinical and medical resources across the state — a harbinger of the community-based approach to medical school training that would develop a quarter century later. He did this by instituting the May clerkship. Until that time, medical students at UND studied almost exclusively a basic science, non-clinical curriculum in Grand Forks. All clinical studies occurred in the third and fourth year at their transfer schools.

The May clerkship was an attempt to give students a first-hand taste of clinical medicine. Each May, graduating students spent four weeks in hospitals around the state, often working with a particular physician. While the program was in no way comprehensive, it gave North Dakota students an extra bit of experience and confidence that often put them ahead of their peers when they transferred the following fall.

In spite of such successes, Potter never seemed comfortable in the job and even confided to some of his colleagues that he did not enjoy being the dean.

"He was a true scholar," recalls a colleague, Dr. Robert Fischer. "He did not appreciate a lot of administration but he was a very fine teacher. He was well liked, but he was not a social person. He suffered in World War I from mustard gas and it affected him throughout his life."

Potter's ambivalence irked John Page, the man who had pushed through the mill levy. Page wrote a memo to then-President John West urging that West fire Potter for incompetence. But Page died shortly after and Potter remained as dean.

In spite of his unhappiness, Potter was popular with students. "In all my years of school," says Phil Dahl, class of '47, "and that includes through my final two years at Northwestern, I think he was the best teacher I ever had. He made you want to have the class last all afternoon."

Sometimes, however, his students referred to Potter, with amusement, as "the Phantom." This was a reference to his extremely low profile on campus. In fact, Potter spent most mornings at home caring for his wife. She also was a physician, but never practiced and was rumored to be ill. Typically, he would arrive in the office of the physiology department about ten minutes before lecture time, announcing, "Well, I'm here. Let's go pick out a few slides."

Donald McIntyre, one of the students who helped him select slides for that day's lecture, remembers that Potter always had a difficult time remembering the name of Bertha Opheim, the long-serving laboratory assistant in the physiology department.

"Whenever we went into the physiology lab area he would always check with me," recalls Dr. McIntyre, class of 1957. "What was her name, now?"

Potter was a chain smoker (in those days smoking was permitted, at least by the professors, in the lecture halls) and kept all of his notes on the inside of a book of matches.

"It used to tickle me," says one of his students, Dr. Clayton Jensen, "because Potter would come in with his outline for the day on a matchbook. It never ceased to amaze me. He was a superb lecturer who would get up in front of the classroom and lecture right off the cuff, never looking at notes."

Potter was matchless
Dr. Wilbur Potter, the third dean of the medical school, was known for outlining his class lectures on the cover of a matchbook. His detailed, flawless matchbook lectures were legendary.

The old Science Hall

Built in 1905, "Science Hall" was the first structure of the medical school. It lasted 44 years, until 1948 when a new medical science building opened. It became known as Med Sci South and it was in use for exactly 44 years as well.

"Dr. Potter was a very enjoyable man," adds Dr. John "Doc" Graham, class of 1952. "Coming from Mississippi, he kind of brought a different impression of a professor to us and he had a little bit of a drawl."

Potter encouraged medical students to consider transferring to southern medical schools for their third and fourth years; Graham became the first UND student accepted at Duke.

Whatever his attitude toward being dean, Potter took maximum advantage of the proceeds of the mill levy to bring the School of Medicine up to date. Medicine was suddenly different; new developments in antibiotics and surgical procedures were forcing medical schools to devise more appropriate curricula and to produce more competent doctors.

Some historians, such as Bruce T. Briggs, a professor at Moorhead State University, refer to the post-war period as the time when medicine went from an emphasis on black bags to white coats — meaning the individual, independent doctor who made house calls was being replaced by centralized hospital care.

As Briggs noted in a 1999 presentation at the state chapter of the Hospital Financial Management Association, this was a time when Congress approved easy funding for building more hospitals, when nursing homes came into wide use for long-term care. Insurance programs like Blue Cross and Blue Shield began the system of third-party payment of bills. Many older North Dakota doctors tell stories of sending a bill to a patient in pre-war days, and if they weren't paid, they simply forgot about it. Now, compensation was no longer just between the doctor and the patient.

Along with more hospitals came a more specialized form of medicine. Briggs notes that in 1946 the Fargo Clinic employed twelve general practitioners. Four years later, they had hired six new specialists. Hospitals now could not get by without modern laboratory or radiology facilities. And doctors no longer had the time or luxury of making house calls.

"If a patient lived twenty-five miles from you, well, you had to figure the amount of time it took to get there and check them out a little bit," says Edward Hagan, class of 1940. "Then, if they were sick enough they had to go to the hospital. You did very little or almost nothing by making a lot of house calls. As you look back and talk about the family doctor in 1945, 1946 and 1947 making house calls or country calls, it really did not have much value, whatsoever. You could go out and sympathize with the patient and that was about all. You used to make more house calls than you would have patients in your office during a day. This rapidly changed. You had to refuse making calls and people agreed to that. All of this transition was going on."

Modernizing the School of Medicine to keep pace with change meant shifting to a more sophisticated emphasis on the basic sciences, many of which began to break off into specialty areas of study. Potter began in his own specialty area of pharmacology and physiology. Before his arrival, students trained in the very basics of pharmacology, known until the 1940s by the old fashioned Latin term "materia medica." With new drugs coming along at a rapid rate, Potter turned pharmacology into a serious discipline at the School of Medicine. He recruited several experts to develop a curriculum, including Benjamin DeBoer, a Ph.D. who had been an associate professor at St. Louis University. DeBoer became the heart and soul of the department, remaining as chair for 25 years. (Incidentally, one of the people DeBoer recruited into the department lasted only six months because he wouldn't sign a statement saying that he was not a Communist — a requirement of all faculty instituted by university President George Starcher in the McCarthy-esque Red-baiting days of the 1950s.)

Potter also brought in Dr. Helge Ederstrom in 1952 to revamp course work in physiology. Ederstrom was not only an experienced teacher, his paintings of North Dakota landscape became immensely popular. Some of them were used on promotional posters for the state. It was Ederstrom who coined the term "Cathedrals of the Prairie" to describe his gritty portraits of ancient grain elevators outlined starkly against a broad Dakota horizon. "He had great ideas and did some splendid work in the area of research," recalls Clayton

Doctor vs. Lawyer

There were about twenty-five in my medical school class. We worked two to a cadaver and we didn't get our cadavers until three or four weeks after we got the bone box, which we got one of the first days. One of the fellows, on the day we got our cadavers, he decided medicine was not for him and he switched to law school.

Eva Gilbertson, M.D., class of 1939.

The student's lair

Looking quaint and somewhat idyllic, this typical UND dorm room reflects student life in the pre- and post- war eras. The hardest part, say many med school grads, was leaving such comfy quarters and transferring to another medical school for their final two years of education.

Jensen, Ederstrom's first graduate student. "He was a very Renaissance kind of man who did everything from sculpturing to painting to boat building. I thought he was one of the most remarkable persons I had ever met. He was a bit sometimes withdrawn or reclusive, but once you got to know him, he was a marvelous individual."

As Potter spent money on new departments and recruited bright, young scientists, the face of the School of Medicine began to change dramatically. What was once an older, sedate faculty was becoming more energetic and daring.

Two of the bright new stars were Dr. Richard Marwin and Robert

Fischer, professors from the University of Minnesota who would spend the rest of their distinguished careers at UND. Marwin became the first chair of the new department of bacteriology and immunology — later to be renamed microbiology and immunology. Fischer would one day succeed him as chair and serve in that post for twenty years.

"I recall the 1949 budget having $200 for equipment and $25 for repairs," says Fischer. "I believe the salaries for the two of us for nine months was approximately $9,500; Dick, being senior, got $500 more. We each taught the medical students, the nurses and

John Page

A stalwart supporter of a four-year medical school, Page is credited with getting the state legislature in 1947 to create a one-mill property tax levy that would support expansion. North Dakota taxpayers went to the polls in 1948 heeding the rallying cry "Vote Yes for More Doctors." The levy passed overwhelmingly.

undergraduate microbiology courses. In addition, Dick taught a course in hygiene and sanitation."

Because they taught students in the university's general population, any new hire for the School of Medicine in those days had to be approved not only by the university president and Dean Potter but by Jack Robertson, dean of the university's School of Arts and Science. Fischer remembers the day Robertson drove him and Marwin around Grand Forks on a cook's tour. Apparently, he felt it necessary with this new crop of young men to point out several supposedly disreputable saloons in town. "Faculty members," he said disapprovingly, "are not seen in these places."

Fischer recalls a more uncomfortable moment with John West, the university president at the time. "He was a very inquisitive man," says Fischer. "One of the first things he asked me was what my religion was. I said, 'What difference does it make?' He said, 'Well, we would like to keep a balance.' I said, 'Okay, now you have a balance.'"

Fischer and Marwin were trained researchers — a rare species the university had not seen much of until then. Even more scarce was grant money, but Fischer quickly proved to be adept at landing grants for equipment and research projects from the American Cancer Society and the National Institutes of Health. One of the first grants the school ever got came when the federal government gave him $5,000 to bring in expert guest lecturers to teach students, staff and medical staff in the community about recent advances in cancer research and treatment.

"There were questions about how much research should be done in basic sciences," says Fischer, "and I was criticized on numerous occasions for doing too much research. But, in order to build a department, you had to have money and if you didn't get money from the state, you had to get it from outside sources."

The NIH was so impressed with his work that it sent a representative to inquire about Fischer's research on insect transmission of viruses. They proposed a long-range, fully-funded project on insects and tumor viruses, which he gladly accepted. He began raising mosquitoes, cockroaches and mice, feeding them infected tissue and then analyzing their droppings.

"I thought it was exciting," he says, "but every time a cockroach was seen in a hallway, I got blamed for it. Those old buildings were full of cockroaches anyway."

Fischer's very first graduate student was a young, recently discharged Navy corpsman from Zahl, North Dakota, named John Vennes. He went on to become chair of the department and interim dean of the entire School of Medicine.

Eager young investigators such as Fischer, Marwin and Vennes were used to graduate programs — studies that were not prevalent in Grand Forks in those days. "We felt it a necessity to establish graduate programs," Fischer says. One of the earliest programs he and Marwin established was a joint venture with the newly-created department of biochemistry and its inventive young chair, Gene Cornatzer.

In the meantime, the list of other new departments kept growing. In 1952, a formal department of medicine — later called internal medicine — was formed. A year later, a department of surgery was organized. In 1949, Fischer offered a course in the nascent science of new gizmos and equipment, heralding the start of the School of Medical Technology.

A department Potter had little to do with starting was neurology. In 1951, university President West told Potter he had met a neurologist in Fargo named Lee Christoferson, Sr. Greatly impressed, West told Potter to get Christoferson to come up to Grand Forks for a series of lectures on neurology and neurosurgery. Potter brought the matter before the curriculum committee and soon after, sophomore students were required to take the six two-hour lectures. Thus began the long association with Dr. Christoferson, whose reputation would soon soar among North Dakota doctors. The subject matter of the course material expanded a year later to include psychiatry, based on the availability of a bright young psychiatrist named Duane Somerness.

One of the pluses of the New Science Building was additional space for a medical library — 2,000 square feet on the first floor, a basement reading room for thirty-six students, plus seventy-five new books to go with the 5,600 volumes that already had been transferred to the new library. The Medical Library Association approved and gave accreditation to the new Harley E. French Medical Library.

The New Science Building also doubled the space available to the physiology department and Potter made good use of it. Until then, students took basic physiology courses in the second semester of freshman year and first semester of sophomore year. In 1953, Potter expanded this to include clinical physiology for sophomores, focusing on physiological interpretation of the disease process. This visionary concept did not become standard in most medical schools until the 1980s.

By the early Fifties, the time seemed especially ripe for going beyond the talk about expansion to a four-year school of medicine to enacting the legislation required to get it done. Improvements in

Army vs. Navy

At the end of our freshman year it was absolutely necessary, if you were physically able, you had to join the Army or Navy and continue your education in that capacity. I remember a group of us went to Dr. French and asked him which he recommended: joining the Army or the Navy. He said, "Well, if you get into trouble when you are in the Army, you can always walk back." I think the majority of the class joined the Army.

Donald Skjei, class of 1944, was born in Kempton, North Dakota. He earned a medical degree at Temple, did his pediatrics residency at Children's Hospital in Detroit, and eventually settled in Williston. He retired in 1985.

I had to sit on a court martial board for people who were being court martialed because of mental problems. One interesting thing was that I was only a first lieutenant, and we had a full colonel with schizophrenia. I said that he had to be cashiered back to the States, but I couldn't make that determination because a lieutenant couldn't say that about a colonel, so they had to get somebody of his rank to say that.

Martin D. Sommerness, M.D., class of 1943, studied psychiatry at the Menninger Center in Topeka, Kansas, and neurology at the University of Minnesota and the Mayo Clinic. He was a partner of neurosurgeon Lee Christoferson, Sr., in Fargo for several years.

healthcare, the mill levy, and people like John Page pushing the idea all played a significant role. But when the idea presented itself in full blossom, it came from the most unexpected place of all: the notoriously tight-fisted state legislature.

Consider that on June 16, 1951, state Senator Joseph B. Bridston, a Grand Forks Republican, appeared before the Medical Center Advisory Council at its semiannual meeting to urge in great detail the conversion to a four-year school.

By law, the advisory council was empowered to distribute mill-levy funds to the State Board of Higher Education without any further legislative approval. Bridston was there to remind the council that the entire legislature had passed a resolution in the session just ended, directing the Board of Higher Education to "proceed with all possible dispatch to get a complete four-year medical school in operation at the University of North Dakota."

This was no hurried decision, he said. The legislature had "studied and investigated developments throughout the country in connection with medical education and progress. There never has been any attempt to rush the program. No one in connection with it has ever gone off 'half-cocked,' and that is why after six years the sponsors are now for the first time asking that a definite program be set up toward the end of establishing a full four-year medical school."

Just in case anyone thought that perhaps the mill levy was adopted for some other reason, Bridston noted, "In all legislative hearings and debates on this program, the establishment of a complete medical school has been openly discussed as the ultimate goal. The financing, which is very important, has been arranged for."

It had to have been a rare sight, that of a state senator more or less asking a state agency to spend the money the way the legislature wanted it spent, please. Bridston argued that it was ridiculous to spend money educating students in North Dakota, and then forcing them to leave, often losing them for good. Only a four-year school would "keep our medical graduates at home and give North Dakota more doctors — which the people demand and voted for."

Although that argument would be forceful even twenty years later, the facts he used to back it up were, at the very least, not of the caliber one might use to persuade, say, a state senator on a powerful legislative committee to appropriate money. For instance, Bridston said legislators were certain that the one-mill levy would bring in enough money to operate a four-year course that would graduate about forty competent general practitioners each year. He based this on an off-the-cuff answer given in a phone conversation he had with a doctor from the AMA

Fierce Competition

The strongest memory I have is one of anxiety. I think all of us that enter medical school have a certain fear. There is a certain whispering that goes on to the effect of, "Well, a few of you won't be here at the end of the year." At that particular time in 1950, a lot of the WWII veterans were entering medical school and there was tremendous competition. As I recall, there were some sixteen hundred applications for the class of 1950.

Robert Jordheim, M.D., class of 1952, practiced for years at The Fargo Clinic.

asked quickly how many doctors could be educated for $525,000.

Bridston also disputed objections of some doctors "who refuse to admit that there is any shortage of doctors — because the large towns seem to be well supplied." As part of his proof that there really was a shortage, he cited recent articles in Reader's Digest and Collier's magazines. He, however, did cite also an AMA report that gave the nation's 1949 ratio of doctors to population as 135 for every 100,000. North Dakota, he said had only seventy-eight per 100,000. Worse, the national ratio of general practitioners was sixty-five per 100,000, while North Dakota's was forty-six. Five counties in the state had no doctor, he said. Neither was there a doctor in the one hundred miles between Jamestown and Bismarck.

"The people in the rural areas and in the small towns in North Dakota voted for a one-mill levy because there was a shortage of doctors and through this one-mill levy saw their only hope of ever securing medical service that their children and families are entitled to. If anyone can prove that there is no shortage, let us forget the whole thing. Let us not kid ourselves," he said.

Bridston said that by using hospitals around the state as training points and by setting up a de-centralized preceptor plan — enlisting private doctors as faculty — an expanded medical school would work in lowly populated North Dakota. Other states, he said, that had no large cities or teeming university hospitals to supply patients for training, had set up such preceptor programs for their rural medical schools.

One such was the University of Vermont's medical school program. It had converted from a two-year school to a four-year school forty years earlier by using a decentralized preceptor plan for clinical clerkships. The entire cost of their program, Bridston said, was about $500,000 a year. This estimate was based on a phone conversation with the dean of the Vermont school, Dr. William E. Brown. Vermont, Bridston noted, had only sixty percent of North Dakota's population and only two cities with more than fifteen thousand. If they could do it, he said, North Dakota could do it.

"Your legislature has spoken," he said. "The voters have supplied the money. It is no longer a question of whether we should establish a complete medical school. The only question is — when, how soon! The mandate of the legislature and the people cannot be ignored or in any way sabotaged by dilatory, delaying tactics!"

The council actually didn't need a lot of persuasion. A year earlier, the secretary of the AMA's Council on Medical Education and his counterpart at the Association of American Medical Colleges after coming to Grand Forks and reviewing the situation, had urged

Getting Priorities in Order

I got married in 1948. In 1949, money became an issue, so I took a year off and went back to Williston and worked in the pharmacy. It was an interim sort of thing. I knew I'd go back to school. But I needed to make money to at least own a car.

John Vennes, PhD., was born in Zahl, North Dakota, joined the faculty at UND in 1952 and has never really left. He has chaired the department of microbiology, served as interim dean and Associate Dean of the School of Medicine.

A Doctor with Wings

Life is what you make it. You get into all sorts of things and each event depends on your attitude and how you look at it. I made use of my G.I. Bill of Rights by going out and getting my pilot's license at six in the morning. If you are going to get a night call, it usually doesn't happen at sunrise, because they will usually wait until the office opens, so that's when I did my flying and got my certification. We had poor roads when I first came up here. Once we had a blizzard that was just beginning to clear and I had a lady, due with her first baby, go into premature labor out where there weren't roads. The snowplows couldn't get to her. So, I took a pilot, as I had learned very rapidly that I could go out on a house call with my airplane, but I couldn't keep the airplane warm and take care of the patient, too, so I flew with a pilot most of the time. But, anyway, we went out in the country with the wind blowing and taxied up to the farm.

(continued on next page)

the school to begin planning for an expansion to a four-year school. In fact, that visit had energized the legislature as well.

One small technical hurdle remained: the School of Medicine was still on probation, dating to the bitter years of the late 1930s. But with the enthusiasm shown by the AMA and the Association of American Medical Colleges, it was apparent that full accreditation would not be a problem.

Thus, following Bridston's appearance, the Medical Center advisory council decided to create a small survey committee to visit the School of Medicine and assess its chances of full accreditation in case of expansion. Two medical educators made up the committee. John Ascott was the respected dean of the medical school at the University of Alberta — a regional and rural school like North Dakota. The second man was William E. Brown, the dean of the School of Medicine at the University of Vermont in Burlington — and the man to whom Bridston had referred in his address.

At the last minute, Brown could not make the trip, so he sent his assistant dean as a substitute. Thus did fortune come to link Dr. Ted Harwood and the University of North Dakota.

Harwood and Ascott arrived and made their inspection. While not calling for an immediate conversion to a four-year school, they suggested a next logical step. Create the structure of a four-year school first, they said. Work out exactly where students would train around the state. Come up with a new, workable curriculum for all four years. When that is done, revisit the idea of expansion. One other small point: Do away with the title and position of director of the largely bureaucratic Medical Center and make its chief officer the dean of the School of Medicine.

Their ideas were accepted and work on a structure and curriculum was begun. By 1952, the school was back in the good graces of both the AMA and the Association of American Medical Colleges. In the meantime, the legislature in 1953 actually adopted a bill that called for the establishment of a four-year school of medicine. It also revised its mill levy authorization, saying, "A sufficient portion of such funds, however, shall be retained by the Board of Higher Education to permit the establishment of a third year course of medicine at the center not later than 1955 and a fourth-year course not later than 1956...."

The matter seemed almost certainly a fait accompli. If it had been an opera, someone would have cued the fat lady.

Before that could happen, though, Wilbur Potter announced he was resigning as dean. Finally, he was going to spend time doing what he enjoyed most — teaching. No one was surprised, but the exit presented a dilemma. In the first forty-two years of its existence, the School of Medicine had known only two deans — each precisely the right man taking over at precisely the right time. With Potter's withdrawal, the university had gone through three deans in less than six years.

Perhaps it was inevitable that the university would need to endure a lengthy transition before it found the right person to replace the stoic and singular Harley French. After all, it's hard to be the man who follows The Man.

But this time around, the university thought it had finally found exactly the right candidate, someone not only to replace Potter but to stick around for a while and turn the two-year School of Medicine into what French wistfully envisioned as "a complete" school.

As luck would have it, that perfect man was practically staring them in the face. He was that quiet, genial doctor from Vermont whom the university had gotten to know on his recent visit. Vermont had already done what North Dakota wanted to do: expand its medical school from two to four years. That is why the one thing they were sure of on the selection committee was that Ted Harwood knew exactly what they wanted.

In fact, he was a man who performed admirably as dean for the next two decades. Students loved him; legislators respected him; he was everybody's friend. He accomplished much in his tenure and brought the school's reputation back to where it was in the glory days under French. Harwood did everything the university asked of him — except, of course, the one thing for which it had embraced him in the first place. In that respect, he was exactly the wrong man for the job.

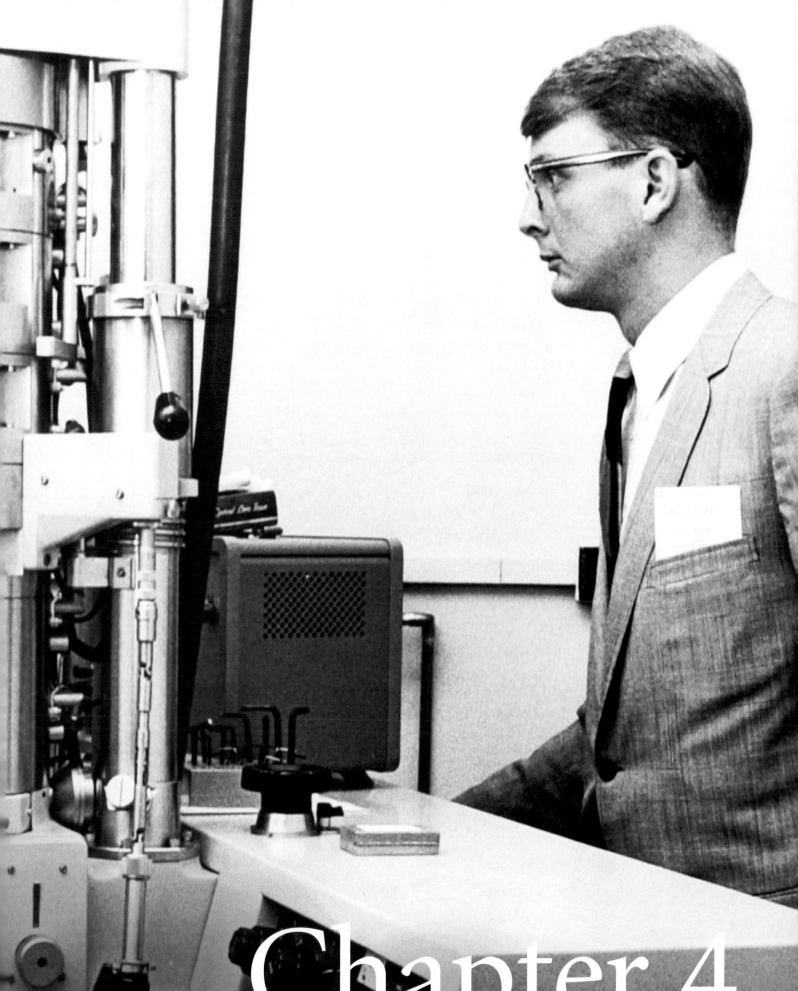

Chapter 4

CHAPTER FOUR

A Word to the Wise is Unnecessary

The first thing Ted Harwood did as dean of the School of Medicine was to type up a letter of resignation and place it on file in the office of university President George Starcher. He later explained the letter to his son, Bill. "Anytime I'm not doing my job," he said, "I expect to get fired."

As far as understanding what his job was, Harwood hung on the wall of his office a copy of the resolution from the state legislature to create a four-year school of medicine. The irony is that Harwood did not intend to expand to a four-year school. In fact, over the next few years he slowly but deliberately suffocated the idea. It took twenty years, but eventually — as he always feared — that strategy would cost him his job.

It was not that Harwood came to North Dakota under false pretenses. Or that he wanted to undermine the School of Medicine, or even to play some kind of power game. "My father had great integrity," says Bill Harwood. "Life for him was a struggle between the moral and what he had to do to be dean. He had a very unbending moral code and it gave him a lot of trouble his whole life."

That moral code was hardwired in young Ted Harwood from the moment he was born in the small Vermont town of Dorsett in 1911 — the year Harley French arrived in Grand Forks. Founded in 1761, Dorsett

Previous page:

Harwood in action
Dr. Ted Harwood, shown in 1969 with medical students around an electron microscope, was brought in as dean to expand the medical school from two to four years. He ended up opposing the idea.

is half way between Burlington and Bennington. It once was known for its marble quarries and for supplying the stone that graces the New York Public Library. In Vermont, stone is not only a major crop, it is a metaphor for bred-in-the-bone New England values. Ted Harwood learned them well. He grew up on a farm, one of seven children raised by strong-willed, Presbyterian parents who, it was said, did not get along. By the time he had grown to adulthood, Harwood developed his life's passions: a nurturing zeal honed in the family garden; a strict sense of frugality common to many New Englanders, and in seeming direct counterpoint, a love for singing.

Harwood was a short man, about five feet eight inches tall, who, later in life, would drily refer to himself as a mesomorph. As a young man, he was shy and reserved but found an outlet singing in the church choir. He graduated in 1932 from Hamilton College in upstate New York, and then went back to Vermont for his medical degree at the university in Burlington. Following internships in Boston and Montréal, he returned to his alma mater in 1939 to teach internal medicine. Two of Harwood's brothers also became doctors. A third became an escalator mechanic, while his three sisters married and settled down in Vermont.

Like the rest of the family, Harwood married and lived a comfortable, conservative life in Burlington. He and his wife were well known for their participation in church and community activities. According to his son, Bill, Ted Harwood would have been content to spend his entire career at the University of Vermont. But after rising to assistant dean at the medical college in 1950, he realized that the university never was going to promote a local doctor to the top spot of dean. Reluctantly, he began looking around for another job.

His inspection tour of the UND School of Medicine came about not long after that decision. One thing Harwood liked immediately about North Dakota was its thick black soil, much richer than the hardscrabble rocky ground he was used to in Vermont. When he moved his wife and three children west in 1953, he bought a working farm on the outskirts of Grand Forks. He leased the land to a farmer who rotated the crops each year among barley, flax and potatoes. The Harwoods lived on the farmstead, and Dr. Harwood had his own garden next to the house, where he lovingly tended vegetables and flowers. But he always gave most of the harvest away to friends or faculty.

"It was one of his rules," recalls Bill. "If you grow vegetables and flowers you had to give them away. That's why you garden. That's why you farm."

Even with his New England accent, a very proper attitude and the shy habit of looking up at the ceiling when he lectured, Harwood earned high marks from students for his kindness and solicitous interest in their welfare. To many, he became a father figure.

"Dean Harwood was a great favorite," recalls one of those students, Dr. George Johnson, class of 1958. "He was a special dean who put the students first. Above all, he knew the students. He always was a bit heartbroken about leaving his beloved state of Vermont to come to roughhewn North Dakota. Yet he understood what this place was about. He knew this was where he was going to spend his career and contribute what talents he had to this place."

The move west was hardest on his mother, says Bill Harwood. "In Vermont, they were locals born and raised and were well known. Going to North Dakota turned things upside down for her. She never quite fit in. She belonged to clubs and was in church, but she always felt like an outsider. She never cozied up to North Dakota."

One of the first faculty members Harwood came across was a young John Vennes. An instructor in the new bacteriology department, he had earned a master's in bacteriology, studying under Dr. Robert Fischer. Vennes was keen to go on to earn a doctorate, but North Dakota had no such program. When the doctoral program at the University of Michigan accepted him, he hesitated because he did not have the money. Harwood stepped in and provided financial help from his School of Medicine budget. Vennes felt so grateful that after getting his doctorate, he returned to North Dakota and began a long and distinguished career as a teacher and administrator. He remembers as the hardest day of his life, some twenty years later, the moment he walked into the dean's office to take over — as Harwood walked out.

"I suppose he may have seen something in me that reminded him of his formative years," recalls Vennes. "In the twenty years he was dean, we were always very good friends. I felt very good about working for him."

So did most of his colleagues, his idiosyncrasies notwithstanding.

"Dean Harwood was a man who liked to talk," says Dr. Wally Wasdahl. "He could talk all day if he wanted to and would be oblivious to what else was going on. He was a very humane and compassionate man. I doubt if he could have made it too well in the private sector as he was too gregarious, but I got along with him."

When he took office, Harwood found himself with a brand-new science building and a faculty that was in many respects also brand-new. Harley French, however, was still there and Harwood, out of respect, invited him to dinner at the farm on occasion. By then, French lived with his daughter, Mary Margaret. She had been a

Ted Harwood

Hardworking and admired by his students, Harwood spent almost two decades as dean ducking the expansion issue, while at the same time enhancing the reputation of the two-year medical school nationwide.

The Harwood family
The 1954 Christmas photo of The Harwood Family with a
Vermont map visible on the wall. From left to right: Ted Jr., 11,
Dr. Harwood, Mrs. Harwood, Bill, 8, Judy, 16.

schoolteacher in Nashville, but came home in the early 1940s when
Mabel was diagnosed with cancer. She continued to teach and kept
house for her parents. When her mother died, she says, "I couldn't
leave Daddy at first. He was very philosophical about Mother's death.
He was stronger than I was. I would have gone to pieces."

Mary Margaret eventually left again to attend library school. She
and her brother, Townsley, both became librarians. She took a job in
Springfield, Illinois, while her father lived in a room on the ground
floor of the Hamline Street house, renting the top floor to two college
girls. When a job came open in Grand Forks, Mary Margaret moved
back to town. In 1957, at the age of forty-five, she married a chemistry
professor at the university named Richard Frank and became head
librarian in her hometown. Her father moved in with the newlyweds.

"It was a little hard on the men," she recalls. "They were both quiet
and gentle, but each was a little uneasy. They didn't know which one
was the boss of the house. They didn't clash but I had to be in the
middle and keep things going. I couldn't say, 'Daddy, I don't want to
live with you anymore.'"

By the time of French's death in 1961 at the age of eighty-seven,
a cadre of scientific leaders whose grant-supported research began
attracting national attention had largely supplanted the old guard on

the faculty. Ted Harwood, in many respects, was an old-school doctor and uneasy with so much change. Yet the medical and scientific revolution of the day was as unavoidable as Dr. Robert Fischer's well-funded cockroaches.

"Harwood was a very New England person," says Fischer. "Very proper. He did not have a great interest in research, although he realized we had to have research. But I think he simply wanted to do an excellent job teaching medical students and making sure they transferred after two years."

Clearly, the most brilliant and energetic of all of the young professors who transformed the faculty in the early Fifties was a man hired by Potter at the behest of the prominent Grand Forks doctor, Ralph Leigh. His son, Jim Leigh, graduated from the UND School of Medicine in 1950 and, along with several other UND classmates including Bill Buckingham and Jim Moses, transferred to Bowman Gray School of Medicine at Wake Forest in North Carolina. The North Dakota students, especially Jim Leigh, struck up a friendship there with an unusual classmate named William Eugene Cornatzer.

He was a young man from a dirt-poor family in the tiny town of Mockville, in the hills of North Carolina. At the time, Cornatzer already held a doctorate in biochemistry from the University of North Carolina. In fact, he actually was an assistant professor at Bowman Gray while also studying for his medical degree. As the story goes, Cornatzer's grades were so high as a med student that when they came to figure the class standing, they automatically started counting below him. His reputation was such that even from the beginning of his career he never had trouble making key associations with top scientists around the world. At Bowman Gray he worked with Dr. Camillo Artom, who was an associate of the legendary Italian physicist Enrico Fermi, who developed the world's first nuclear reactor. Through Fermi's work, the radionuclide 32-P had become available for metabolic studies. Artom and Cornatzer used it at Bowman Gray in pioneering research.

When Jim Leigh told his father in Grand Forks about his brilliant classmate, the elder Leigh — the first director of UND's Alumni Association — thought immediately of recruiting Cornatzer to UND. At the time, Dean Wilbur Potter was interested in starting a department of biochemistry. But Wake Forest University in Winston-Salem got to Cornatzer first and appointed him to their newly formed biochemistry department. Undeterred, Ralph Leigh flew to Winston-Salem and convinced Cornatzer to come to Grand Forks for an interview with Potter.

William Cornatzer

Perhaps the greatest scientist the medical school has ever seen, Cornatzer practically invented the department of biochemistry in 1951. Through his achievements and national reputation he brought millions of dollars in research funds to the university.

Scientists at work
Paul Ray, left, and Robert Nordlie, right, both Ph.D's (now professors emeritus) were two of the shining stars in Gene Cornatzer's groundbreaking biochemistry department.

Thus, the young Professor Cornatzer, still a medical student, arrived in Grand Forks in December 1950 in the middle of a blizzard. When the airplane landed, the snow was so thick on the runway the plane could not taxi all the way to the terminal. Cornatzer and other passengers had to jump out into the snow and hoof it from there. Why that did not discourage a Southern boy from coming to North Dakota, when his grades and contacts could have landed him a job almost anywhere in the country, remains a mystery to many. His friends say Cornatzer simply loved a challenge. They also note that he was a man so full of energy that it is possible he might not have noticed the snow. Not very likely, says Cornatzer's son, William, a Bismarck physician and himself a UND med school alum. "He'd only seen snow once in his life, until then," he says. "He loved it, and he loved the folks he met in Grand Forks and at the medical school."

Potter was so impressed he hired Cornatzer essentially to invent the department of biochemistry. Cornatzer finished his medical degree at Bowman Gray in June 1951 and started work at UND on July 1. His father's plan, says Bill Cornatzer, "was to come for two years, get the department started and then leave. Several different schools offered him departmental chairs. He could have gone anyplace he wanted, but he loved the area and loved the people here."

"Gene hired a couple of faculty, took over a student laboratory and made it a research laboratory," recalls John Vennes. "Immediately he went out and picked up equipment for working with radioisotopes. His car was always on full speed. He only had one speed."

As chairman, Cornatzer focused his department on research into clinical chemistry, enzymology, biological regulation, amino acid and lipid transport, mitochondrial function and the mechanism of hormones. He was one of the first scientists to use a radioisotope of phosphorous in his studies of phospholid metabolism in membranes.

Cornatzer never was afraid of recruiting faculty with more talent. One of them was Bob Nordlie, so brimming with talent that Cornatzer offered him tenure at the tender age of twenty-eight, just two years out of graduate school. It was a move upsetting to some of the more traditional- minded faculty that were not at all sure about biochemistry or radioisotopes and were not convinced that anyone should be doing "that sort of thing" in North Dakota. But as they would soon learn, Gene Cornatzer never took no for an answer in anything.

"Nobody can fully describe Dr. Cornatzer," says Nordlie, now retired after a brilliant career capped by his chairing the department

Robert Nordlie

Hired by the brilliant Gene Cornatzer, Nordlie was deemed such an up and coming talent that he was offered tenure at the age of 28, only two years removed from graduate school. One of his teachers was John Vennes who remembers giving him an A.

Johnson's Liver Problem

I had trouble studying the liver. We had a female cadaver and I did what Dr. Hamre told us never to do. He opened the class by saying, "If you take any human tissues out of the laboratory, you are out of medical school now." Well, in all the stresses of this, I forgot his admonitions, stern though they were, and I took the liver to my dormitory room in Sayer Hall to study all the hollows and curves of the liver, of which I was certainly unsure. I was the last one before the Christmas vacation to finish the anatomy exam and I never heard sweeter words before that or since, than when Dr. Hamre finally said to me, 'Johnson finish up, you're going to pass anyway.' I hurried home to Bismarck, forgetting the frozen liver right outside the window at Sayer Hall, which was on the ground floor. I called Lyle Hillman, my lifelong best friend and I said, "Oh, my God, Lyle, that liver is sitting there in the snow!" He was there in Mountain, North Dakota, his home, and I said, "Are you going to go to Grand Forks to see if you can find that liver?" And he said, "No, I'm not going to Grand Forks." So I had the most uncomfortable Christmas vacation I ever had. I just

(continued on next page)

Cornatzer founded. "He was an absolutely unique individual. He came up here full of ambition and full of energy. I've never seen anybody more energetic than Gene Cornatzer. He was bound and determined not only to educate medical students and do an outstanding job, but to create a department that had a graduate program to educate people as master's and Ph.D's in biochemistry, and he did just that."

Cornatzer was a short man with very thin hair, known for his brown shoes and nervous energy. His boisterous, outgoing friendliness and Southern accent intrigued everyone. He also owned the first Volkswagen in town and was very proud of it.

His students immediately took to him, though not necessarily for his lecturing skills. An extremely animated man, Cornatzer paced up and down the aisles of his classrooms, buttoning and unbuttoning his coat as he jumped from one topic to the next. He often showed slides and, according to legend, he was so wound up that he would put a slide into the projector, turn it on and rush forward, beating the image to the screen.

"He wasn't a particularly good lecturer because he was difficult to follow," says Clayton Jensen. "Ideas kept popping up in his head like popcorn, and he sometimes wouldn't follow through on his train of thought before he got off on another tangent. It was sometimes difficult to follow him. His lectures were always interesting but you had to make sure you took notes so you could follow on a particular area he was talking about."

"We had been taught organic chemistry by Dr. Moran," recalls Dr. Al Samuelson, "and then Dr. Cornatzer came and introduced a dynamism into biochemistry that had never been there. He was a hyperkinetic, marvelous person. Not the best lecturer in the world, but his heart was as big as all outdoors."

His students called him Corny and knew him for his bubbly smile and intense desire to see them succeed. "When you took your oral exams from Gene Cornatzer, you could tell by the way he moved his head if your answer was right or not," recalls Dr. Robert Eelkema. "He wanted you to be right. He was a good instructor and he was fun to be with."

Dr. George Johnson remembers Cornatzer pulling a twenty-dollar bill out of his pocket and stuffing it into the pocket of a student who had arrived at medical school with no extra clothes. "Well," Johnson recalls, "you don't find that happening in the large medical schools when there are 150-250 students."

Cornatzer's enthusiasm was contagious. Before long, he began a relationship with physicians at the Grand Forks Clinic and involved them in several research projects. He did not stop there. He befriended Guy and Bertha Ireland, who owned a lumberyard in Grand Forks. They became convinced that his research ideas on investigating the basic molecular biology of the cell during growth and development would help in the fight against cancer. In 1953, they donated $11,200 to have a special laboratory built. It opened in 1956 and the keynote speaker at the dedication was Dr. Fritz Lipmann, the Nobel Prize laureate in medicine and physiology.

In its early stages, the Ireland Research Laboratory was a one-story structure. In 1957, Mrs. Ireland donated $75,000 for an expansion. Cornatzer wangled another $75,000 from the old federal Department of Health, Education and Welfare, and $50,000 from the state legislature. Before he was done over the next few years, he arranged another $500,000 from various federal sources.

"Through his energy and determination, he got money to add four stories to the building," says Nordlie. "This was the beginning of biomedical research at the University of North Dakota. It provided quarters for housing people not only for biochemistry, but also for microbiology, physiology, pharmacology and anatomy. All of these departments had people there and were able to hire people not only to teach, but to do research as well. Cornatzer then went ahead and located staff and funding for them."

Not only was outside money coming in to hire new people, but also the salaries paid to them began finding their way into the economy of Grand Forks and surrounding areas. It was the start of something big that has grown every year since — the positive economic impact of medical research on the city and state.

When the completed Ireland Research Laboratory was dedicated in 1963, Cornatzer seemed to have no trouble coaxing to Grand Forks two more international Nobel Prize laureates for guest lectures.

Over a thirty-year period, Cornatzer and his department pulled in almost $7 million in outside funds for various projects and laboratories. This included one of Cornatzer's crowning touches, the establishment of the Hill Research Professorships. Early in his tenure, Cornatzer approached the Hill Family Foundation in St. Paul, whose endowment came from James J. Hill, the empire builder of the Great Northern Railway. The Foundation created the Hill Professorships program, which funded in full the salaries and research projects of top-notch scientists. Robert Nordlie was the first recipient and John Vennes, a newly minted Ph.D., was among the first five Hill professors.

Another of Cornatzer's coups came out of his appointment to

Christopher Hamre

Brusque, stiffly formal and derided by some students as "the Danish Field Marshall," Hamre inspired fear in his anatomy classes, although few would argue they didn't learn a great deal from him.

the human nutrition and consumer use research advisory committee of the U.S. Department of Agriculture. He parlayed that into the first-of-its-kind, federally funded Human Nutrition Research Laboratory, which opened in Grand Forks in 1970. Never before had a laboratory been built for the sole purpose of studying the trace elements. Since its opening in 1970, it has tripled in size. "That was a real feather in the cap for North Dakota and the city of Grand Forks," says Nordlie.

"He knew what it took to do good research," says Vennes. "He knew the kind of energy it took to get things going. Gene essentially wrote his own ticket. He did it in a scholarly, professional way. He put the school on the map in terms of research. He was known nationally and he attracted some very good people." It was not at all uncommon for Cornatzer to show up at a lecture in the company of a Nobel Prize winner he had invited to North Dakota. In his office, Cornatzer hung a map of the world to pinpoint every city and country that had sent him requests for reprints of journal articles written by his faculty. As he and his department published more than two hundred papers and abstracts, pins covered the map.

More than one observer from those days says that Ted Harwood's greatest contribution while dean was to give the hard-charging Cornatzer his head and not to interfere with any of his projects. Actually, Harwood got along fine with Cornatzer. Bill Harwood recalls the many times his parents had the Cornatzers over to the farmhouse to play Bridge.

"My parents loved to play bridge and played with the Cornatzers quite a bit," he says. "I remember one night when they were over. I was ten. They were playing and Cornatzer sat at the table and I noticed he was not paying attention. Afterward, I asked my father, 'What's wrong with Dr. Cornatzer? He didn't seem to be enjoying the game.' My father said, 'Dr. Cornatzer is a very intelligent man, but he doesn't like to play bridge. He likes doing other things more. Some people don't like to play games.'"

Both during and after the Harwood era, research at the medical school was led not only by Cornatzer, Nordlie, Fischer and Vennes, but also by a number of talented scientists including Paul Ray, John Duerre, Helge Ederstrom, Frank Lowe and many others skilled at balancing research projects with teaching duties. And while students dearly loved and respected brilliant faculty members such as Cornatzer, such was not always the case with the curious Christopher Hamre, Ph.D. A brusque anatomy professor, he inspired cold fear in his students. Even his faculty colleagues felt some disdain for his style. "The Danish Field Marshall," sniffs Robert Fischer in recollection of Hamre's imperious manner.

In the early Fifties, with the infusion of young blood into the school, Hamre was one of the old guard. He had earned a doctorate from the University of Wisconsin and arrived at UND in 1949. He

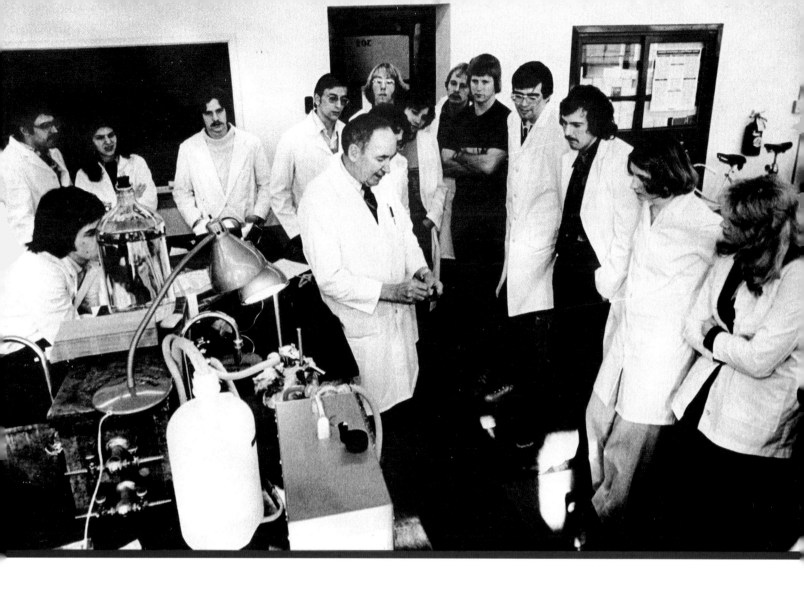

chaired the admissions committee at the School of Medicine, was dean of the graduate school, and also chaired the department of anatomy. Tall, moustachioed and supremely formal, he was known as The Dr. Hamre and addressed all students as Mr., Miss or Mrs.

"He came off as being a curmudgeon but he was very interested in student welfare," says Vennes. "I liked him because you knew what you were getting. He was upfront. When they completed their course in gross anatomy, they damn well knew their gross anatomy. Hamre made sure that when people completed a Ph.D., they were worthy of that degree."

Hamre was an excellent chalkboard artist. Most afternoons after students had gone, or sometimes very early in the mornings, Hamre would draw freehand on the chalkboard — without referring to any book — a detailed cross-section for the next day's anatomy lecture.

"He was particularly fond of some of his drawings," says a former student, Edward Carlson, Ph.D., the chair of the department of anatomy and cell biology. "I can remember one day. Imagine this very formal gentleman, coming in early and working particularly hard on two or three chalkboards full of colored drawings. He generated these drawings beautifully and when he got done, he looked at them and thought they were particularly good. He then walked down the hall to find Ted Snook, who was not only a faculty member in the department, but kind of the department photographer. Ted Snook

Helge holds forth

Helge Ederstrom, Ph.D., chatting here with students in a physiology class, joined the department in 1952. Ederstrom was not only an experienced teacher, his paintings of North Dakota landscape became immensely popular. It was Ederstrom who coined the term "Cathedrals of the Prairie" to describe his gritty portraits of ancient grain elevators outlined starkly against a broad Dakota horizon.

Ted Snook

Gentle and shy, Ted Snook, Ph.D.,was a top-flight scientist and teacher with a national reputation. He developed the Snook Reticulum a light, microscopic stain for slides, still used in pathology labs across the country. Known for thrift and doing research on a shoestring, he spent only $125 on supplies over 15 years.

had his camera, and Dr. Hamre asked him if he would come and take some pictures of these drawings he had made while getting ready for the students in gross anatomy. Ted found his camera and got the color film together and walked down the hall with Dr. Hamre into the lab only to find the custodian wiping all the drawings from the board, because he thought he needed to clean the boards before the class started. Dr. Hamre didn't take that very well and had several words with him."

The wrath of Hamre was something to be avoided at all costs.

"We were deathly afraid of Hamre," recalls Dr. Richard Olafson, class of 1957. "He was a very demanding taskmaster, very bright but quite self-centered. He was firm, but fair, although some didn't think he was particularly fair."

"I was so respectful and fearful of him," adds Donald McIntyre, class of 1957, "that when I took the oral part of my gross anatomy final, he asked about a certain facial structure that he expected me to know. And I knew it. It happened to be the duct of the parotid gland. Prior to that, he had mistakenly named the parotid gland as the sub maxillary gland. As I didn't want to offend him, even though I knew the structure he had in his hand was not the duct that was to be named, I named it anyway because he had named it incorrectly and I didn't want to offend him. And he called me on it. So I was a loser both ways."

Another student who ran afoul of Hamre was Robert Eelkema, class of 1958. Eelkema already was a working veterinarian when he entered the School of Medicine. While the experience helped, especially in dissecting lab with human cadavers, it also got him into trouble.

"I was used to posting out animals," says Eelkema. "In Dr. Hamre's lab, we had our cadavers and we got to the kidney and I went ahead and took out the kidney and sliced it vertically and horizontally to look at the cortex and so forth. Then Hamre announced, 'Do not take your kidney out of the cadaver and do not cut into your kidney.' I thought, 'Oh, oh, we're in big trouble.' So I tried to use my surgical skills to re-do the kidney and re-sew it back into the cadaver. But when we set our cadaver up horizontally, the kidney fell out. I tried to hide it from Hamre, but I almost got kicked out of anatomy."

George Johnson may have the distinction of being the most anxious of all of Hamre's students.

"Dr. Hamre's anatomy class was tough, tough, tough," he recalls, "psychologically and physically. It was so stressful to me that on the first practical examination in anatomy lab, I performed a flub that was known thereafter as Johnson's Flub. This was an examination where parts of the body were tagged around the room and we had to look at the tags. When I shakily approached a prone leg on the table with a tiny tag on it, I got so distraught and upset I managed, in my anxiety, to knock the leg off the table and it rolled across the floor. Later, I guess because of the stress, I developed a neuro-dermatitis and I got a secondary infection on my hands. I'm sure the formaldehyde had something to do with it, but in all honesty, I think my psyche had something to do with it, too. I had such a bad time that I had to turn the pages of the anatomy book with my elbows and I sat in the lectures dripping rather unmentionable fluids from my hands onto the floor. Finally, Dr. Hamre leaned over the lectern and said, 'Johnson, go see a doctor and get yourself fixed.' And, of course, the class laughed."

Hamre, though, could be equally hard on himself. "While chairing the department of anatomy and cell biology," says Carlson, "he was also the Dean of the Graduate School, which sometimes put him in a very interesting situation. Once he wanted to get an additional stipend for a graduate student so he wrote a letter to the dean of the graduate school, which was himself, asking for the stipend. He then walked over to the graduate school and answered his own letter. He realized he didn't have the money to do it and he turned himself down."

Not surprising, some of his students sought to exact revenge. One night some of them hired a stripper to come to Hamre's surface anatomy class at 8 a.m. the next morning. The woman arrived, showed surface anatomy to all the students, triggering a memorable Hamre tirade.

"To show how immature we were at the time," says George Johnson, "one dark January day, about a half dozen of us were gathered over in the medical school building at about 7 a.m., waiting for this not well liked anatomy lab to open. Dr. Hamre came down the hall and it so happened that some dogs were being delivered from Fort Totten to the physiology lab. There was a chute at the south end of the building and Fred Campos, the janitor and friend of all beleaguered medical students, was helping unload the dogs. Well, Fred was getting pretty old, hc was bent over at that time, and the dogs got loose. The dogs flooded into the hall and started to chase Dr. Hamre. Now Dr. Hamre, who was always serious, hustled down the hall. There were five of us, and Donald Breen shouted above the din of the dogs, 'Go get him, Shep!' He was our hero forever after, because at that point, we students had had it with Dr. Hamre."

Actually, their dean wasn't all that enamored of Hamre, either.

"Dr. Hamre was the bane of Father's existence," says Bill Harwood. He remembers dinner conversations on many nights when something Hamre had done that day upset Dean Harwood. "I don't know of anybody who liked Hamre. He was very conservative and stuck in his ways, a bureaucratic infighter. My father said, 'Hamre works with cadavers; it fits his personality.' My father told me that after students were finished with their dissection, Hamre would go back to the anatomy department to make sure that all of the bones were wrapped properly. He was obsessive. And it was difficult, since he was dean of the graduate school and was of equivalent academic rank as father."

Donald McIntyre remembers the day when he was on duty as a physician at the Mayo Clinic in Minnesota, and Hamre showed up as a patient. He had developed a serious problem with a blood vessel that was in an obscure location but thought to be correctable.

"He had surgery, but his post-operative course was very complicated," recalls McIntyre. "He was alone except for either a professional person or, otherwise, me. I did spend a lot of time with him with his post-operative respiratory problems. I talked with his wife several times on the phone to update her on his condition. He was a wonderful fellow. I think probably the fear we had was not really warranted. I don't think he meant to come on that way. He was a very dignified and serious person and that was the way it was."

He did not recover from that episode. When Hamre died, he left a generous trust to the department of anatomy and cell biology, and, says Carlson, "We operate on the interest of that trust yet today. To that I am very grateful to Dr. Hamre."

Hamre made some excellent hires as chair of the anatomy department, including the man who liked to take the photos of his chalkboard work. Ted Snook used his photography skills to produce large lantern slides — done on his own time — big enough to be seen without a projector. Each was labeled with minute detail and were handy enough that students could flip through them over lunch and be well prepared for an afternoon lab.

Snook arrived at UND in 1951 from medical school posts at the universities of Cornell, Syracuse and Pittsburgh. He was gentle and shy, a man easily embarrassed who found it difficult to make eye contact. Yet he was a top-flight scientist and teacher with a national reputation. Some of the things that he did, even as a graduate student, remain in use today. For instance, he developed light, microscopic stains for slides. One of them, known as the Snook Reticulum, is still used in pathology labs across the country.

"Ted Snook was one of those individuals who could do research on

Fred Campos

A popular janitor at the School of Medicine, Fred Campos was revered by students for his kindness to them and good humor. Once, when the Gross Anatomy lab was being moved across campus, Fred noticed something had been left behind. He nonchalantly hoisted a cadaver over his shoulders and carried it across campus to the new lab.

almost no money," says Carlson. "He was very conservative and made his own things. He was just one of those guys that could do it alone. When Ted Snook retired, there was an account in his name that he had been using for supplies for his research. There was $375 in it. Dr. Ollerich, the chair, checked to see what the original amount had been 15 years before. It was $500. Snook had spent $125 in the fifteen years on razor blades and light bulbs and things like that. He was one of those guys who could publish a paper and didn't need the technology that we have today. A more gentle person you can't possible imagine and an outstanding mentor."

One day in a histology class, Carlson recalls, Snook was about to begin his lecture on the mammary gland. "His drawings were exquisite and he was extremely formal and careful about those drawings, but also very shy. He started his lecture by saying, 'Today folks, we are going to touch lightly on the breast.' Suddenly he realized what he said and he turned about four shades of purple and almost couldn't go on. Of course, the class thought it was wonderful and applauded him. But he was so shy he simply had to turn away. What a wonderful guy and tremendous person. We all loved him

Cornatzer at work
Biochemistry chair Gene Cornatzer, discusses an experiment with then-graduate student Eric Uthus. Cornatzer held both an M.D. and a Ph.D. He started the Ireland Research Laboratory and the Human Nutrition Research Laboratory and regularly brought Novel Prize winners to campus for lectures.

(continued on next page)

A Tribute to Frank Lowe

Frank Lowe was a true academician and a true intellect. He was an outstanding person who came here when he was about fifty-five or fifty-six years old in the mid 1960's among four or five other outstanding scientists who were recruited as the Hill Research Professorship. In my estimation, the entire program made a quantum leap in the School of Medicine with regard to do what we were able to do and whom we were able to attract, not only as faculty, but also as students in those years. Frank Lowe trained most of the students in the department of anatomy and cell biology. He literally gave himself to that program. He was a bachelor who considered his students his family, and I happened to be one of his very fortunate sons. With his help, I was given an outstanding education in electron microscopy. This gentleman made it his life's ambition and drive to see that his students were not only well educated scientifically, but that they matured into true gentlemen and ladies and learned how to handle themselves in the scientific community. He was an outstanding scholar in art,

dearly. Ted Snook is just an icon. He is known nationally and internationally for his work."

In the meantime, back in the dean's office, Ted Harwood was typing another fascinating letter to university President Starcher. In his first, he had offered an undated resignation. Now, only a few weeks after he was hired to extend the medical school, he wasted no time declaring his real intent.

In the first paragraph he told Starcher, "There is one very obvious fact about a medical school, and particularly a four-year medical school, which I am sure is universally true and which has recently become very obvious to me. I refer to the fact that a state really cannot afford to run a four-year school if the only advantage accruing to it is the graduation of physicians."

This had to have been a jolt to Starcher. Citizens of the state had gone to the polls in 1947 and approved a mill levy based on the cultivated belief — one that the university had actively supported — that a yes vote meant more doctors for North Dakota. The state legislature had felt the fire at their feet and approved — even demanded — the expansion. Starcher then had hired the one man everyone was sure could get the job done.

But here was Dr. Harwood, suggesting that other than the doctors it would produce, a complete medical school in North Dakota really was not needed. In his letter, he based this conundrum on a comparison to what had happened in Vermont. There, he said, the $335,000 per year that the legislature appropriated for the support of the medical school not only produced doctors, it produced "byproducts of service which benefit the state greatly." These included "physician services given the state in the way of home visits, outpatient department visits, hospitalization, operations, deliveries, and consultations." Add up those byproducts, said Harwood, and you get about $500,000 worth of extras.

"In other words," he said, Vermont "is obtaining as a byproduct more in the way of benefit to its people than it is putting into the school."

The point, he said, was that North Dakota did not need its medical school to provide those extra services. The present welfare system, he said, covered most of those needs. "There is no volume of patients which is going without medical care; therefore we cannot attract patients to this area for teaching purposes without interfering with our welfare arrangement."

This was a subtle challenge to the notion — advanced in 1944 by Harley French and picked up by many others — that a four-year school could succeed in North Dakota if a new teaching hospital aimed at serving low-income patients were constructed. The model most had in mind was something along the lines of a publicly funded institution such as Cook County General Hospital in Chicago. But if such a hospital were not built, a four-year medical school would need to siphon off patients for study, and that, Harwood suggested, would not work. "The many hospitals throughout the state need all the patients they have at present and more if they are to remain solvent."

Whatever Starcher thought, he knew that as a matter of practical reality, the conversion of the School of Medicine to four-year status depended almost completely on the energy of the dean to get it done. It was not so much that Harwood had to fight enormous battles to knock down the idea of a four-year school. All he had to do, really, was nothing. Or, more to the point, do nothing about the four-year idea. Harwood had not really come to North Dakota to do nothing. He was able to deflect his critics and supporters of expansion with plenty of other projects aimed at bolstering the two-year medical school. They were projects you could not really argue with, as long as they succeeded. It was a risky strategy for a conservative man, but one that came straight from that bedrock of marble.

"He knew he had that mandate," says Bill Harwood. "He had it posted on his wall in his office. This is what he was supposed to do. He had to live with it and it distressed him greatly. But Father still retained his Vermont virtues, like thrift. An inch of water in the bathtub is enough, he'd tell us. You don't need anymore. That explains his character on saving money and spending money. That's why we lived on a sharecropped farm."

And that's where his misgivings over an expansion came from.

"He looked at the money it would cost for a four-year school and he said the state can't afford it. Who's going to pay for it and who will persuade graduates to stay in North Dakota? His mantra was 'If you can show me tax payers getting their moneys worth I'll do it.'"

Harwood's nineteen-year tactic of deflection began in that letter to Starcher as he outlined briefly his first priority as dean. The one gap, he said, in North Dakota's medical care program lay in the field of rehabilitation. He was right. People from a rural farm- and ranch-oriented state such as North Dakota sustained more than their share of physical injuries that needed both long-term care and short-term therapy to get people productive again. The state had no capacity for such care at the time, although a department of physiotherapy was on the university's drawing board. Yet it would need clinical

A Tribute to Frank Lowe

(continued)

history, literature and music. He was a naturalist and a mountain climber who climbed mountains in Switzerland. He was an outstanding gardener, but his true pioneering area was the area of electron microscopy. He developed marvelous new techniques for transmission and scanning with the electron microscope that are currently being used. I have nothing but a grateful heart for this man. He retired in 1981 and at that time, Tom Johnson, dean of the medical school, decided it would be appropriate for the School of Medicine to designate one day each year when individuals from the entire School of Medicine, both clinical and basic sciences, could make presentations and have plenary speakers from outside come for an entire day dedicated to research. Knowing that Frank Lowe's attitude and his mentoring while he was here were so important in the history of our research enterprise, the School of Medicine made a decision to name that day for Frank Lowe. Since that time, we have had almost twenty-five years of Frank Lowe Days every spring, and each year they have gotten more and more well attended.

Edward Carlson, Ph.D., is chair of the department of anatomy and cell biology.

material — patients — to fuel its operation.

Harwood suggested that by incorporating such a department into the medical school, a needy population previously unserved by the welfare system or other state hospitals could be cared for with occupational, psychological and sociological support and rehabilitation.

"It would be a very logical approach to our medical care and medical school problem to develop our local facilities for rehabilitation," Harwood wrote. "An excellent selling point is that a rehabilitated patient may once again support himself and relieve society of the cost of his support."

A further sweetener: Federal funds on a matching basis were soon to be available for such a rehab center. "These funds could be used to build one central plant for all aspects of the program here in Grand Forks."

If properly done, he said, rehabilitation meant a complete medical team — all the way from diagnosis to complete treatment. Such a program would encompass everything from orthopedic surgery to eye surgery to treatment of heart failure.

"Furthermore, if we emphasized rehabilitation in our teaching program there is a good possibility that one of the larger educational foundations might give us considerable help. You may know that the University of Iowa built its medical school with a grant of, I believe, millions of dollars from the Rockefeller Foundation."

With his intriguing closing line, "Let's talk about this sometime," Harwood set in motion a change in emphasis that would gradually neutralize talk of a four-year school. Starting with that rehab hospital, Harwood kept busy over the next two decades steadily improving the two-year school while being too busy to pay attention to expansion. Critics labeled his strategy one of "benign neglect." But there was not much they could do, for Harwood showed a real talent in gathering support from the people who mattered most.

"My father was good at going to the legislature and talking to farmers," says Bill Harwood. "He was one of them, a small-town boy. He'd say, let's get by for two more years. I don't want to rock the boat. And they'd give him the money."

Among his accomplishments was doubling the size of the faculty as well as increasing the number of students accepted each year. The average class size during his tenure grew from thirty-five under Potter to forty-two. That was made possible, in part, by Harwood's concern that medical students could not afford their tuition and other college expenses and support themselves at the same time. He convinced legislators that by helping medical students, the state could get more of them to go into medicine. Thus was created a loan fund aimed exclusively at relieving the financial burdens of medical students.

Harwood made another positive impact with several of his hires. In 1959, he brought in Dr. Walt Wasdahl to join the department of

Donald Barcome

Ted Harwood hired Dr. Barcome in 1963 to run the medical school's under utilized rehabilitation hospital. The first trained rehab specialist in the state, Barcome increased hospital usage dramatically, first expanding its quarters to meet demand and then getting state authority to erect a new building.

pathology. The plainspoken Wasdahl was known for eschewing lectures in favor of hands-on clinical work and getting his students to think for themselves. In 1968, Harwood hired Robert Eelkema — the former veterinarian who nearly was kicked out of Hamre's anatomy class — to start a department of community medicine, with the idea of addressing healthcare delivery issues across the state. Eelkema proved himself a master at finding grant monies and establishing community-based programs.

Harwood named Dr. Wallace Nelson the first dean of students at the medical school, and saw to it that medical school faculty — including himself — taught students in allied health fields and in the nursing school. And it was under Harwood's leadership that Harvard University came to be almost a regular transfer point for North Dakota graduates.

As dean, he was able to share credit — along with Cornatzer — for the establishment of the Hill Research Professorships. With Harwood's help, Cornatzer was able to secure funding for the construction of the Ireland Research Laboratory — benefiting all basic science departments.

As Vennes remembers it, Harwood's open-door policy for students, faculty and staff characterized his easygoing management style. He was known widely for his favorite saying, "A word to the

Walter Wasdahl, M.D.
The plainspoken Wasdahl, known as Waz by his students, was known for eschewing lectures in favor of hands-on clinical work and getting his students to think for themselves.

We Had No Beepers

We worked very, very hard and we made house calls. In our office practice in Bismarck, there were never enough physicians and we could never get caught up. We would end up with ten to twenty phone calls that we had to return each evening between five and six and that took a while. We always made rounds twice a day on our own patients and we were on call, in our small group of five people, twice a week and weekends. Then we made rounds on everybody's patients. We made over 300 house calls a year. Sometimes we had to leave while we were in the office and other times we would do them early in the morning or in the middle of the night. We would make those calls for $3, including medication patients would need. The largest charge we ever made was $10. Nowadays house calls are out because you can't do that much in the home. We couldn't then, either, but we could do as much as they could in the hospital, unless it was a true illness that required hospitalization. You must recall that we had no emergency room physicians until the Seventies. If you had the patient go to the emergency room, you had to go down to see them whether it was a sore throat or sprained wrist or rash, you had to get up and go the emergency room. I don't think the first ten years of my practice I ever slept through one night when I was in town. If you were on vacation, it didn't make any difference if you stayed in town. There was really no freedom. The only way you could be reached was by telephone. We had no beepers or cell phones, so even at home if I was going to work on the lawn, my wife would have to stay in the house to answer the phone. If I went uptown, I would have to call back every fifteen minutes to see if there were any calls. You would make a house call in the middle of the night, and then when you got home your wife would have a message for you. You can't imagine the freedom that the beeper gave you. It was like a whole new world. Now everybody hates the beeper but everyone is wearing one. When I was practicing, you couldn't answer back on a beeper. Now you have a cell phone so you can go out to dinner and still take care of things. For some twenty years, until the Seventies, the hospital administrators were right on your back if you didn't go down when the nurse called. I don't care if it was an earache, a rash, a sore throat or a drunk, you had to get up and go down to the emergency room. If you were working in the middle of the day and were behind, you still had to go over to the emergency room. You can't imagine what freedom the emergency room physician gave us. Nowadays, a physician gets a telephone call and there isn't any doubt in his mind; he isn't going to come out. The patient is going to the emergency room to see a physician. The physician may never go down there until the next day to work him up. We had to go down and see the patient if we admitted him and we had to stay there and work him up and get the orders going. But I loved medicine. I really did.

Phil Dahl, M.D., class of 1947.

I had a rancher come in who was coughing and running a fever. I said to him, "I better get an X-ray." He had no insurance and said, "What are you going to do differently if you get an X-ray than if you don't?" I said, "Probably nothing." He said, "Then don't get it." I knew he would never sue me; he was a man of his word. That is the difference from what is happening today. There is a tremendous amount of defensive medicine and I think that is unfortunate. In western North Dakota, it was a different time frame and a different family thing. You knew your patients and their families and they knew you. That is not always true nowadays.

Keith Foster, M.D., a native of Mandan, North Dakota, is a UND grad who earned his medical degree at Marquette University. He practiced for many years in Dickinson, North Dakota, and was the first dean at the Bismarck campus of the School of Medicine, serving for sixteen years.

By this time, Dr. Sathe, Dr. Ellis, Dr. Borrud and I had decided we were going to have a little clinic of our own out in Williston. There had been an oil boom out there, so the population had expanded significantly and there were no additional physicians. Dr. Borrud's father put his neck out and signed a note for us so we could get money together to erect a building, which we did. By the time we finished with our training in Fargo, the building was pretty well ready so we could go on out and start work. Things were different in those days than they are now. I remember going to the banker and telling Mr. Davidson, we were starting this clinic and we needed some money but we didn't have any money in order to get started. He said, "Well, how much do you need." And I said, "I don't know, we've never done it before." He said, "Well, you sign the note and I'll put this much in the bank. When you run out, I'll put some more in and then you can pay it off as you are able to." That was the way of financing back in 1965. You couldn't do that today."

Dean Strinden, M.D., class of 1950.

wise is unnecessary." He took his own advice, continuing to say nothing of the four-year plan. The year 1956, when the legislature had ordained that a four-year medical school be fully operational, came and went. Interest in the idea faded. Still, mention of the third and fourth years of medical school training continued to show up in the legislation every two years that funded the medical school. It was enough to keep up the pressure on Harwood and perhaps remind him of his gamble.

He dealt with his stresses, says Bill Harwood, by maintaining a daily ritual that indulged his passion for gardening. He arrived home for lunch from medical school every day at noon. He ate lunch, took a five-minute nap, and went into the garden. He drove back to campus for the afternoon, but in the evening he would go back out to the garden. When he didn't putter with his vegetables, he played the violin or the guitar.

"He loved entertaining," says Bill. "They'd have a Christmas party in one of the labs and father would play guitar and sing and lead the singing. He was completely different when he had a guitar."

In 1967, the pressure eased. The legislature amended its 1953 legislation by deleting references to third- and fourth-year courses in medicine. The four-year medical school was now officially dead.

There was only one problem. Two years earlier, Congress enacted a new law that would change forever the way medicine was practiced and paid for. Within three years, Medicare would change everything at the University of North Dakota's School of Medicine. And it would start a process that would result in two dramatic events: the creation of a four-year school of medicine and the firing of Ted Harwood.

Of Harwood's many accomplishments, certainly the most visible was the building of the rehabilitation hospital. Even so, it might have been his hiring of the man who finally made the building work that deserves the most recognition.

From the time he first floated the idea to Starcher, it took Harwood three years to get the hospital built and another six until he found Donald Barcome, M.D. That he was the right man for the job became evident when Barcome passed the Great North Dakota Recruiting Test: He flew into Grand Forks for his interview in a raging blizzard — and took the position anyway.

Born in Oconto Falls, Wisconsin, Barcome was schooled in Green Bay, graduated from St. Norbert's College in DePere and earned a medical degree at the University of Wisconsin in Madison. It was not until he joined the Navy and was practicing at Balboa Navy Hospital in San Diego that he made his first North Dakota connection. There he met and married Shirley Shepard, a physical therapist from Burnstad, North Dakota. They moved back to Wisconsin, where Barcome worked as a general practitioner and his wife as a therapist. He soon found that four out of five of his patients suffered from some kind of long-term

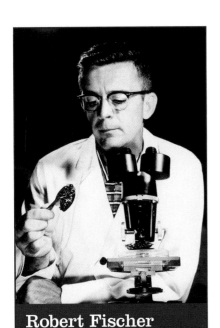

Robert Fischer

Well known for his federally funded research on the transmission of viruses, Fischer performed experiments with mice and insects. Everytime someone found a cockroach in the halls, they blamed it on him. His work was nationally recognized and he eventually became chair of the department of microbiology.

illness or chronic disease. He started to think that Shirley was better prepared than he to deal with such a population. So he contacted her teachers at the Texas Medical Center at Baylor University in Houston and embarked on a three-year training course in chronic disease and rehabilitation.

"My mother-in-law in Logan County, North Dakota, was a patient of Dr. Cliff Peters in Bismarck," Barcome recalls. "One day he asked her what her son-in-law was doing and she said he was in physical medicine and rehab in Houston. She was told they needed him up here."

Not long after, Ted Harwood called Barcome. He had just finished his residency and was waiting to take the second part of his Boards. Harwood invited him to Grand Forks for an interview, and Barcome remembers pulling into Grand Forks between Christmas and New Year's Eve in 1962, in the middle of a blizzard. He stopped at a phone booth and called Harwood. "Here I am," said Barcome. Harwood replied, "Well, I'm so glad you're here, but I can't see you tonight because I have choir practice." Barcome had a room at the North Star Inn. When he got there, the bar and restaurant were closed due to the snow. A salesman gave him a bag of popcorn and he got a soda from the machine and settled in for the night.

The next day he had his first glimpse of the McCannel Building, the three-story structure next to the medical school that housed what officially was called the Rehabilitation Unit of the North Dakota State Medical Center. Barcome liked the people he met and liked the building. He noticed, however, one oddity. There were fourteen staff and no patients. Correction, said the administrator, there was one patient but he had gone home for the Christmas holiday.

As Barcome recalls, "That was when I got out of the building and called Shirley. She said, 'Don, there is something in your voice.' I said, 'Yes, honey, we are coming up here. All I need is two patients and I have a one hundred percent increase in patient population!'"

The single-story McCannel Hall was built in 1956 as an outpatient facility. By 1962, it had gotten so little usage that two floors were added and it was converted to a forty-two-bed inpatient-outpatient hospital and renamed a Vocational Rehabilitation Center.

Still no takers. When Barcome arrived, however, he started getting the word out that the hospital was now in the hands of a trained rehabilitation specialist — he was the first physiatrist in North Dakota. With his own money and on his own time, he started attending meetings of the various district medical societies, delivering his pitch on the importance of rehab. Once word spread, the patients started pouring in. Within a few months of his arrival in 1963, the forty-two-bed inpatient unit had a six- to eight-week waiting list for patients who needed comprehensive rehabilitation. Meanwhile, the outpatient load in his first year went from five thousand to fifty thousand patient visits.

Barcome was not afraid of change. He immediately sent one of his assistants, Larry Eichman, to UCLA to take a prosthetics and orthotics course. Not long after Eichman returned to start a new orthotics department, it became one of the highest rated departments in the country.

The children's program Barcome started in 1965 became the model at the Cerebral Palsy Association for treatment and management of handicapped children in the United States.

"We built a great facility dedicated to patient care," Barcome says. "We were about the first fully accredited rehab hospital in the country. Within about three years' time we were the only facility between Chicago and Seattle. I remember the medical school accreditation team coming up in those years and actually making a comment in their report how fantastic it was for the medical school to be able to have a facility like this so its students could be exposed to chronic disease."

As Barcome had always envisioned, his work went beyond patient care. He trained medical students and was a proponent of starting a department of physical therapy. It opened in 1967, founded by one of the physical therapists Barcome had recruited to the rehab center. He was Bud Wessman, yet another of those stalwart hopefuls who arrived in Grand Forks in a snowstorm and was happy to be there.

Wessman remembers space being so tight in McCannel Hall that his office was in a converted bathroom. One day the governor at the time, Bill Guy, visited the center and stopped by Wessman's office. "We were talking for awhile and he said, 'By the way, where's the men's room?' And I had to keep from saying you're sitting in it."

Wessman also recalls Dr. Barcome's energy.

"That man would come in after working all day in the clinic and lecture to the physical therapy and occupational therapy students. I still marvel. He never brought notes with him but he was so strong in what he knew and how well he knew it."

Eventually the program was so successful that it outgrew McCannel Hall. A new facility was needed, but where to find it? A group of doctors at the old Grand Forks Clinic solved that problem by buying a large parcel of land on Columbia Road for a medical park. They donated a portion of that land to the building of what was to become United Hospital (and is today Altru Health Systems — the merged result of United and the Grand Forks Clinic.) The hospital people in turn gave seven acres to the rehabilitation center. It would become the first building erected at the new medical park.

Because the demand on the first rehab center grew so quickly, Barcome and others designed a new hospital and then they went to the state for authority to build it. The land had to be signed over to the state because the hospital was a part of the State Medical Center. The hospital was built by selling bonds. Its ratings were so high that the bonds sold within twenty-four hours and later were paid off independent of any state funds. Yet, even though not one cent of state money went into the new building, the legislature dragged its feet for two years before giving its approval.

Even then the lawmakers were full of suspicions. Barcome remembered that at the ground breaking for this new North Dakota State Medical Center Rehabilitation Hospital, the elderly Enoch Thorsgaard, the Republican chair of the House Appropriations Committee and a long holdout against approval, took hold of his hand and shook it. "He said, 'Congratulations, Doctor, but I still think you put one over on us.'"

In fact, the financing of rehabilitation medical services is an area in which the state really has no complaint.

"In the twenty-six years, twenty-seven years that I was chairman of the department of physical therapy," says Bud Wessman, "at no time did we ever have more than twenty-six percent state money in the budget of that program. The lion's share came from Allied Health grants. We had some tremendous stalwarts in Congress at that time: Senators Milt Young, Mark Andrews and Quentin Burdick. They knew how to pay attention to the things that truly mattered and so when you went after an Allied Health grant or a Rehab Services Administration grant, you could be fairly confident that if you did it right, if you wrote it right, that the funds would be there."

And Casey Ryan, M.D., president of Altru Health Systems in Grand Forks, attests to the energy Barcome used to make rehabilitation work in North Dakota.

"They started almost with nothing at the university," says Ryan, "Don Barcome pulled in some unique individuals such as Ken Koch. They were able to fund totally the building that ultimately became part of the state's holdings, into which the state never put a nickel. They were ahead of their time in providing a lot of service to the whole state."

The switch to the new rehabilitation hospital took place in 1972. The first week it opened, the inpatient load was eighty-eight, every bed full. It remained at capacity with another one hundred outpatients every day for several years.

"We never expected that and we just didn't have staff to handle it," says Barcome. "We had patients coming from all over. On an average, we would have a minimum of one in-patient from every county in the state of North Dakota. We averaged seventeen other states on an annual average of patients transferred. We had patients from four foreign countries."

Demand became so high that Barcome contacted a religious order of nuns to supply a corps of volunteer nurses while he hired and trained more staff.

In a way, though, the hospital became a victim of its own success. Across North Dakota, smaller communities began to understand much better the concept and need for rehabilitation services. Soon, others

First library
Medical Librarian Loretta
Swift and her assistant
Melba Youngren at work in
the medical school's very
first library, located on part
of a floor of the Med Sci
South Building.

built smaller rehab centers, and as a result the hospital in Grand
Forks lost patients and referrals. What was once an eighty-eight-bed
hospital is now a thirty-two-bed unit, no longer officially connected
to the School of Medicine, but operated as part of Altru Health
Systems. "Certainly, for the medical park," says Altru's Dr. Ryan,
"rehabilitation medicine is an important part of what we do."

But Barcome worries that the proliferation of the smaller rehab
centers ultimately undermines the main center.

"They have inhibited the growth and development of
rehabilitation medicine," he says. "We were the leading edge in
the country when we started. Even in the surgical aftercare of
orthopedics, we started things that people were coming up here to
see. We don't have that anymore. If you have a rare disease, where
do you go for its management? You go where the rare disease is a
common patient! This rehab hospital should have continued to be
the only rehab hospital, but for whatever reason we have multiple
inpatient rehab facilities, none of which is capable of sustaining a
patient population to maintain the leading edge."

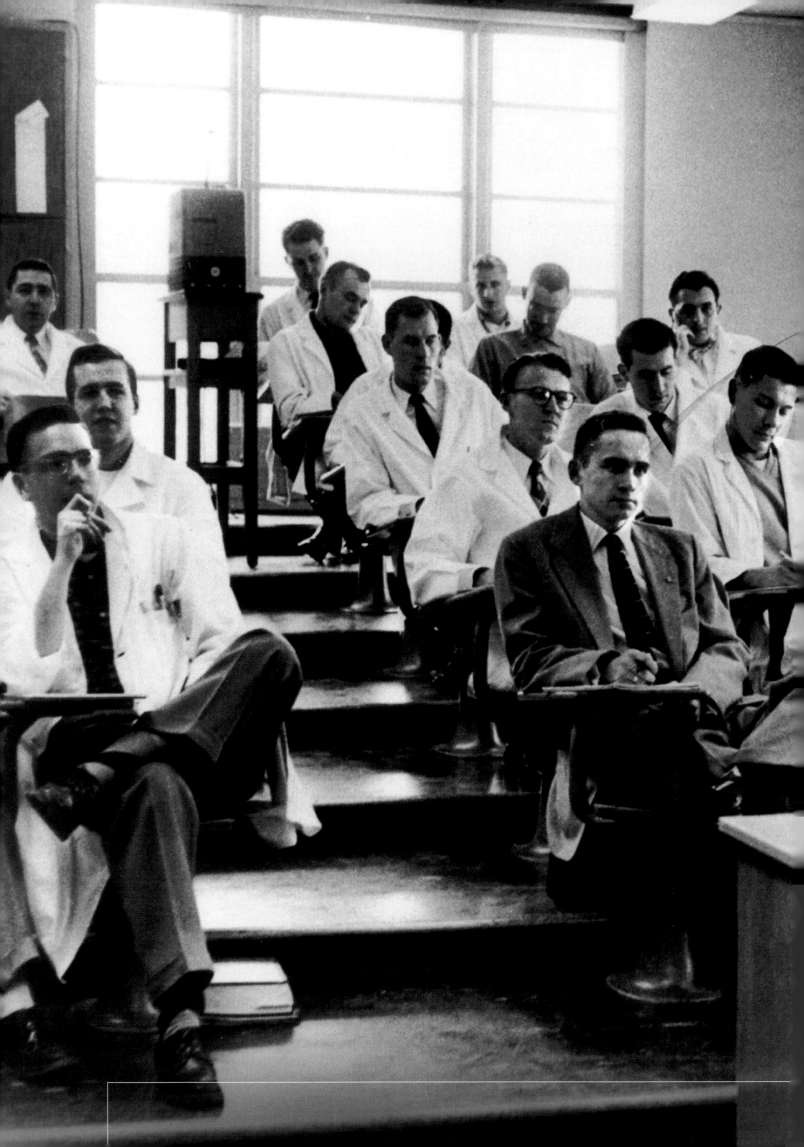

Chapter 5

CHAPTER FIVE

Clifford's Gamble

CLIFFORD'S GAMBLE

History is ripe with pivotal moments that portentously announced to one and all that nothing would ever be the same again. Museum walls sag under the weight of gilded scenes that portray such seismic shifts in human momentum.

There is no law, however, that a pivotal moment cannot be subtle, perhaps even unrecognized at the instant for the upheaval it portends. Such as the crack in time that occurred in January of 1971 in an ordinary meeting of the curriculum committee at the School of Medicine at the University of North Dakota.

Among those seated around the table that day were John Vennes, the committee chairman, Ted Harwood, the dean, and Wallace Nelson, M.D., the assistant dean for student affairs. Nelson, the colorful Nebraska transplant known for cowboy hats, string ties, pointy-toed boots and bracing candor, announced that he had gotten a handful of disturbing letters in recent days. They came from medical schools across the country. These were not just any schools, but the very places to which North Dakota had been transferring its two-year graduates for years.

All of the letters said the same thing: Given the extraordinary nature of the times, they did not see how they would be able to accept any more transfers after 1975. Perplexed, Nelson did some checking with other

Previous page:

The old curriculum
For the first 68 years of its existence, the medical school was a two-year program, specializing in basic science courses built around lab work and lectures such as this one. Grads were forced to transfer to four year schools elsewhere for clinical training and to finish their degree.

medical schools. He quickly got a mailbag full of discouraging news. More than half of the 40 schools that had accepted transfer students from North Dakota in the past decade were now saying they would not be able to guarantee open slots. Again, they cited as the reason the recent shifts in the theory and perception of medical practice and medical education.

The shift in thought had everything to do with the stunning advances made in medical science since the end of World War II. Not only were new antibiotics knocking down illnesses, but also vaccinations for polio, measles, mumps and chicken pox were wiping out diseases altogether. Seriously ill patients were no longer treated exclusively by their family doctor, but more likely in a hospital with new diagnostic procedures and surgical techniques. But those costly new tools required sophisticated training, and that was expensive. In response, Congress called for massive funding of research and had placed a new emphasis on doctor training. Congress also invented Medicare in the mid-Sixties, designed to offset healthcare costs of the elderly, and Medicaid to fund care for low-income and indigent patients.

Wally Nelson himself was among the pioneers who had made good use of those medical advances. After graduating from the school of medicine in his home state of Nebraska, he moved to North Dakota to work as an obstetrician-gynecologist in the Grand Forks Clinic. He was one of the first doctors in town to show an interest in and to encourage women to undergo a Pap test. This procedure, developed by Dr. Papanicolaou in 1943, examined a tissue sample from the cervix in order to head off cancer. The test was expensive because it required a trained pathologist to make a microscopic laboratory diagnosis of the cell sample.

In the Fifties, when the Pap test first came into use, it was recommended for all women of a certain age. But laboratory facilities were not readily available in Grand Forks, and local pathologists seemed reluctant to recommend them. That didn't stop Nelson. A colleague at the time, Dr. Rodney Clark, a fellow OB-GYN specialist, recalls the many times he went with Nelson to meetings of various women's clubs in the area to encourage them to seek a Pap test. Nelson even processed the tissue samples and read the slides on his own time in a makeshift lab at his home.

"He probably read about twenty slides a week," says Clark. Finally, Nelson, Clark and a third Grand Forks Clinic OB-GYN specialist, Frank Hill, decided to do a Pap test on every new OB patient. Nelson kept reading the slides at home and ultimately hired

a technician, sending her away for training as a Pap screener

"It grew and grew," says Clark. "And then pathologists began to see this was going to be something."

In the meantime, Dr. Wally Wasdahl, a pathologist at the School of Medicine and a friend of Nelson, started a Pap lab at the university. It eventually performed five thousand Pap tests a year. Nelson soon shifted all of the Grand Forks Clinic tests to the university lab. In fact, he left the clinic to run the UND Pap lab and to become assistant dean of students.

But not all doctors were as caring as Nelson. As more and more emphasis in medicine nationwide went toward the technical, and more and more federal dollars went to support development of these sophisticated advances, a negative perception developed among the public. It wasn't just that their medical care had become more expensive. It seemed to more and more patients that the caring family doctor they were used to had been supplanted by a colder, more distant specialist less interested in them as people than in their disease.

In fact, there were more specialists. The excitement of the many new fields of medicine saw more medical students opting out of

Wally Nelson
The colorful Dr. Nelson, known for his cowboy boots and dry wit, was the first to raise the alarm that the old two-year medical school system was in danger of collapse.

primary care for a specialized niche. Meanwhile, the federal government, in its attempts to insure the public against huge medical bills, was much more likely to reimburse a specialist than a primary care doctor. Thus, for economic reasons, many general practitioners left their field and went into the specialized world. This brought the public complaint full circle by creating a shortage of general practice physicians and a flurry of specialized experts.

By 1971, when Wally Nelson opened his mail, these factors and others had worked a subtle but lasting impact on the world of medical education. Americans were just beginning to realize that with a better chance of living a longer, healthier life, they needed more direct healthcare providers. Public discontent with the way medicine was organized translated to political pressure. Congress began talking about appropriating less money for research and more for the training of primary care doctors. Medical schools, likewise, were pressured to emphasize the needs of the patient and not the doctor.

To offset a shortage of general-practice doctors, The American Medical Association developed new residency programs in family practice and in general internal medicine. Suddenly medical schools saw great increases in the number of student applications. Not only were there more of them, they were smarter and better prepared than ever before. In 1972, for example, thirty thousand students applied for the thirteen thousand open slots in medical schools in the United States.

Dropout rates in medical schools fell off dramatically. It used to be that in any given freshman class at a four-year medical school, a certain percentage would drop out. This is what created vacancies that, by the third year, allowed these "complete" medical schools to accept transfers from two-year schools.

By 1971, not only were the dropouts not dropping out, but another suddenly large group of students was competing for the once common third-year transfer slots. Because there just were not enough openings, thousands of qualified students rejected by American medical schools went off to foreign schools for their first two years. They planned to transfer back to an American medical school in their third year. Add to this group the large body of science oriented graduate students who, instead of completing work toward a doctorate, had decided, in all the excitement, to become medical doctors instead. They, too, were looking to transfer into a medical school's third year class.

Finally, there were the graduates of the two-year medical schools, now standing at the end of a long line for a chance to complete their education. The unprecedented competition for transfer slots made it more and more unlikely that they would be able to do that.

This was the news Nelson delivered to his colleagues at the regular curriculum meeting in January 1971. The fear that Harley French had once expressed in the 1940s, and then quickly dismissed, had come to pass.

As the members of the curriculum committee digested the news, they began asking themselves what alternatives they had. Nelson, ever the man to get right to the point, put it bluntly. Either we close the two-year School of Medicine, or we expand into a four-year school and not be dependent on anyone.

This was not just an off-the-cuff idea. For the same Carnegie Commission that had once hired Abraham Flexner to pass judgment on all of the medical schools in the country had already addressed the issue. Two-year medical schools, it had recently stated, should do exactly as Nelson was suggesting — either phase out or become a complete school that could grant a medical degree. Congress heard that message and was on the verge of making available federal money to help two-year schools convert to the four-year variety. In fact, on the drawing board was a plan to give two-year schools up to $50,000 per student to convert to a four-year institution.

Nelson told the group that, morally, UND had no choice. The School of Medicine could not go on accepting students in its two-year school without being able to guarantee their transfer to complete their degree. "The handwriting," he said, "is on the wall."

But if that final point seemed to make the next move a no-brainer, there was at least one man at the table that day who did not want any part of it. Ted Harwood, who had been hired to make a four-year school happen, quickly opposed the idea. When others at the table seemed to embrace the concept, Harwood got up and walked out.

It wasn't just Ted Harwood who opposed the idea of a four-year school. The legislature, which had once championed the idea, was now skeptical — not only of a four-year school but also of any medical school at all. The measuring stick many legislators used to judge the school was how much money it cost to graduate how many students. They saw more than a million dollars in mill-levy funds paying for the

What Makes a Good Doc?

It starts early. Having been on the farm as a youngster, you learn to care for things. You care for growing things. You care for animals. You grow up and you want to take care of people. You only want to be a physician if you really feel it in your heart that's your job in life. You are willing to sacrifice and go the whole nine yards in order to get there and there's no easy trick to get there. There is a caring nurturing part of me that you can't help but see.

Clay Klakeg, M.D., class of 1943.

I rankle when I hear talk about "clients" or when doctors talk about "customers." I like to think I have patients. That word implies a relationship that is really what is the unique part of our profession and what determines the essence of it. This business environment of clients and customers may be appropriate for other types of circumstances, but I really don't think it should be applied to physicians.

William Newman, M.D., class of 1972, is Assistant Dean for Veterans' Affairs and Chair of Internal Medicine.

We are calling patients "customers" and we are counting them as numbers and we aren't seeing patients anymore. The bean counters are trying to have the physicians see more and more patients to make the ends meet. I like to spend as much time as I can with patients and I know that I have to see a certain number a day. The difficult part of medicine is the business side of it, but I love seeing patients.

Richard Larson, M.D., a graduate of the INMED program at the UND medical school, now practices in Belcourt on the Turtle Mountain Reservation.

Willard Wright

Often unsung for his yeoman work behind the scenes, it was Dr. Willard Wright's experience in medical politics and his persuasive powers that brought many of the state's doctors into line in support of expanding the medical school to four years.

graduation of about fifty students a year. Compared to the other colleges in the state that graduated many more on a lower cost-per-student ratio, the medical school did not make sense. What they never seemed to take into consideration, of course, was the large number of graduate students and those studying in applied health and science fields at the School of Medicine.

In the meantime, the honeymoon with the mill levy had ended. The levy was supposed to keep the School of Medicine funded more or less on its own, without the legislature having to cough up anything extra. In 1967, the mill levy supplied the School of Medicine with $1.4 million. But that year, Harwood for the first time had to ask the state for extra money — $1.2 million extra.

They paid it, but ever since, the legislature was in a bad mood when it came to requests for more funding. In fact, in 1969, Harwood became so upset at the legislature's changing mood toward him that he wrote yet another letter to George Starcher resigning as dean. He told Starcher that the legislature acted as if he were hiding something and did not believe him when he told them the new rehab hospital was self-sustaining. Starcher apparently talked Harwood into staying, for nothing further ever came of the offered resignation. But it was clear that the prospects of getting the legislature to agree to something as grand as an expanded School of Medicine were not good.

Early in 1971, however, in an intriguing bit of serendipity, a doctor named Willard Wright entered the picture and things began to happen. Wright was born in Manitoba in 1899 and attended medical school in Winnipeg and Edinburgh, Scotland. He served in the Canadian army during World War I and then emigrated to America, settling as a country doctor in Williston. In 1924, he delivered a baby boy from the small town of Zahl, some thirty miles north of Williston. Mr. and Mrs. Vennes named their little son John.

Wright was more than a country doctor, however. He had a gift for listening and for imparting advice that always came across as supreme wisdom. Tall, imposing and sometimes gruff, he reminded some of Moses, but others of Genghis Kahn. He proved to be a gifted politician who became active in the North Dakota Medical Association, serving as president and later rising to the number two position in the American Medical Association.

In 1971, Wright's work as director of the federal Regional Medical Program (RMP) brought him frequently into contact with the School of Medicine, and in particular with Dr. Robert Eelkema, chair of the

department of community medicine. Wright was a fan of Eelkema's MEDEX program, which used federal funds to train former military corpsmen from Vietnam as physician assistants. The university was only the second in the country to establish a MEDEX program. Its graduates settled in rural communities with doctor shortages all over the United States. They were trained to handle routine medical emergencies and were under the preceptorship of a supervising physician.

Wright, of course, already was familiar with John Vennes, and became part of an informal brain trust with him, Wally Nelson and Eelkema. It was natural that they discussed with him the problem of transfers. Wright's mission with the RMP was to enhance the training of doctors, and he believed the state needed a four-year school of medicine. Being a savvy politician, he also knew that if not handled right, the powers that be would never agree to it.

And he didn't necessarily mean the state legislature. Wright knew that the legislature's approval would mean little if the state's doctors did not first approve the idea of a four-year school. To get their approval, he said, would require more than a subjective argument from the School of Medicine. An outsider's view was needed, someone with credentials who could objectively come in and assess

Clifford and Eelkema

In 1973, then-UND President Tom Clifford (left) asked his handball partner, Dr. Robert Eelkema (right) to head an ad hoc group aimed at getting a four-year medical school funded and through the state legislature. The two recounted the successful campaign in the 2003 book "Good Medicine."

How I Got to North Dakota

I was originally scheduled to go to Concordia College. I think this was largely because I had a girlfriend who was going to Concordia and it was a very fine Lutheran school and seemed to fit very well. My parents took me down to Moorhead this one particular fall day to enroll and there was an uneasiness in the car about my going to Concordia. But I thought, what the heck, I'll go through it. We went to unload my clothes in a dormitory room and found there were four students assigned to the room and the other three were already there and had taken all of the treasured spots. I looked sort of cross-eyed at my parents as I was unloading. It was then that my long-standing love for the University of North Dakota started coming through. I had always been a Sioux fan and that was a family tradition. We went out for lunch and we talked a little, came back, loaded the stuff in the car, headed for Grand Forks and had the wonderful opportunity to meet with the Dean that afternoon. He could remember my grandfather, who had been a professor here in the early part of the century. He put together a curriculum for me that would meet my science needs and suggested that I not take band because he thought that might take too much time from my studies. I was just as happy as a clam to be here and off I went.

Jon Tinglestad, M.D., class of 1958.

the situation and show the state's Medical Association that such an expansion was a necessity. Get the docs behind you, he said, and the legislators would follow.

At this point, it was clear that Vennes, Eelkema and Nelson were operating ad hoc, without their dean's approval. But they liked what Wright had to say and wondered who the outside expert should be. Wright had in mind two prominent doctors high up in the hierarchy of the AMA. When neither man was free to take on the job, Eelkema proposed an alternate. His name was Gary Dunn, the associate dean at the school of medicine at the University of Alabama. Dunn had consulted with Eelkema on the curriculum of his MEDEX program and the two had become fast friends.

Eelkema was born in Mankato, Minnesota, in 1930, but spent much of his early teens in Drayton, North Dakota, where his father was once a superintendent of schools and farmer. Eelkema became a veterinarian in 1956 in Valley City, but decided to go on to earn his medical degree. He graduated from UND in 1958 and got his medical degree at the University of Washington. Ted Harwood hired him to run the student health service, and later, when Eelkema earned a master's degree in public health at Berkeley, named him as the first chair of the department of community medicine. In 1970, a year after taking that job, Eelkema got federal funding for his MEDEX program. The $1.7 million was the largest grant anyone at the university had ever landed.

Eelkema shifted $38,000 of that money to Willard Wright to hire Gary Dunn on behalf of the North Dakota Medical Association. In July 1971, Dunn started work on his analysis of the expansion question.

Eelkema, meanwhile, had formed another unusual friendship, this one on the university's old cement handball courts during his medical school days. His frequent playing partner was the popular dean of the business school, Tom Clifford, a likable young man from Langdon who came back from World War II a much-decorated Marine combat hero.

In January of 1971, the same month that Wally Nelson broke the bad news to the curriculum committee, the state Board of Higher Education named Clifford president of the university. It was a controversial move for Clifford, who was not academic and made no bones about it. He was a doer, not a talker; his hands-off management style gave you enough rope to either get the job done or hang.

Clifford didn't take office until July. In the meantime, he continued to play handball several times a week with his old pal Bob Eelkema, who kept him apprised of the transfer problem at the School of Medicine, the Gary Dunn hire and the fact-finding trips.

"It was the first thing on my agenda when I took office," says Clifford. "One of the first letters I received from the American Medical Association said, 'You can either change or go out of business.' That news was difficult to accept because we had a very good two-year school, great research, and great acceptance of our students. It was hard to think that all that would come to an end and yet that was exactly what the letter was telling me. We had to go into uncharted waters and we started immediately."

Clifford left the problem of winning the support of doctors to Dunn and Eelkema and began plotting a political strategy. He knew immediately that the cost-conscious legislature never would agree to expansion if he suddenly placed a bill before them — even with all of his charm. They had to be convinced long before any vote was taken that this was the right thing to do. It would take time, but Clifford had time on his side. North Dakota's legislature meets every two years and the next session did not begin for eighteen months, in January 1973.

He knew he needed to be careful in broaching the expansion subject with the Board of Higher Education. His sense was that board members would be reluctant to approve expansion because of the cost issue. In fact, he worried that even bringing it up for discussion could trigger a pre-emptive stance against expansion that would be impossible to overcome. His strategy: Say nothing for the time being. In fact, appear oblivious to the entire question.

That left the legislature, an animal Clifford understood well. He knew for certain that if the legislature wanted a four-year medical school, it did not matter what the Faculty Senate wanted or what the Board of Higher Education wanted.

That is why he had John Odegard wheel out one of the university's small planes one morning and fly him down to Fessenden. Actually, they landed at nearby Harvey International Airport, a state-funded project of Fessenden's leading citizen, Bryce Streibel. It was a telling fact of Clifford's importance that Streibel himself, the Republican floor leader of the state's House of Representatives in the 1971-73 legislature, met the plane. He drove Clifford back to his modest home for lunch.

Earl Strinden

As a powerful state legislator, Earl Strinden did much to convince his colleagues of the merits of medical school expansion. "He was probably the best legislator we ever had in the state," says former UND president Tom Clifford. "He figured out what opponents were going to say against the school and he had an answer for it."

Streibel was a tight-fisted fiscal conservative, but he had two soft spots: roads and education. Not that he was a pushover for those, but they were the areas he would consider what he called "investing" in North Dakota. He was well respected in the legislature on both sides of the aisle, easily one of the most powerful men in the state. He also was chairman of the all-important Legislative Council. Almost all successful bills that passed in any given session began first as study topics of an interim committee of the Legislative Council. Legislators felt comfortable supporting a bill that came out of an interim committee with a favorable recommendation.

Clifford had a hunch that Streibel would favor a four-year medical school and he was right. When he asked him to appoint a special interim committee to study the future of the medical school, Streibel readily agreed. He went up to Grand Forks and met with Clifford's great ally, Earl Strinden, a UND grad, a former Marine and another prominent House Republican. Though Strinden went on to become the majority leader of the House, in 1973 he was the assistant majority leader. He tends to downplay his role in those days, but Clifford and others credit him with yeoman behind-the-scenes work that often gets lost in the retelling of the story of those days.

"Earl was probably the most competent and most powerful political legislative leader we've had in the last fifty years," says retired Bismarck physician Phil Dahl.

"Earl is a dynamic guy," adds Clifford today, "a workaholic. Smart guy. Great at organizing. He was probably the best legislator we ever had in the state. He outthought everybody. He figured out what opponents were going to say against the school and he had an answer for it. And he had Bryce Streibel, another alum, as House Majority Leader and they really put the pressure on."

Together, Streibel and Strinden stacked the interim committee with Republicans and Democrats already known to be leaning toward a four-year school.

With that plot underway, Clifford finally decided he had to approach the Board of Higher Education — but carefully. If North Dakota were going to establish a four-year medical school, it would need to take advantage of pending federal funding for conversion of two-year schools. That funding was essential, but to get it the university had to be at the head of the line when the monies became available. Wright and Eelkema had urged Clifford to start the application process immediately. But to do that he needed the approval of the Board of Higher Education. Clifford gambled that as long as the board wasn't being asked to approve a four-year school outright, they would give that blessing for the funding application. The request, however, could not come from him, lest he give away his real intent.

Clifford knew he had one strong ally on the board in chairman Peter Hinrichs, a Lutheran pastor from Dickinson and well liked by just about everyone. "He was a good supporter of the school," says Gerald Vanderwalle, an assistant attorney general at the time assigned to the Board, and later Chief Justice of the State Supreme Court. "And Peter had a feel for people, obviously, since he counseled a lot of them in his position. So he understood North Dakotans pretty well."

John Vennes remembers sitting with Hinrichs at a meeting in Bismarck when the four-year school was mentioned. "I remember him saying, 'North Dakotans only worry about two things: the weather and their health.'" Other members of the board, though, were less friendly toward the idea. George Sinner — a future governor — was a Democrat from Casselton who had serious doubt about the ability of the university to produce quality doctors. And Ken Raschke, the state's commissioner of higher education who reported to the board, was known to very skeptical, says Vanderwalle.

"I remember telling him one day, this will pass so don't worry about it," says Vanderwalle. "I said most of these legislators come from small towns where they are having trouble getting doctors. And I think it will pass with the hope that the medical school will start supplying more doctors for the state of North Dakota. He just looked at me."

All of these uncertainties made Clifford wary about stating his own position. The way he finally couched it was to say that the university had been urged to apply for funds by Gary Dunn and Dr. Willard Wright, two men who represented the state's Medical Association as well as the federal Regional Medical Program. He made no mention that they were also key operatives on the university's behalf.

When board members asked him what he himself thought, Clifford shrugged as if he were just considering the idea. He said it looked like they had no choice but to apply.

So the board approved. It was important not only because it gave the university a chance to get federal seed money, but also because it gave Clifford the political flexibility to now appear up front as a public supporter of the four-year idea and not have to work quietly behind the scenes. Whether or not the skittish board saw this end run for what it was, it was the last time Clifford ever

Brynhilde Haugland

The support of this fiery legislator from Minot was critical to the medical school's hopes for expansion. Haugland was not only for it, she did much to make sure the state backed the idea. Haugland served longer as a state legislator – almost fifty years – than anyone in North Dakota history.

Transferring: A Disruption in Our Lives

There was always the issue of transfer. Where are we going to transfer? Dr. Harwood had come to the medical school in 1953 and he took a real hard line as far as transfers were concerned. It had been the practice to negotiate with different medical schools, but he took it upon himself to say, "You can apply to two or three, but the first acceptance that comes through, you have to take." That was the way it went. We had to pick up after two years and move to a different place in the country and acquaint ourselves with a different faculty and new peers. It was a difficult transition to make. I moved to Cincinnati. A lot of students went to Chicago and a few to the East Coast. It was a disruption in our lives, but it worked out okay. It was a new experience, but an experience we had to have.

Al Samuelson, M.D., class of 1954, is a Bismarck psychiatrist and a member of the medical school's teaching faculty.

Getting into Harvard was interesting. I went to Dean Harwood and he said, "You can't get into Harvard!" I said, "If you will just write the letter of recommendation, everything will be fine." He wrote the letter and the secretary read it and said, "This isn't good enough." So she wrote the letter and the glorious day I got that telegram of acceptance was one of the finer days in my life. I then went to medical school at Harvard but it was an incredibly cold environment. I have never been so frightened in my life. Here I was at twenty-five years old. I had been around the world twice, had four years in the

(continued on next page)

raised the four-year expansion with them.

Interestingly, at the first meeting of Bryce Streibel's interim committee, the stacked members made it clear they were not about to go forward until they knew where the state's doctors stood on the issue. Brynhilde Haugland, the charismatic legislator from Minot, emphasized that "unanimous approval" of the North Dakota Medical Association, was required, "or there is no point in the state trying to establish" a four-year school.

The big issue with the legislature, of course, was cost. But doctors had separate concerns. Willard Wright knew that doctors needed to be convinced that a UND four-year school — without a university hospital attached to it — could turn out quality doctors. There was plenty of skepticism that it couldn't be done.

Much of that skepticism was centered in Fargo, a long-time rival of Grand Forks in many areas, from football to beets. It was the home to the all-powerful Fargo Clinic, which employed the majority of the doctors in the area. Many of its physicians were specialists and sub-specialists, those representatives of the new wave of medicine. Almost all had received their training in the traditional way — in large city hospitals — and couldn't imagine any other way of becoming a doctor. Their opposition to expansion was fierce.

"The old guard in Fargo, then the Fargo Clinic, thought that little school up there in Grand Forks just has no business to continue because they can't have a university hospital," says Dr. George Magnus Johnson. "They can't do things like our great universities did and they deserve to die. Besides, they were saying parenthetically, 'We don't want to be bothered with teaching residents and students anyway.' "

Johnson, who worked in Fargo in 1971 as a pediatrician and whose uncles at the Johnson Clinic in Rugby were all UND graduates, took a lot of heat from colleagues for his support of expansion. "This was a tough time for me," he says. "I was sternly warned, 'We don't like your support of the University of North Dakota School of Medicine.' The old guard didn't realize that times were a-changing. That meant that you could have a community-based medical school. I think John Vennes and any number of others thought the doctors of the state could, in essence, be the faculty. And at a much lower cost and perhaps be a better faculty than professors that lectured from afar and never knew their students very well."

It was not just doctors in Fargo, but also local legislators who did not like the idea. In fact, C. Warner Litten, the majority leader of the State Senate, also was the administrator of the Fargo Clinic. Even Bryce Streibel remembers warnings from opponents that anyone who supported a four-year school would be voted out of office.

In spite of Fargo's stance, there were still plenty of doctors in the state in favor of the expanded medical school. One of their most prominent leaders was Bismarck internist Phil Dahl, such a confident UND graduate that he blithely rejected Harvard's offer of a transfer in favor of finishing his degree at Northwestern.

"We felt if we did not have a four-year medical school ourselves here in North Dakota," he says, "we would be denying the opportunity of our students to get into medical school. There are so many applicants to medical schools all over the country that they are very reluctant to take out-of-state students — particularly the state universities. There just weren't enough of them and they had an overwhelming number of applicants as well."

Dunn and Eelkema, in the meantime, gathered ammunition against the oft-stated Fargo complaint that North Dakota did not have the patient population to support a "complete" medical school. While no single hospital in North Dakota came close to having the 200,000 patients a year seen by the Mayo Clinic — whose school of medicine trained 550 residents — the two hospitals in Bismarck alone saw a combined 300,000 patients a year.

That point hit hard in March 1972 when Dunn delivered his famous report, "North Dakota Health Manpower," to Wright's Regional Medical Program. The RMP's board members were the same as the board of the North Dakota Medical Association.

The so-called Dunn Report touched on the overcrowding of the nation's medical schools and the competition for slots faced by North Dakota students. It offered four options: Close the two-year School of Medicine; pay some four-year medical school to take North Dakota transfers; expand to four years or do nothing.

Dunn noted that two out of three UND students said they would not be in medical school at all if the state did not have its own institution. Even so, only one out of five said they would come back to North Dakota to practice — a prediction upheld by fact: Fewer than one in four graduates of the School of Medicine returned to North Dakota to practice. On the other hand, Dunn made the same prediction Harley French had voiced almost thirty years earlier: A four-year school likely would mean that half of all grads would return.

As for cost, Dunn estimated $3 million to $5 million a year was needed to run a four-year school. He also said nine out of ten doctors in North Dakota pledged to volunteer their services as faculty.

It was now clearly up to the doctors — through their Medical Association — to decide the future of the School of Medicine at their annual May convention in Minot. While many doctors seemed impressed by the Dunn Report, there were many still opposed. The night before the vote on whether to recommend the medical school expand to four years, a rumor circulated that even though the measure would pass, those opposed were going to issue a minority report. The words of Brynhilde Haugland echoed ominously in the ears of Eelkema, Wright, Dunn, Vennes and Nelson: The vote the next day had to be unanimous or the interim legislative committee would not proceed with its study.

It fell to the doctor known as "Moses" to lead everyone to the promised land. Wright had been president of the Medical Association ten years before and knew its workings and its members well. He also had been nearly elected president of the AMA and his stature among doctors was very high. Late into the night at the Ramada Inn in Minot, Wright knocked on doors and chatted with groups of doctors debating their stand. By the time morning came, the minority report had been talked to death. Later that day, the Medical Association unanimously approved a resolution calling for a four-year medical school. Just as significantly, it committed the state's doctors to becoming faculty members and allowing students the access to their patients and facilities.

As welcome as that news was, Eelkema provided more excitement a few days later when he told Clifford about a new grant program he had stumbled upon in Washington. He had been there visiting with his federal MEDEX liaison in the NIH's Division of Health Manpower. That man, Doug Fenderson, turned out to be a North Dakota native who had moved to Minnesota as a boy and later to Washington. He told Eelkema of a program called Area Health Education Centers — AHEC — and that it sounded perfect for North Dakota's medical school expansion. The brand-new program was designed to give federal funds to designated AHEC localities set up by communities within a state to rectify medical manpower shortages. Nothing prevented the university, Fenderson told Eelkema, from declaring the entire state of North Dakota an AHEC.

This meant very big bucks — more than a million dollars a year for up to ten years if the university's application was granted. But only a handful of projects would be funded, Fenderson stressed. There was a great deal of grass roots organizing to do and less than a month to get it done and the grant application written. Eelkema and Dunn were off in a cloud of frenzied activity. They made a lightning tour of the state following Fenderson's formula: Form an AHEC structure in the four main cities — Fargo, Bismarck, Minot and Grand Forks — and put someone in charge of each. Those AHEC centers became "campuses" of the expanded medical school, and each was charged with finding space for clinical training and recruiting faculty from local physicians. Back in Grand Forks, Dunn, his wife Nancy Hepburn, and Eelkema began putting the grant together.

On the political front, now that the doctors had approved the expansion, Clifford's campaign moved into high gear. His daily habit was to have his breakfast at the Chuck House restaurant in the old Westward Ho Motel on Gateway Drive. One morning in July, Clifford invited Eelkema, Nelson and John Vennes to join him. Harwood was excluded. Over eggs and bacon, Clifford established the trio as his Medical Affairs Committee or MAC. He placed Eelkema in charge. Each week, the MAC met in a corner booth of the Chuck House and reported to the president on the status of their various assignments. They became known as the Chuck House Gang and that summer of 1972 they and their allies fanned out across the state to give speeches, show slides and talk up the four-year school to farmer-legislators, doctors and anyone else who would listen.

"It took a lot of lobbying," says Clifford, "as not all communities were in favor of this. We had a group that met at the Westward Ho and we plotted the future. Dr. Wright, Gary Dunn, John Vennes and Bob Eelkema did a fine job going to the grass roots. Vennes came from Williston, so he automatically was accepted in the western part of the state and he did a terrific job. He was always there. He was the thread that kept it together."

At Dunn's suggestion, the gang hired a colleague of his from Alabama, a cardiologist-turned-academic named Dr. Bill Harlan. He was the real thing, with stellar credentials both as a physician and as a health education administrator. He signed on as a consultant and most often he paired with Dunn in a curious dog and pony show that played out in community meeting rooms across the state. Typically, at these sessions, Dunn stepped to the podium and played fast and loose with facts, while painting a glowing picture of what a four-year school of medicine would mean to the state. Immediately after he sat down, Harlan would get up. More reflective by nature,

Lee Christoferson, Sr.

The first neurosurgeon in North Dakota, Christoferson made his mark with his successful TNI clinic in Fargo and later his Neuropsychiatric Research Institute. His support for the four-year medical school persuaded many of his colleagues in that direction. He was the first chair of the medical school's department of neuroscience.

The One Person that I Look Back on in Medical School

OB was not a field that I ever intended to enter into. I never wanted that as my specialty until I ran into Dr. Bury in Bismarck. He really loved doing what he was doing. I remember he was very busy in those days. I think he has slowed down a bit now, but he was very busy and we would do ten deliveries a day. I remember by the end of the day I was totally exhausted and he was still going strong in spite of the fact that he was probably twenty years my senior. That influenced me to look into OB/GYN and I am happy that I did. That is the one person that I look back on in medical school, in my clinical years, that influenced my choice. OB/GYN is generally a good field in terms of "feel good." You get good outcomes and you get close relationships with your patients because you see them so often. I have one family of six sisters and sisters-in-law and I just delivered the twenty-eighth child in that family group. I was personally there for twenty-six of the deliveries. I took care of the other two also but I was not there for their deliveries because they delivered before I could get

(continued on next page)

Harlan's practical approach to the problem was the perfect antidote to too much Gary Dunn. Audiences warmed to his logic as he frequently chided Dunn in his talks for stretching the facts a bit.

Eelkema and Vennes, and even Harwood at times, hit the road on behalf of the cause. Harwood was less an opponent of the plan than an ambivalent party. Along the way, the Chuck House Gang recruited people in each of the AHEC regions to spread the word. Phil Dahl was the point man in Bismarck and often traveled around the state. Clifford likes to cite the support of the Williston physician Dean Strinden, brother of Earl, who became president of the State Medical Association in 1973. "Dean Strinden gave some of the greatest speeches on helping the medical school that I have ever heard," recalls Clifford.

What Dr. William Cornatzer remembers strongly from those days was his father's frequent forays to Bismarck with Vennes to lobby legislators on behalf of the medical school. In fact, says Bill Cornatzer, "John Vennes was the number-one person responsible for that four-year school. He was always up there lobbying."

Vennes, who also traveled the entire state, speaking before various medical and community groups, says today, "I have learned that gaining support from the entire state is critical to anything that the university does. Placing our major emphases in the four major cities in the state was a brilliant move. We needed those hospitals as teaching sites for our students."

Though many people needed convincing around North Dakota, the real trouble, Clifford knew, would come from Fargo. The state's most populous city wielded a heavy political club. Yet while many doctors there opposed the expansion because of the lack of a big teaching hospital, and concerns over quality, others had a more personal reason.

"There was a nasty group," says Dr. Richard Olafson, a Fargo neurosurgeon at the time. "They didn't want any competition. The medical school would take patients away."

Clifford knew he needed an ally in Fargo, someone with political clout among doctors, someone who actually liked the idea of a four-year school. Not surprisingly, he knew just the man.

Lee Christoferson, Sr., who died in 2000, was the first, and for years the only neurosurgeon in North Dakota. He had built a strong national reputation for his surgical skills. By taking referrals from all over the state, he also knew just about every general practitioner in North Dakota. When patients in need of brain surgery could not be moved, Christoferson often went to them, flying in a private plane up to remote towns to perform surgery.

His association with the School of Medicine at Grand Forks began almost as soon as he arrived in Fargo in the early Fifties. It seems UND President John West discovered him and urged Wilbur Potter to use Christoferson in setting up a curriculum in the neurosciences.

"Dr. Christoferson used to come and give us a lecture in neurosurgery," recalls Dr. John Graham, class of 1952. "He built an empire of neurosurgery and neurology. I remember a medical school grad a year or two ahead of me by the name of O'Toole, who practiced in Park River. He had a patient from an automobile accident who had a subdural hematoma that needed to be drained. O'Toole called Christoferson, but he said, 'I'm sorry, I've got four cases here. But I'll put one of my neurosurgical kits on the bus and send it up to you.' And he sent a kit up to Park River and Dr. O'Toole drilled the burr holes and drained the fluid. Now, they don't recommend doing that, but in those days men did things they had to do."

Lean, lanky, and balding, Christoferson radiated energy. "Anything he decided to take an interest in he pursued with a vengeance," says Olafson, his partner. "He was like a pit bull."

Born and raised in Minnesota, he earned his medical degree at the University of Minnesota. He decided to settle in Fargo for many of the same reasons Harley French stayed in Grand Forks. He was a very large frog in a very small pond. He started his own clinic in Fargo — the Neuropsychiatric Institute, or TNI — and began recruiting other neurosurgeons and psychiatrists. One of them was Olafson who, like Christoferson, believed strongly in the School of Medicine.

"The medical school was part of Lee's overall vision," says Olafson, "that we in North Dakota had medical capabilities far beyond what people believed. He saw that the medical school could attract more people into medicine who would stabilize our medical care and allow growth in specialty areas."

Christoferson obtained federal funding to build a 120-bed neuropsychiatric hospital on one of the floors of St. Luke's Hospital in Fargo. Devoted to neurology, neurosurgery and psychiatry, it was later sold to the Fargo Clinic and St. Luke's. Christoferson used the proceeds to start a Neuropsychiatric Research Institute (NRI) in Fargo that is now affiliated with the School of Medicine.

Christoferson's talents as a surgeon combined with a dynamic personality. "He was a very forceful guy who knew what he wanted," says Al Samuelson, a Bismarck psychiatrist who used to play golf with Christoferson. "He was very persuasive, very political and had a lot of clout."

Eventually, John Vennes, when he became the interim dean, offered Christoferson the job of chairing a department of neurosurgery in the new four-year school — if it ever got going, that is. Christoferson had little trouble drumming up support in Fargo among some of his fence-sitting colleagues.

That same summer, Gary Dunn made contact with Michigan State University in East Lansing. The university there had an unusual but successful School of Medicine — a so-called school without walls — based on the very community model North Dakota was considering. Dunn arranged for the Michigan State people to host a visit by a North Dakota contingent so they could actually see a working model of the theory whose virtues they had been extolling.

Eelkema arranged with John Odegard, the head of the nascent department of aviation at UND (later to become the Odegard School of Aerospace Sciences) to borrow a very used DC-3 for the flight to Michigan. Odegard even sent smaller planes out to various spots in North Dakota to bring community leaders, doctors, hospital administrators and skeptical legislators to Grand Forks for the big flight.

About twenty dignitaries made the trip to East Lansing and the two-day visit worked wonders. The disparate group bonded and came to the simultaneous conclusion that if Michigan could do it, so could North Dakota. The doctors on the trip were especially impressed. They got to see that their Michigan colleagues were quite comfortable with the community model and the way things worked in East Lansing. It was a highly enthused group that returned to Grand Forks, spreading out like zealous missionaries, convinced more than ever that a non-traditional model of a medical school would work.

That fall, Eelkema received word that the NIH grant he and Dunn submitted had been approved — one of the biggest grants in the university's history. At about the same time, the interim study committee of the Legislative Council met again, pleased to see that the state Medical Association had approved the expansion idea. Lee Christoferson, Sr., spoke forcefully in favor of a four-year school and the impact it would likely have on the economy of the state. The outspoken Brynhilde Haugland then pronounced that citizens of North Dakota had been waiting for a complete medical school since 1947 when they approved the mill levy. "It's time," she said, "to

deliver on this implied promise."

To win ultimate state approval and the accreditation of the Association of American Medical Colleges, the Chuck House Gang had to quickly put in place the four-campus structure so glibly described in the grant application. That meant hiring deans of the four campuses, permanent chairs of the various departments, and working out myriad details such as where the students would live, what exactly they would be taught and by whom.

John Vennes and Bill Harlan worked feverishly on curriculum and logistical issues, while Gary Dunn was in charge of recruiting new faculty.

Dunn's charm, however, had begun to wear thin. By the fall of 1972, those who had heard him talk, or had run-ins with him, were calling his credentials and character into question. While Clifford and Eelkema viewed him as a flawed fraud with hidden talent, others were much less accepting. Some, like Harwood, simply didn't trust him.

Dunn's reputation was important because the bedrock of the approval of the state's doctors was the supposedly objective Dunn Report. By fall, with Dunn's credibility becoming an issue — especially among the volatile Fargo crowd who now viewed the Dunn Report as the work of a partisan — Tom Clifford worried that the entire expansion question was in jeopardy. He acted peremptorily to cut off a controversy before it arose. He hired the consulting firm of Booz, Allen and Hamilton to come to North Dakota and conduct

Medical Science South
Following World War Two a new medical science building was erected on campus. Now called O'Kelly Hall (after a long time arts professor), medical students knew it for 44 years as Med Sci South.

an independent study of the medical school question.

Two weeks before the 1973 legislative session was to begin, Booz, Allen delivered its surprising report to the interim legislative committee. It suggested that developing a four-year medical school was not a good idea unless residency programs were developed at the same time. Once students earn a degree from medical school, it pointed out they almost always went on to serve a one- to four-year residency at a hospital or clinic in a chosen specialty area.

Clifford and his Chuck House Gang did not disagree with the need for residency programs. In fact, a big argument in favor of the four-year expansion — that graduates most often settle within one hundred miles of where they finish schooling — was flawed without residency programs. Conceivably, a person could graduate from North Dakota's four-year school and still go off to Michigan or Harvard for residency training and never be seen again. It is just that Clifford hadn't counted on asking for extra state money for residency programs in the same breath as asking for a four-year expansion. The politicians would never bite.

The biggest surprise of the Booz, Allen report, though, was its recommendation that instead of a four-year school, the state consider a three-year school. That is, pay Minnesota medical schools to take all third-year students into their clinical training programs, which were based on the traditional big hospital model. Then, take those same students back to North Dakota as fourth-year students when elective courses would be more suited to community training.

This concept probably arose from UND graduates practicing in Minneapolis. It became known as the 2-1-1 plan: two years at UND, one year in Minnesota and one year at UND. Even with the cost of paying Minnesota — at an estimated $11,000 per student — the system would be cheaper than a full four-year bill. The idea intrigued the interim committee. So much that Clifford and Vennes, along with members of the Board of Higher Education were dispatched to negotiate with the University of Minnesota and the Mayo Clinic. They did this immediately and by early January they reported to the interim committee that Minnesota, facing budget crunches, was only too happy to get the money.

A last-minute wrinkle was smoothed out when the committee realized that the Booz, Allen 2-1-1 plan called for funding of residency programs. Vennes worked hard the weekend before the legislative session convened, getting the four AHEC campus deans to agree to find local funding in their communities to finance residency programs. The following Monday, the interim committee approved the 2-1-1 plan and two months later the full legislature adopted the bill without much debate at all. All of the wheels had been greased.

But had Clifford blinked in the face of the enemy at the last minute? Was 2-1-1 really what he wanted? Was it a victory or a defeat for the movement?

In answer, Clifford cites his experience as a Marine tank commander in the South Pacific. The islands held by the Japanese, he reminds, were taken back one at a time, not all at once. Others agreed that the 2-1-1 was the compromise needed at the moment to move things forward. There would be plenty of time in the near future to get the third year back.

"There was a time when we were in doubt," says Clifford. "We would go back and forth and we had to scratch and fumble around, but it came. John Vennes followed the academic work and Gary Dunn was a good recruiter."

Fellow Marine Earl Strinden lays the success to the work with the state's doctors.

"If I were to put my finger on one prevailing argument," says Earl Strinden, "it was the respect that the physicians are held in our state and their influence on their individual legislators. If we had not had a medical school, very few North Dakotans would have an opportunity for a medical education."

"If I were to put my finger on one prevailing argument," says Earl Strinden, "it was the respect that the physicians are held in our state and their influence on their individual legislators. If we had not had a medical school, very few North Dakotans would have an opportunity for a medical education. There was a full realization that good health is everyone's priority. Having that available, especially in rural North Dakota, was very much in the minds of the legislators."

The Clifford-engineered 2-1-1 compromise thus made it possible in that spring of 1973 for both sides of the medical school issue to feel a degree of satisfaction. Yet even as the School of Medicine prepared for a new era, there was one man who felt only dread.

"My father knew exactly where he stood," says Bill Harwood. "He was no fool. The world changed and he didn't change with it. He knew what was coming down the track."

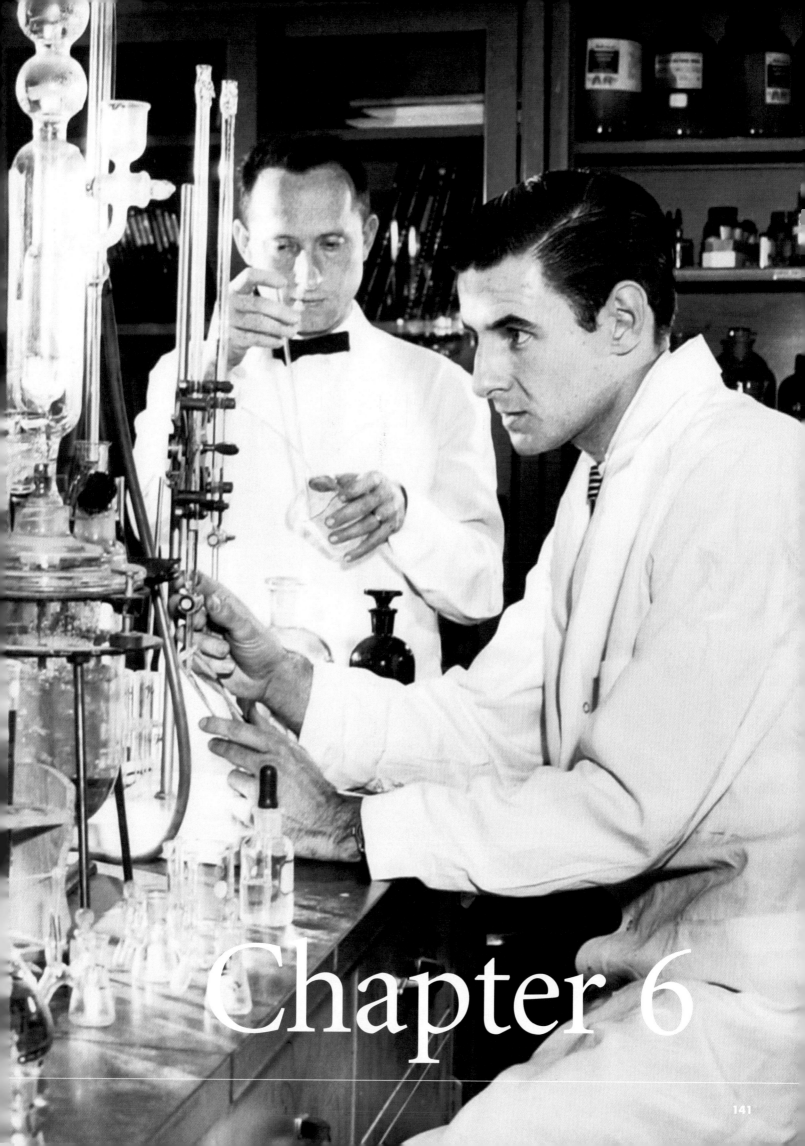

Chapter 6

CHAPTER SIX

Tears in My Eyes

Could two men have been more exquisitely opposite than Ted Harwood and Tom Clifford? Clifford was the larger-than-life native North Dakotan, Harwood the meek New England outsider.

Clifford was the wild Irishman, a maverick with a magical knack for negotiating himself into and out of tight spots. Harwood was the quiet, Presbyterian homebody who preferred the potential of his garden to a cocktail party full of politicians. Clifford loved the smash and sweat of handball. Harwood belonged to the local country club only one year before quitting; he didn't play golf and membership cost too much money.

Often, says Bill Harwood, his father would ask his children, "Do you know what a Puritan is?" The answer never varied: "Someone afraid that somebody someplace is having a good time."

"That's the way I was raised," says Bill Harwood. "Life is difficult, life is mean, you did not have a good time. So it was oil and water with Clifford and my father. He was not entrepreneurial. He was not a hale fellow, not a backslapper. He was a small town kid from Vermont who was fortunate to go to medical school. He was grateful for everything. His only goal was to provide for his family and do his job. He didn't have big ambitions for himself. He looked after the med school the way he looked after his garden. You take care, you nurture, but you don't take a big risk. He was not a risktaker."

Previous page:

Easy does it
Gene Cornatzer and his then-grad student Fred Snyder — now a Ph.D., in the medical school's biochemistry department — conduct research in a lab setting.

Still, for two decades Ted Harwood did more than merely hold the two-year medical school together. He vastly improved it, not only in the quality of its faculty and curriculum, but in reputation, too. In the end, very few people disliked him, including Clifford.

"He was a fine guy," says Clifford. "But he was the dean and he didn't think we needed the four-year medical school. I think he was ill at the time. I think he just couldn't bear the thought of doing that. But you had to move on. You could either do it or you could go like Wyoming and Montana and not have a medical school. And they suffer for it. But there were a lot of things that pointed to the fact that we should do it. So we just had to figure out how."

In fact, Harwood was ill, suffering from prostate cancer. Bill Harwood, then a graduate student in history in San Francisco, noticed the change in his father during a visit Harwood made to the Bay Area during all the debates over the four-year expansion.

"I spent a day with him and I knew he was not well. He knew he was not well. But he treated it the way medical people treat it. He ignored it."

Bill Harwood says his father just was not able to take on a large challenge like expansion. "No way, psychologically, could he have taken on that big a project like Clifford. He knew his limits. For him to stay on was just not in the cards. I think he would have retired at the end of twenty years and gone away. My mother was just counting the days until she could get out of North Dakota and go back to Vermont."

Harwood never spoke much to his family about what happened next. Clifford ultimately told him he had to step down. He paid Harwood a year's salary to leave the medical school. That extra year gave Harwood exactly twenty years of service and qualified him for his pension. "He never said a word about it," says Bill Harwood. "This was off limits. It hurt him so much. He was a very proud man. He always felt he'd been wronged but he never talked about it."

Harwood told his colleagues he wanted no gifts or big fuss. The school held a small luncheon for him, says Bill, and "then he just packed up his stuff and went home."

Clifford had asked John Vennes, the man whose career Harwood enabled with the funding of his Michigan scholarship, to become interim dean until a successor was found. "The toughest day I had," says Vennes, "was the day I walked into his office as interim dean and Ted walked out. It was a strange experience."

Shortly afterward, Harwood and his wife moved back to Vermont. He spent his year's severance — $35,000 — to buy a farm and a tractor. He would tell people that he had earned in his lifetime only a third of what his medical school classmates had made.

"Oh, God, could I feel the bitterness," says Bill. "He never got over it. That's part of old-fashioned Vermont heritage."

Harwood went back to where he had left off twenty years earlier. He was elected to the school board, became president of the Rotary Club, served on the town council. The man who had done so well in North Dakota in everything but politics now threw his every energy into the art of persuading, compromising and getting along.

The prostate cancer finally claimed him in 1979. Many of his old colleagues from the University of Vermont attended his funeral. Though Vennes and other friends from Grand Forks sent heartfelt condolences, Harwood's family remembers to this day that there was no one at the graveside from North Dakota.

The baby boy delivered by country doctor Willard Wright in 1924 in the remote northwestern corner of North Dakota marks perhaps the happiest and most profound coincidence in the history of the School of Medicine. Though the two would not meet up again for almost fifty years, Wright and Vennes became two of the leaders most responsible for saving the School of Medicine from extinction.

Many, however, first point out the redundancy of calling the northwest corner of North Dakota remote. Unless, that is, you zero in on the tiny town of Zahl, the old Great Northern rail stop of 250 souls into which John Vennes emerged that summer. At last count, the population stood at seventeen.

Young John spent his formative years during the Dust Bowl days of the Depression. He has memories of riding to school in a horse and buggy, of seeing the thick smoke of Montana forest fires darkening the skies, of a summer day when a strong wind blew down the family livery stable.

Zahl was predominantly Scandinavian and though it never was overendowed with people, it did have two Lutheran churches. Vennes remembers wondering about that one family in town who drove seven miles west each Sunday to Hanks and the nearest Catholic church.

When he was ten years old, his parents divorced and his mother raised her six boys by renting out space in their three-bedroom house to boarders. She supplemented that with a monthly state welfare stipend plus $5 a month from her ex-husband in child support. Every year on June 1, Vennes remembers taking off his shoes and spending the summer barefoot — less out of a boyish desire to feel free than his mother's concern about preserving the leather. "We were unaware of the affluent lifestyles of others," he recalls, "so we had no reason to think what we were doing was anything different

John Vennes

Born in Zahl, North Dakota, Vennes joined the faculty at UND in 1952 and has never really left. He has chaired the department of microbiology, served as interim dean and associate dean. His speeches and presentations on behalf of the four-year expansion are credited with changing the minds of many opponents.

than what anyone else did."

Like most children in Zahl, John grew up skiing, hunting and playing baseball and basketball. He remembers that he seldom missed a day of school. Infectious diseases were rare out on the open range. "If I didn't have a birth certificate, I wouldn't know that I was born with the help of a physician," he says. "I never saw a doctor in my first eighteen years of life." The closest hospital was fifteen miles west. Once a year a Williams County nurse came up from Williston to perform immunizations.

Zahl was big enough in those days to have a three-room schoolhouse, with grades one through four in one room, five through eight in another and four years of high school in the third. School was not a challenge — Vennes can't remember ever doing homework — and he felt no special stimulation from the field of science. He does count, however, the reading of Sinclair Lewis's novel "Arrowsmith" as something of a foreshadowing of his career. The hero of the book, Martin Arrowsmith, grows up in a small town in the Midwest, attends medical school and becomes fascinated with bacteriology and infectious disease.

During the summer of 1940, John worked in a hardware store in Zahl. The owner took sick and Vennes, at fifteen, became the sole operator of the store. In 1941, after only three years of high school, Vennes graduated — one of only seven in his class. His mother moved the family to Williston, some thirty miles to the south and arranged for her son to work in the drugstore as a soda jerk. She told the owner that John would work on Saturdays until high school graduation and if he did not like the work John did, he did not have to pay him.

The owner subsequently tried to persuade him to go to pharmacy school. He even wrote a letter to the dean of the pharmacy school at North Dakota State University in Fargo on his behalf. The dean wrote back saying he would accept him as a student and find him a job. But World War II intervened and as soon as he turned eighteen, Vennes followed three of his brothers and his father into the Navy. His pharmacy experience landed him in a medical corpsman school, and he spent two years at a naval hospital in Seattle. After the war and three years in the Navy, Vennes was excited by what he had learned in medicine and decided to go to Grand Forks to study biology. He took a part-time job in the department of bacteriology and decided that was his calling. Later, when John came back from Michigan with his doctorate, the great Dr. Hamre tried to persuade him to go into medical school. But during his years at Michigan, the field of microbiology had lit up like a prairie fire with the discovery of the DNA molecule. "I was completely convinced," he says, "that microbiology was the greatest field in science. That's where all the action was. So I told Dr. Hamre, 'I've found my niche.'"

When Tom Clifford decided he needed a new dean of the School of Medicine — at least someone to fill in temporarily after Ted Harwood's departure — he had several choices. There was his good friend, Bob Eelkema, and there was Wally Nelson, both of them medical doctors. In the end, he settled on John Vennes, an extremely organized man who understood the curriculum and what it would take to keep the two-year school going while everyone learned how to convert to four years — or at least the three allowed under the 2-1-1 plan.

Vennes and Clifford got along well. Once a month the two would meet for breakfast at the Chuck House and Vennes would bring a notepad and run down a list of what he was doing. "Tom would say, 'Fine. Are you comfortable with that?' I had a great working relationship with him. That was his style," says Vennes.

As interim dean, Vennes soon found that getting the legislature to approve the 2-1-1 plan was not the end of the struggle, but just the beginning.

"My job was to hold the ship together," he says. "My goal was to continue the credibility of basic sciences in the eyes of the physician teachers in the state and to develop a four-year school in an environment where the basic sciences world had changed. They no longer were the darlings of the system."

Still, his colleagues in the basic sciences were delighted that Vennes — and not a medical doctor — was in charge. He remembers coming back from an appearance before the legislature in Bismarck and attending a party that evening. A couple of faculty approached him and asked how it had gone. "Oh it was fine," he said. They smiled and one said, "We knew you'd take care of us."

The rivalry between basic scientists and clinicians was a longstanding one. Vennes knew it wouldn't do to appear to favor one side versus the other, and he always managed to walk the thin line between the two. "John Vennes is probably one of the neatest guys I've ever come across," says Clayton Jensen, who himself served a term as interim dean at the school in the Nineties. "John had a good clinical sense about him though he was a basic scientist."

In fact, he pulled off a major clinical coup not long after taking over.

It was agreed in negotiations with the legislature that the school would not seek to build a hospital. The cost was too high and — so the fear went — there would not be enough patients to make it worthwhile as a teaching hospital. Yet in one stunning bit of legerdemain, Vennes and Gary Dunn made a clinical hospital materialize before the very eyes of their biggest critics.

They began with a modest grant proposal to the Veterans Administration, which had announced the availability of unspecified funds for programs of cooperation between the VA and medical schools. Through the influence of North Dakota's senior senator, Milton Young, they reeled in an unheard of $12 million in federal funds. The money was used to set up an alliance between the School of Medicine, the VA and its hospital in Fargo. The grant, spread out over seven years, established a Dean's Committee to oversee the new relationship. It erected new medical school buildings on the VA campus, including a 30,000-square-foot educational building adjacent to the VA hospital. It also established residency programs in psychiatry, surgery and internal medicine at the VA hospital. Combined with the AHEC grant, it meant the school not only had found its so-called missing piece — a teaching hospital — but federal money essentially ran it. For skeptical state legislators, it was a beautiful thing to behold.

In the meantime, the non-clinical Vennes had more clinical projects ahead of him. He helped establish residency programs in family medicine at all four AHEC campuses and arranged alliances with hospitals in those cities, including in Bismarck St. Alexius and the Bismarck Hospital; United Hospital in Grand Forks; Trinity and St. Joseph's in Minot and St. Luke's, the Dakota Clinic and St. John's in Fargo.

Until the 2-1-1 plan was approved, most of the school's clinical departments had been part-time endeavors. But with the addition of the fourth year to the two-year curriculum came a need for a full-time coordination of electives for those fourth-year returnees from Minnesota. To manage this, Vennes began appointing full-time chairs to various clinical departments, all of them physicians.

Dr. Reed Keller, a UND alumnus who had earned his medical degree at The Case Western Reserve, became chair of the department of internal medicine; Dr. Howard Joos chaired the department of pediatrics; Dr. Preston Dilts became the first chair of obstetrics and gynecology; Dr. Ed Donatelle chaired family medicine; Dr. Neil Thomford took over at the department of surgery, and Dr. Lee Christoferson, Sr., as promised, was named chair of the department of neuroscience.

But even with all of this attention to the clinical side, and with all of his credentials as a respected scientist and faculty star — not to mention his title of dean — Vennes still felt the cold shoulder. He can't forget one of the first meetings of the North Dakota Medical Association that he attended in Bismarck early on as interim dean. Vern Wagner, the executive director and also the chair of the House Appropriations Committee, introduced him to the doctors as the dean and asked him to give a report on the medical school. "I got up and gave my report," Vennes recalls, "and then Vern said, 'John, you can leave now, we're going to have our meeting.' And I said to myself, now there's an example of a good old boys' club. I think one of the characteristics I had — I was aware of the fact that I was not part of the club. The people who counted were the docs."

It did not faze Tom Clifford, a man used to being slighted by academics because he, too, wasn't part of the club. One morning at their regular Chuck House breakfast, Clifford asked Vennes if he would become the permanent dean. Vennes had never aspired to the job, and always knew his tenure was limited. "My contribution was maintaining a sense of decency in the whole process of change," he says, "and not allowing territorial differences to impact where we were and what our goals were. I may have been the right person at that time, but I was not the right person for the long term. I was not one of them."

After thinking it over, Vennes told Clifford that the school really needed an M.D. as its permanent dean. Thus, in 1975, after increasing the average class size to sixty-five students and readying the school for its first awarding of medical degrees, Vennes stepped aside for Dr. Richard Davis. He was a psychiatrist from Missouri, who left the dean's post after nine months. Davis's story, however, had a better ending than Harwood's. He went back to Kansas City, where he practiced medicine and also invented a barbecue sauce called KC Masterpiece.

Clifford then appointed Neil Thomford, M.D., (recruited by Vennes from Ohio State, as the first full-time professor and chair of the department of surgery) to be the new interim dean. Thomford took over in the spring of 1976. He presided over the very first awarding of medical degrees at the School of Medicine to forty students who had spent their third year in Minnesota. The very first graduate was Robert M. Arusell, who went on to study internal medicine and radiation-oncology and is now a member of the staff at MeritCare Clinic in Fargo.

Neal Thomford

Appointed interim dean of the medical school after the departure of Richard Davis, Dr. Thomford presided over the first awarding of medical degrees in 1976 to a class of 40 students who had spent their third year in Minnesota, finishing their degrees in the newly expanded UND medical school.

Even as Thomford was awarding those first medical degrees, a search committee was looking for a permanent dean. Thomford himself hoped to get the job and lobbied Vennes — who remained as associate dean — because of his closeness to Clifford.

But instead, Clifford hired a man who had many of his own leadership traits, people skills and even the same first name. Dr. Tom Johnson, an associate dean at Michigan State's medical school, already knew many of the players in North Dakota. He had been leader of the reception committee back in the summer of 1972 when the rickety DC-3 carrying Vennes and Eelkema and their group of dignitaries landed in East Lansing. He had given the group briefings on Michigan State's community approach to medical school training. In subsequent years, Johnson had acted as a consultant to the University of South Dakota when it expanded its two-year school of medicine to four years. At the time Clifford hired him, Johnson was on a leave from Michigan State, working for the Association of American Medical Colleges as one of its field examiners on accreditation visits. He knew exactly what a school of medicine needed to succeed.

Once again, the University of North Dakota felt it had hired the right man at the right time. And as it had done once before, it made clear to this new dean that the mission was all about getting North Dakota to that "complete" four-year status. It would mean finding a way to convince the legislature to undo what they had been lobbied so hard to do just a few years earlier. It meant wrenching that third year of medical school out of the glad hands in Minnesota.

Johnson came in not just with a winning smile and energy, but with a thoughtfulness about the nature of the problem in North Dakota. He believed sincerely that no matter where you lived, you had the right to expect decent healthcare. He talked a little fast and had the habit of saying to people, "Okay, you got that?" Sometimes he appeared gruff, but it was mostly a facade. Almost everyone took an instant liking to his genuine down-home style. Earl Strinden compared him to an old shoe.

"He was the most uncommon common man I've ever met," says Pamela Knudson, the medical school's long-time director of public affairs and editor of The Review. "He had a gift of relating to everyone with simple sincerity. He didn't show a shred of snobbery and genuinely appreciated North Dakota people, their work ethic and integrity."

Johnson lived on a farm out near the Grand Forks airport, where he spent his free time on a never-ending restoration of his house. It seemed to visitors that there was always a part of the house in shambles. He also loved to tinker with cars and kept the Quonset hut on the farm full of old Studebakers. Whenever John Odegard flew

him across the state to a meeting, he would make a mental note of the junkyards he saw from the sky and, weeks later, would drive out to take a closer look. Often he took with him Randy Eken, his director of finance (now an associate dean) in an ancient blue Dodge Omni with 200,000 miles on it.

"He drove a crummy car!" laughs Eken. "The damn thing had a hole in the floorboard. We're driving along and it's raining cats and dogs and my feet are getting wet. You'd never know he was the dean of the medical school. He took pride in just being an ordinary person who wasn't afraid to get dirty."

While everyone else was delighted, Neil Thomford was not one of Johnson's biggest fans. The interim dean who had wanted the full-time job, made his unhappiness clear to Johnson almost immediately. In the spring of 1977, about a month before Johnson was scheduled to take over, Thomford held a spring retreat for his administrators in Scottsdale, Arizona. Johnson was told he could attend, that it would be a good chance to get acquainted with the faculty and staff.

"When I got there," he recalls, "I asked Neil if I could talk to him. We went out by the pool. Neil was an excellent surgeon. But I had never seen anybody play his cards as close to vest as he did. I

The first degree

In 1976, Robert Arusell, M.D., became the first student to receive a medical degree from the UND medical school. Now a practicing physician in Fargo, Arusell and his classmates were the first to go through the 2-1-1 compromise expansion program.

Tom Johnson

Down to earth and self-effacing, Dr. Tom Johnson's challenge as dean was to persuade the state legislature to convert the UND medical school to a complete four-year, degree granting institution.

couldn't get any information out of him. He finally said, 'Look, I'm the dean now. You start May 15. Until then, I make the decisions.'"

Their relationship got worse after Johnson became dean. An exchange of frosty letters between the two shows that Thomford developed a residency program and hired a man to run it without informing Johnson. Thomford finally left in 1979 and became chair of the department of surgery at the Medical College of Ohio in Toledo. But it was not the last personality clash Johnson faced.

When Tom Clifford hired Johnson he told him that he "had the blessing" of Gary Dunn — who was by now an associate dean at the School of Medicine. By then Dunn's reputation had split the faculty into two hardened camps: ardent supporters on one side and those who simply couldn't stand or trust him on the other. Technically, he reported to Johnson, but Dunn always had Clifford's ear and frequently would run things by the president without informing Johnson. Critics of Dunn complained that there were, in essence, two deans. Some even accused Johnson of "being Gary Dunn's boy." When Johnson mentioned this to the president, the response was typical Clifford: "That's a lot of crap; you're my boy."

In fact, say those who knew him, Johnson succeeded precisely because he managed to remain his own man — which meant that it was eventually clear to everyone that he was not Gary Dunn's boy. While he managed to maintain Clifford's respect and friendship, his relationship with Dunn slowly fell apart.

In the beginning, Johnson recalls, Dunn was extremely outgoing and friendly toward him. Before his wife and family joined him from Michigan, Johnson spent many of his early weeks staying with Gary and Nancy Dunn.

"He was really important," says Johnson. "He could be the most charming or brutal individual. And God, he brought in a lot of money. One time we went to Washington. He saved us about $800,000 that they were gonna take back. On the trip back, we were in first class and Gary was making everyone laugh. I have never laughed so hard in my life. When I got to St. Paul, I hurt. All of the flight attendants came over to him and started talking to him. He was unbelievable."

But Johnson, whose undergraduate degree was in psychology, sensed that Dunn saw him as someone he could control and manipulate. It made him uncomfortable. "I was walking into a situation where I was the fifth dean in four years. I had more than a little trepidation because Gary didn't work for anyone. He reported to me, but Gary worked for Gary."

Even so, Johnson slowly built his own reputation across the state, especially with legislators.

"Tom had about the best way of working with the legislature of any person I have come across," says Clayton Jensen. "The only one who could possibly supersede him would be Tom Clifford, who was a master in working with the legislature. Tom Johnson could walk up and converse with anybody. He knew things about rural North Dakota that surprised me for a guy who didn't grow up here. He knew about the farms and he would go out and walk into a barn and sit down with the local farmer and talk about the local crop conditions. That is truly a talent. Let me tell you, there were legislators out there who would literally eat out of his hand."

But the more Johnson began to branch out, the more Dunn sensed he was no longer in control. "My relationship with Gary degenerated," he recalls. "It got pretty bad there. Gary was a sociopath and a genius. He's a type you only meet one or two of in a lifetime — and that's enough."

One thing Dunn did, says Johnson, was to foment crises that only he could solve. Or simply foment rebellion. He says it was Dunn who put a faculty sycophant up to charging Johnson with violating principles of academic freedom. It resulted in a drawn out process of hearings and trials before the Faculty Senate, which ultimately exonerated the dean.

"I think Tom found out fairly quickly that there was an awful lot more to being a dean than he had anticipated," says Dr. Hank Slotnick, who ran the school's office of medical education in those days. "The first couple of years he was here, things were a little tough and the problems were very often not of Tom's making. As he settled in, he developed a really good detector in terms of what was worth worrying about and what wasn't. He became seen not as Tom Johnson, the dean, but as The Dean. I think things began to improve dramatically for him."

Johnson worked well not just with legislators, but also with his faculty, especially the basic science members who were always leery about those on the clinical side.

"There was always that friction between myself and the basic science departments," he recalls. "They felt I didn't understand research and there may be some truth to that, as I am not a researcher. I got that kicked out of me when I was in medical school. But there was friction from the comfort of doing things the way we had always done them. I mean change is difficult. I came from a school, Michigan State, where sometimes they changed things for change's sake and not for a good reason. I didn't like that either."

His changes at North Dakota, however, made sense, says Vennes. "Tom was the first person to actually get basic scientists to think about

Everyman
Tom Johnson's down-home, Everyman style resonated with state legislators who appreciated that he took time to stop at their farms and stores and chat sincerely about everyday problems. They finally agreed with him and allowed the medical school to become a four-year school.

what it was like to problem-solve in clinical medicine. He put basic science chairs and clinical science chairs on the curriculum committee. Quite frankly, it was a refreshing change for the school."

Johnson is remembered as a man who never pushed an agenda, though he always had one.

"He always had a plan but it wasn't always clear to people around him what that plan was," says Judy DeMers, a former nurse who has worked as an administrator at the medical school since 1977. She is currently associate dean for student affairs and admissions at the School of Medicine and for eighteen years served terms in the state House and Senate. "Tom believed a lot in soliciting input. It was not uncommon for him to walk around the school every day and stop in people's offices to find out how they were doing and what their issues were. It was a very informal approach to people who worked for him. I thought his door was always open to provide help, but he was willing to give you a lot of leeway in terms of developing your own program."

That informal sense of confidence trickled down even to the students.

"One of the highlights of my first two years was during our orientation," says Dr. David Theige, the internal medicine residency program director who graduated in 1985. "Tom Johnson invited the whole class and their families to his home. When we met him there for the very first time, I think he had been working on some of his old cars. He had bluejeans on and grease on his hands and he was a down-to-earth, real person, which really impressed my family."

Families were always high on his agenda.

"We set up the oldest parent-teacher organization in the state and we went out and met with all the parents of our students on a regular basis," says Johnson. "I truly believed that this was the people's School of Medicine and the only way you get to the people is going out there. These were really fun meetings and the parents were very supportive. They would have a son or daughter in medical school and they would go to their legislator and say it was really a good school and how much their child was learning. And that never hurt."

From the very beginning, Johnson knew not only what was expected of him, but also how difficult it would be to succeed. If it had ever seemed from Michigan State that bringing the third year of medical school training to North Dakota would be fairly simple — given the legislature's approval of the 2-1-1 plan — he was quickly disabused of that notion.

Two weeks before he assumed office, Johnson met with the state hospital association — representatives of the seven facilities in those four AHEC centers where the medical school hoped to clinically train its third-year students as well as its residents. "They went around the table, one by one," he recalls, "and told me how bad the School of Medicine was and what a foolish person I was for taking the job. How the issue of them paying for residency programs was as far-fetched as it could ever get. It went on, a litany of complaints and absolutes that 'we will not' and 'never will.' It went around the whole table and then went around again and repeated it in case I didn't understand."

When he walked out of the meeting, he says, "I said we'd try to come up with a plan, but all I could do was laugh. It was so outlandish. Here I had taken the job, there were new residents coming aboard in six or seven weeks, and there was no way we were going to be able to pay for them. That was my introduction to the school."

He realized then that the issue of the very survival of the School of Medicine was still very much at stake. Having a 2-1-1 plan meant nothing to opponents, many of them doctors who believed that if Johnson failed, the school would simply have to close. On the other hand, opponents knew also that "if the third year came to North Dakota, the School of Medicine was here for good and you weren't going to get rid of it."

Johnson spent much of his first year working with Gary Dunn on a plan to convince hospital administrators, legislators, and doctors that adding the third year would work. The result was a five-year plan that was sent to every power broker in the state, along with a note asking for feedback. Johnson then held meetings on the plan across the state, generating a good bit of interest and consensus on key elements. The plan was modified, printed up and published.

"It was one of most helpful things we did and we never deviated from it," says Johnson. "When anybody would say, 'Why are you doing this?' or 'I don't want this done,' we would say, 'People agreed to it and we're going to develop this program.' I think consistency was important. The hospitals began to see that there were advantages to it. And there was a group of physicians who believed in it and wanted it."

The devil, however, was not just in the details of the plan. Hard-line, budget-conscious legislators asked tough questions about whether the medical school was really worth the money. Those first grants for the VA and for the AHEC program were phasing into the time when the state needed to assume responsibility for its share. It seems as if money is always tight in North Dakota, but never before had legislators introduced bills to out-and-out close the School of Medicine.

"It was not business as usual," says Vennes. "This was a period where there was a lot of concern about the amount of money going into school versus what came out. There were even some on the main campus who felt the med school budget was too large and was taking money away from them. Our philosophy always was, just because the money went to the med school doesn't mean it would automatically go to your community."

To counteract the negativity, Earl Strinden, who was by then the majority leader in the State House of Representatives — and also head of the UND Alumni Association — borrowed a page from the 1972 strategy. He kept alive the interim committee of the legislature that studied the medical school. It meant key legislators once again became very involved and very knowledgeable.

"I knew it would have a tremendous influence on how other legislators voted," says Strinden, "and what they knew and what they thought on the importance of it all. I am sure it was a pain for the people at the medical school to have this interim committee continuing and all the meetings that were held that they had to go to and testify at for so many years, but it gave the legislature that pride of ownership. This was our program."

Thus, did Tom Johnson and his Dodge Omni become a familiar sight in every corner of the state. For four years, he crisscrossed

North Dakota, speaking at Medical Association meetings, Farm Bureau meetings and hearings of the state legislature's interim committee. Dick Davison, the executive secretary of the State Board of Higher Education, was one of the many impressed by Johnson's tirelessness. "He knew nothing else to be important to him than contributing to people's understanding of the medical school and its impact on the quality of health in North Dakota. If he had a call from somebody in Crosby who was interested in learning more, he would get in his car and drive to Crosby and there he would meet with two legislators. They thought that was great and then there was more support for the medical school."

Whenever he could, Johnson would drop in unannounced on a legislator in his home or his place of business. "Whenever I traveled with him," says Eken, "we always had to take some side trips. Or we'd stop at a bank because there was a legislator that worked there. And he'd have coffee. He liked to do that not just for politics, he just liked to talk to people. He had a very good political base. He worked hard at it. He had a knack for driving down the road and stopping to see someone just to say hi. People really liked that and remembered that."

Johnson says he learned along the way that politics in North Dakota is very different from politics in Michigan.

"In North Dakota, it's a personal matter," he says. "You get to know people and they are pretty open and honest with you. There were people in Fargo you couldn't get to first base with. But at least they told you why."

Al Samuelson, the psychiatrist who worked hard to develop the AHEC campus in Bismarck, says Johnson's charisma even impacted fashion. "I remember he probably wasn't the best dresser in the world," says Samuelson. "He used to wear these high snow boots with his suits. And I recall him coming down here to Bismarck with his snow boots and it became kind of faddish at that point. Everybody started wearing snow boots with their suits like Tom Johnson. That was their way of identifying with him. He was a very personable guy who was a lot of fun but also astute and conscientious."

But it wasn't all fun and fashion.

"I believe this was very tiring for Tom Johnson," says Dr. Dick Olafson, whose work in Fargo built support among many of his colleagues. "Tom was a very bright man and very charismatic, but there were people who didn't like him. He could have a very strong temper but he did hold it in check most of the time even though he was tested on a variety of situations...almost put on a spit and roasted over a fire by some of the practicing physicians who didn't

Nothing is Nothing

It wasn't too hard to fit in. For some strange reason, I had grown up as a Boston Red Sox fan and Ted Williams was my idol. Fenway Park was only a few blocks from Harvard Medical School. I remember going to Sears Roebuck and buying a rain coat because I didn't have one and you needed one in Boston. One night I walked to a Red Sox game, put on my raincoat, and turned up the collar so I looked like Sam Spade or something like that, and went to the game. What a wonderful experience. Unfortunately, I didn't earn any money the first year I was a resident. They gave us room, board and laundry, but then my second year was the first year they paid any residents and I got $108 a month, plus room, board and laundry. When I hear residents today complain about their salaries, I say, "Well, I didn't get anything my first year." The response of course is "Well, times were different." I respond by saying, "Well, nothing is nothing, regardless of the times."

Jon Tinglestad, M.D., class of 1958, is the former chair of pediatrics, East Carolina School of Medicine.

Yearning for North Dakota

When I went to Minnesota, I went with the attitude that I think many young North Dakotans have, that I was probably leaving permanently and that I was moving on to bigger and better things, so to speak. I did have a fantastic year at the University of Minnesota, but I remember sitting on the porch of a house I was renting with some classmates in the spring of my third year. We had an ideal apartment on the second floor of a house on Mississippi River Boulevard in St. Paul, which is kind of an idyllic setting right near the Shriner's Hospital. This is a place where medical students with no money really didn't belong, but somehow we had ended up with an apartment in this beautiful neighborhood. But even there, you couldn't escape all the noise, that's one of the things I remember. I was sitting out on the porch listening to all the traffic somewhere nearby that I couldn't see, and I was thinking to myself, as much as I liked this year, I really missed being back in North Dakota. As fortune had it, I was soon on my way back to do some elective rotations and graduate. When I came back to UND, my first rotation was an elective in gastroenterology with the department chair, Reed Keller, who recruited me very aggressively for the relatively new residency program. He was really a tremendous influence in my subsequent career. By the time I finished a month with Reed, I had decided not only that I was going to do my residency in North Dakota, but that I was likely to stay beyond that.

David Theige, M.D., class of 1985, is the internal medicine residency program director and associate professor of internal medicine.

think it was very practical for North Dakota to go into the expensive venture of having a four-year medical school."

On top of accreditation visits in the late Seventies and early Eighties, there were legislative interim studies to prepare and a State Board of Higher Education study that was crucial.

"It seemed as though we were always having to prove our existence," says Eken. "Many people doubted the state could support a medical school. We have a good deal of data today to support what we are doing. But in the early Eighties it was more conjecture: This is what we think we can do. It wasn't an easy ride."

In fact, Johnson began referring to the whole process sardonically as "Paralysis by Analysis."

The paralysis seemed to get worse when the Board of Higher Education hired an outside consultant — shades of the Dunn Report and the Booz, Allen report — to assess the situation. He was Dr. Stanley Olson, a former dean at the University of Illinois College of Medicine and at Baylor University, a director of several federal research programs and currently the provost at Northeastern Ohio University's College of Medicine.

Olson immediately changed the semantics of how North Dakotans had been viewing their challenge. Johnson and others had been talking of getting the third year "back from Minnesota." Olson, though, questioned how you could get something back that had never been there in the first place. Instead, he used the term "repatriation of the third year." Johnson latched onto the phrase as a glimmer of hope that, perhaps, this outsider's report might turn out positively.

Johnson, of course, did not carry the banner of repatriation into battle alone. He drew on the loyalty and hard work of a core of dedicated individuals including, among others, Dick Olafson, George Johnson and John Magness in Fargo; Ralph Dunnigan, Keith Foster, Phil Dahl and Al Samuelson in Bismarck; Brynhilde Haugland the fiery legislator from Minot, and John Vennes and Bob Eelkema in Grand Forks.

Olafson specifically recalls several primary care physicians who had just joined their practices with the Fargo Clinic — including Drs. Don Breen of Hillsboro, Ron Kloster and Glenn Thorson of Mayville — who warned the Clinic they would stop referring patients to them if they continued their opposition to expansion.

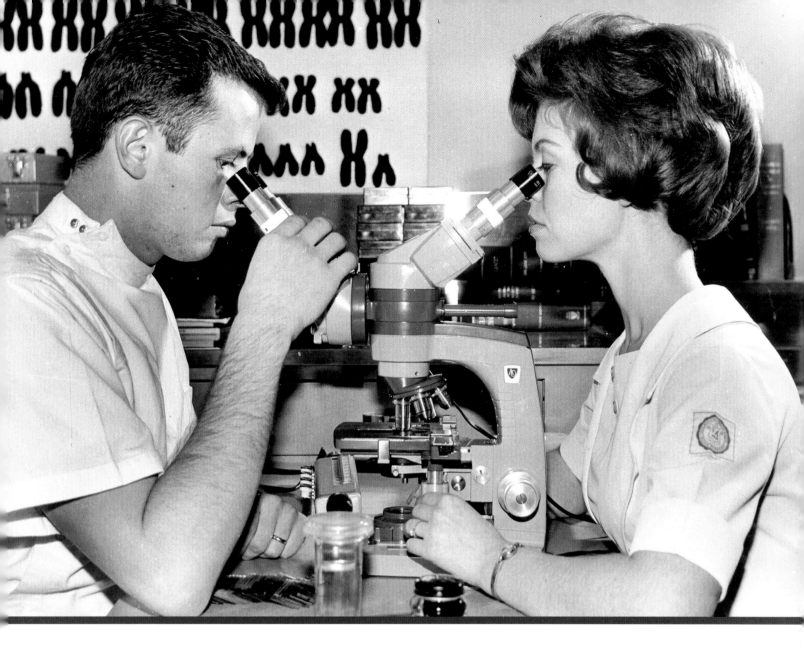

Olafson remembers also meeting not only with doctors and legislators in his travels through the state, but with newspaper editors. "This established a broader sense of recognition in the public mind," he says, "not just in the medical community, of what the purpose of the School of Medicine was."

In Grand Forks, meanwhile, Tom Johnson was grateful for the support of Lee Christoferson, Sr. "Lee was really helpful to me," says Johnson. "When Thomford departed, Lee took the department of surgery as the interim chair. He had such good stature in the state. He understood much better than I the politics of medicine. At a meeting of the doctors in Minot, once, I got frustrated and said to him, 'I really don't give a damn.' He said, 'Yes, you do give a damn and you'd better do this.' And I did. Lee was really important."

Johnson even had the ad hoc help of Tom Clifford in lining up votes. Clifford recalls one particular state senator, a rancher, who was opposed to the medical school. He saw the man one day at the State House in Bismarck, favoring a swollen, black and blue thumb. He told Clifford he had dropped a hay hitch on it.

"I said, 'That looks bad, you ought to take care of it.' He said, 'Aw, forget it.' I said, 'Well, you might develop arthritis from it.' I

Tech work

As the medical school grew and became more modern it began training its own staff of medical technicians to operate new equipment and handle emerging technologies. These technicians, circa 1960, are examining slides in the cytology lab.

The Reassurance of Coffee

I have recollections of the kindness and reassuring nature of very fine people from my first year of medical school when my confidence was faltering. Dr. John Oberpriller and Dr. Jean Oberpriller, Dr. Robert Nordlie and, of course, Dr. Cornatzer. Even a brief talk with them about how good the coffee was that day or how well we were on schedule with our lessons was immensely reassuring. I don't know why, but it was.

Mark Hinrichs, M.D., class of 1978.

Dr. Cardy told us, "If you don't think of it, you won't make the diagnosis." It seemed so trite at the time, but it really is important to teach the power of organization and observation.

Richard Olafson, M.D., class of 1957.

didn't know that. But I could see it in his eyes. Arthritis. I said, 'We've got a family practice clinic down here. I can get you an appointment and they'll take care of it.' I called the clinic and made an appointment. I said to the doctor, 'Tell this guy when you're through with him that because of the treatment, you doubt if he'll ever have trouble with arthritis.' The next morning at breakfast in the Senate cafeteria, he comes in and sits down. I said, 'How did it go?' He said, 'Oh, it went great. I feel wonderful.' I had a few more bites of oatmeal and he says in a whisper, 'He told me it wouldn't be arthritic.' Now, two months later at a Senate hearing, a senator got up and opposed our budget. And this rancher with the thumb, he says, 'Dummy, don't you know what these people do for us? How dare you talk about that?' We never lost a vote from him after that."

There was only one other person in the state who could match Clifford's guerilla warfare tactics. Luckily, Minot's Brynhilde Haugland was on the side of the medical school.

Haugland, a small but determined woman, was a legend in state politics, having served almost fifty years in office, longer than anyone else in state history.

"Brynhilde was one of the most unique human beings I've ever known," says Johnson. "I loved her. She was almost prototypic North Dakota. She was a little bit stout. She had a warm countenance. She could be cynical and cutting to the nth degree. She didn't take crap from anybody. You know, she voted against the Equal Rights Amendment. When asked why, she said, 'I've never needed that.'"

She took to Johnson right away, telling him "It's so nice to have a Scandinavian back in our dean's office."

The close relationship between Haugland and Johnson paid off on many occasions. Johnson would often call and ask for her advice on a strategy, and she would move quickly to quash any anti-medical school dissent on her committees. But at one meeting in Bismarck, Johnson recalls, she outdid herself.

At the time, one of the leading critics of the medical school was a Minot doctor who, even though he had graduated from UND, seldom missed a chance to criticize the school's plan for expansion. In fact, he thought it should be closed.

Because he was a member of the powerful Board of Higher Education, he could not easily be dismissed. He was among those at a meeting in Bismarck called by Tom Clifford. It was held in the small AHEC office where members of the interim legislative committee, including Haugland, squeezed in with Johnson and a group of local faculty and TV people. Johnson takes the narrative from there:

"This doctor got up and he said, 'Well, isn't this interesting. The dean brought his cronies in to tell us how wonderful the school is. But when I get with doctors by themselves in the lounge, they really don't want this medical school.' A hand went up. Brynhilde said, 'Doctor, do you mean to tell me and these people here in front of these TV cameras, that when you doctor fellas are with yourselves you tell the truth, but when you're out here in committee with us peons, you lie? Is that what you say, Doctor?"

As Johnson tells it, everyone had a big chuckle watching the look of defeat on the doctor's face. For months afterward, every time Clifford saw Johnson he would grin and spit out, "Peons!" in homage to the inimitable style of Brynhilde Haugland.

"I learned a lot from Brynhilde," says Judy DeMers, the associate dean of students who, while working at the medical school was simultaneously pursuing a career as a state legislator. DeMers started out as an assistant professor in the Department of Community Medicine in the early 1970s. She worked with Dr. Robert Eelkema and the MEDEX program that trained former combat medics to be physician assistants. After earning a master's degree at the University of Washington, she came back to UND in 1977 as head of the Family Nurse Practitioner's program.

While in Seattle, she studied the teaching of problem solving and clinical decision making. It was a subject that Tom Johnson was interested in when he became dean. He drew on DeMers's expertise when he began making changes in the curriculum and later he appointed her dean of students.

Simultaneously, DeMers became concerned that the state was not adequately appreciating education. "I wanted to get involved," she says. In 1983, she was elected to her first of five terms in the State House of Representatives. She then served two four-year terms in the state Senate, remaining focused on health and social policies of the state.

As a Democrat, whose party was often the minority party in the legislature, DeMers says she learned, "Even if you're in the minority, you can still make an impact if you're smart enough to know how to work in the committee structure."

She learned those lessons, she says, not from a fellow Democrat, but from Republican Brynhilde Haugland. In 1985, the lesson paid off when a young, maverick legislator submitted a bill to shut down the medical school because it cost too much. His mistake was introducing the bill into the State and Federal Government Committee, of which DeMers was a member. Already familiar with the ins and outs of the committee system, DeMers took the bill to Earl Strinden, a

Learning the Snake Dance

The things that drove me crazy were the Block exams. They were hard on an individual. You cycled so much and then crammed for the test at the end of the Block and the day after your exam you were totally exhausted. That is where I learned the snake dance from the younger group of medical students, and I don't even remember where it was, but some bar down at the old City Center Mall in Grand Forks. I don't remember the name, but after the first Block exam we were all having a good time at the local bar, and David Covington, the youngest member of the class, taught me what a snake dance was.

Lloyd Bakken, M.D., class of 1986.

Lo, and Behold

After graduating from here, I went to the University of Colorado. Dr. Harold Haugen, Dr. Bill McCullen and I were the three from that class who transferred out to Colorado. I felt that my education here put me very much on a par with those who had been educated in Colorado. I married Kathleen in 1950. She was trained as a nurse. She worked as soon as we got out to Colorado and put me through the last two years. I remember thinking that the good Lord does look after us, because when we went out there everything we owned we threw in the back seat of an old, broken-down Oldsmobile. We got out there and, of course, we didn't have a penny to our name. Like most young people who had come through in the 30's, money was not an abundant thing. We went to the medical school office and they had two card indexes listing apartments or rooms for single and for married. We went through the married ones and there wasn't anything listed that we could possibly afford. Just by chance, I picked up the single ones and, lo and behold, someone had mixed up a married in the

(continued on next page)

Republican and the House majority leader at the time. Strinden, of course, was another stalwart supporter of the medical school. He handed the bill to fellow Republican Bryndhilde Haugland, telling her he thought it belonged in the human services committee. When the legislator who introduced the bill showed up for the committee hearing, he found Haugland chatting amiably with Tom Johnson. Everyone in the room knew that bill was going nowhere.

Perhaps the most crystallizing moment of the entire four-year struggle came at a showdown meeting in Carrington in the spring of 1980. All of the principals were there: the interim committee, the Board of Higher Education, Johnson and his team, and doctors from across the state. The anti-expansion forces from the Fargo Clinic turned out en masse.

The occasion of this meeting was a presentation by Dr. Stanley Olson of his recommendations for the School of Medicine. Olson surprised critics by essentially saying that the "repatriation" of the third-year students was a necessary and very doable enterprise.

He said the school could not survive indefinitely under the 2-1-1 plan. More, not only were there enough clinical resources in the state to train fifty third-year students, he said, but the university had made a satisfactory beginning in creating a third-year curriculum. He said the money saved by not paying Minnesota to train North Dakota students would be sufficient, with normal state budgetary increases, to pay the bill.

He was scarcely finished, says Johnson, when opponents started hammering away. Attacks on Olson's statistics easily were proven false, taking some steam out of the critic's assault. Then a young Fargo doctor stood up and said he had gone to Johns Hopkins and had trained at the Ohio State University. His colleagues, he said, were from Stanford, Yale and Harvard. His point: If they allowed the four-year school of medicine to happen, it would mean the school's student body would be all North Dakota people. "And it will truly be second-rate," he said. "You can't compare to those schools. We will become inbred and all the physicians will become this inbred group of people from North Dakota."

Upon that, an older doctor from the small town of Harvey got to his feet.

"Let me tell you something," he said in a thick European accent to the young critic. "I don't know how much you know about the School of Medicine, but my son is at the School of Medicine in his second year and he says it is a good School of Medicine. And I know, because I compared it to a lot of other schools and I know what he knows and what he is learning. And he is getting a hell of a good education there. So don't tell me about being second-rate and that my son is second-rate."

It was the kind of outburst that took one's breath away. With perfect timing, the old doctor applied the coup de grace.

"Let me tell you something else, mister," he said. "There ain't nobody from Harvard in Harvey."

The room fell silent.

Doctors from the Fargo Clinic, says Johnson, immediately began assessing the damage. Rather than convincing anyone of their point of view, they now saw that they were alienating their referral base. Doctors like this old man from Harvey weren't going to refer many patients to them if they kept up this kind of elitist talk.

"That was one of the turning points in the expansion movement," says Johnson. "I think the Fargo Clinic said, 'We like those patients from Harvey and we're not going to get them anymore.'"

One immediate result was that the Fargo Clinic softened its public stance. Rather than take a unified position against the expansion, it decided to let individual departments make their own decision on whether they would cooperate with the medical school or not. That was major a concession. Before long, doctors who previously had felt constrained by their employer's blanket opposition began voicing support.

It would be almost another year before the legislature met and voted to repatriate the third year. But the minds of the interim committee were just about made up. And to add a final punctuation to that mounting feeling of support, there was the tiny drama enacted by Brynhilde Haugland toward the end of that meeting in Carrington.

A woman administrator at the Quain and Ramstad Clinic in Bismarck told the committee there should be no medical school. Brynhilde Haugland raised her hand.

"Now, miss," she said, "Where are you from, originally?"

The woman noted she was from out of state.

"And how long have you lived in North Dakota?"

Four months, she said.

Haugland let the comment hang for a long moment. She then said, very graciously, "On behalf of myself and the committee and the citizens of North Dakota, I just want to thank you for your testimony."

And that, pretty much, was the end of it.

"At its next meeting, the interim committee voted to repatriate the third year," says Johnson. "I had tears in my eyes."

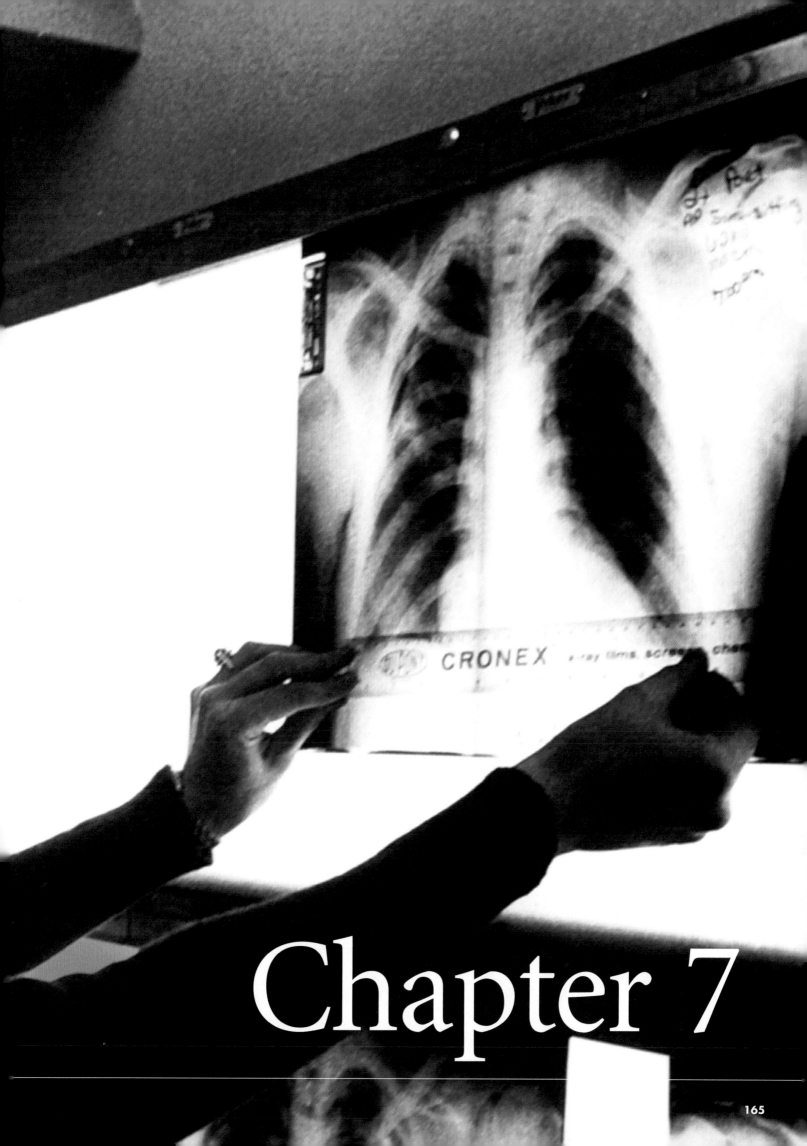

Chapter 7

CHAPTER SEVEN

Seeing it Through

By the time Tom Johnson took over as dean, it was clear to many in the School of Medicine that the Minnesota experiment was not really working the way the 2-1-1 plan had promised.

It sounded good enough on paper, but in practice the students who spent their third year at either the University of Minnesota or the Mayo Clinic were too often falling through the cracks. As was typical at many large medical schools, North Dakota students got little personal attention from their professors. In fact, most of their training was done by residents, who were only a year or two removed from being students themselves.

"They were lost in the whole milieu," says Dr. Keith Foster, the internist who became the first dean of the Bismarck AHEC campus. "But they were bright and they were survivors. They went through there and took what they could get, although they didn't get the choice spots."

Students told stories of spending hours in a surgery, for example, at the back of a crush of other students, all straining to get a glimpse of what was going on, and relying on the student in front of them for a running commentary. It seemed as if North Dakota students were always the ones in the back.

"That going-away experience to Minnesota was not a good one," adds Dr. Al Samuelson, the psychiatrist who worked with Foster to develop the AHEC program in Bismarck. "I guess it was all we could do but I don't feel

Previous page:

Measuring up
Maria Hardinsky, now an M.D., was a fourth year medical student at UND when this photo was taken in 1975.

What It Means to Be a Doctor

If you are going to be in primary care medicine, you can't be a good doctor unless your patient comes first. Somebody has to be available for the needs of the patient, the needs of people. That is what being a doctor is all about.

Dean Strinden, M.D., class of 1950.

You have the opportunity to be with people at the most important times of their life: birth and death. The intimacy can sometimes be overwhelming, but it is also something that one always grows from. It is also a heavy responsibility, and true professionals should always try to put the needs of their patients first. In the world we live in, I think that's become difficult and I worry that that standard is slipping away. Even in my own life, I find that there are lots of competing interests, including my own family life. Today, it's less acceptable to put your family second than it was in previous generations. It's a dilemma we continue to struggle with.

David Theige, M.D., class of 1985.

that those students got the type of experience that they should have had. After a couple rotations of students went down to Minnesota, I had the impression that they weren't getting the kind of experience they needed. A lot of people who went down there got lost. We knew we could do better."

Even so, most agree today that had the university begun a "complete" four-year school back in 1973, the task of creating two extra years almost overnight would have been impossibly daunting. As it was, just organizing those AHEC campuses to be able to teach the fourth year was itself a huge challenge.

According to the 2-1-1 plan approved in 1973, the first two years of basic science training were still to be taught at the School of Medicine's main campus in Grand Forks. That gave the AHEC deans in Bismarck, Minot, Fargo and Grand Forks about two years to recruit a faculty, write a fourth-year curriculum, develop full residency training programs from scratch and secure teaching space, student living quarters and clinical facilities to handle the first batch of Minnesota returnees in the fall of 1975.

One of the immediate problems was winning cooperation in those AHEC cities of the local doctors and hospital administrators, many of whom had been opponents of the expansion plan, even the modified 2-1-1 version.

"I think that the meetings with hospital administrators became an important issue for the school because it was an area that the school had not dealt with before," says Dr. Richard Olafson. "They had dealt with Deaconess, St. Michael's and United Hospital in Grand Forks, but on a much smaller scale than anything that we had to do to develop a third year and coordinate fourth-year teaching programs."

Typically, administrators worried that the presence of the medical school within their city would tip the competitive balance to a rival hospital. Doctors were worried that they would be training their future competition. Such issues had not been fully resolved by the time Tom Johnson repatriated the third year from Minnesota — especially the funding of residency training. The School of Medicine began to understand that in negotiating such agreements with hospitals, one size did not fit all.

"We tried to get the hospitals together to meet with common policies and procedures and how they handle residency programs, but it didn't work very well," says Randy Eken, associate dean for finance, who helped Johnson negotiate working agreements with hospitals in the early 1980s. "You can't treat Grand Forks the same as Fargo or Fargo the same as Bismarck. They have different administrators, different styles of administration within the hospitals and clinics, and it doesn't work. So, we basically try to work individually with programs in each community."

The immediate issue to resolve was who should bear the lion's share of residency training — a hospital with its own money or the university using state funds.

"In the early Eighties, folks weren't as understanding about graduate medical education funding," says Eken. "They felt like the state should pay for it. We have gradually moved from where the state paid for ninety per cent of graduate medical education, to now where the state picks up twenty per cent. The hospital contributions have followed suit. Those have been, as far as my tenure here, the most difficult negotiations that have occurred — getting the hospitals to pay more of their share of the funding."

Ultimately, says Olafson, private hospitals in the state were persuaded it was better to have students than not. "The AHEC board said we need this education to bring our people back to their own communities to provide patient care," he says. Those returning doctors, of course, would represent a referrals base for the hospital. In essence, by cooperating with the medical school they were creating a feeder system for their future business.

> "We always thought that teaching is learning and learning is teaching," says Dr. Bob Eelkema. "If you have a group of practicing physicians that are taking on medical students and residents, you get an openness and honesty you wouldn't get if you didn't have the university influence."

Another critical issue for the AHEC campuses to resolve was the recruiting of faculty. The theory all along was that doctors would pretty much volunteer their time to mentor students. "We always thought that teaching is learning and learning is teaching," says Dr. Bob Eelkema. "If you have a group of practicing physicians that are taking on medical students and residents, you get an openness and honesty you wouldn't get if you didn't have the university influence."

In some clinics around the state, older doctors — often those running the clinic — frowned on the idea and for a time they had a negative influence on recruitment. Ultimately, however, the natural instinct of a doctor to teach won out. "We had docs around the state that participated and gave generously of their time," says

Keith G. Foster

The tireless first dean of the Bismarck campus, Foster helped recruit prominent local doctors to become the essentially volunteer teaching staff. The first campus office was a walk-up above a railroad station where it got so loud when engines roared by, no one could talk.

Clayton Jensen, who helped develop the family practice residency program. "In my opinion, those docs that participated in the formation and the ultimate teaching in the medical school are the true unsung heroes around the state."

In fact, says Altru Health System's president, Casey Ryan, "My personal bias is we should only hire physicians who want to be involved in education at the medical school. We are far enough along in the development of healthcare in Grand Forks that if people want to come to Grand Forks and practice here, they should really have an interest in teaching. I think there has always been a close relationship between us and the medical school and that needs to be retained and pushed even more."

While each physician volunteer receives a modest stipend, the amount is far below what they might have earned by simply seeing more patients, or if they were paid as full-time staff at a traditional medical school.

"Sometimes when physicians teach," says Ryan, "they are doing that out of their own personal time, and they are not getting compensated for it. They do it because it is part of their inner drive. Any teaching I ever did was because I wanted to do it. It wasn't what are you going to pay me to do it, but what are the opportunities?"

Teaching students to be doctors, adds Jensen, means teaching them to be teachers, as well.

"In my opinion, good patient care is about teaching," he says. "You must develop the ability to sit down and explain to your patient what the disease entity is and how it is going to be approached and what sort of medication they might need. That just naturally flows into a teaching mode for medical students."

The advantage of the community medical school model, he notes, is that there is no crush of students trying to peek over another's shoulder to see what is going on. "This is a one-on-one with the attending physician and the resident or the medical student," he says. "They develop a collaborative, collegial relationship that really enhances the educational aspect. It is different from a conventional medical center like the University of Minnesota where they have layers and layers of residents all the way down to the lowly medical students. That doesn't happen in North Dakota."

Each of the four AHEC centers had its own specific problems in getting started as a medical school campus. But each had its own exceptional leaders dedicated to getting the job done. Here, then, are four stories of success.

Up Thirty-five Stairs in Bismarck

"The early part of it was a selling process," says Dr. Keith Foster, M.D., an internist born in Mandan, raised in Dickinson, trained at Marquette University Medical School and the man who became the first dean of the Bismarck AHEC campus. "There was some ambivalence among the medical community here as to whether we were sophisticated enough to become a four-year medical school. The idea was somewhat threatening to the established medical community, and we had to sell it because we needed their support to get the thing done."

Among those most threatened was the leadership of the powerful Quain & Ramstad clinic. The Q&R was founded at the turn of the Twentieth century by Dr. Eric Quain and Dr. Niles Ramstad. Quain also was one of the founders — with the Evangelical Church — of Bismarck Evangelical Hospital in 1907. The Q&R is the second oldest clinic in the United States, behind the Mayo Clinic. Through its relationship with Bismarck Hospital, it had use of the earliest X-ray machine, cobalt machine and laboratory areas in the state. Later, in the Forties and Fifties, Dr. Leonard Larson, who led the clinic's laboratory became nationally recognized and served as chair of the Board of American Pathologists. (Bismarck Hospital changed its name to Medcenter One in 1984 and ten years later the Q&R and Medcenter One merged into a single, non-profit entity.)

In 1973, just after the 2-1-1 plan was approved, Foster was working at Q&R. Its head, Dr. Cliff Peters, was a staunch opponent of an expanded school of medicine and tried to get Foster fired when John Vennes wanted to name him the local dean. Peters tried pulling strings with close friends of Tom Clifford, warning that if Foster were named dean, the Q&R Clinic would refuse to cooperate with the school. But Foster was not without supporters, who urged Clifford to leave politics out of the selection. Clifford's reply: "Sounds good to me."

That fight over, Foster went about setting up shop. "Things were pretty primitive when we started out," he says. "We had an office in a little room above the railroad station and every time a train went by, we couldn't talk. We had to climb thirty-five stairs to get up there, but as time progressed our facilities got better and better."

Foster served as dean for sixteen years, organizing fourth-year electives and third-year clerkships and helping to develop the Family Practice Center. "He made a signal contribution to the actual existence of the medical school," says Vennes. One of Foster's great talents was his persuasiveness as a recruiter of faculty; he was a man who would not take no for an answer.

"I was busy practicing one day when Dr. Foster came to me and said, 'You have to take over the surgical section here in Bismarck,'" recalls Dr. Wayne Swenson, a 1959 graduate of the medical school. "I said, 'I don't want to do that. I don't want to be bothered with that.' But Dr. Foster said, 'You must apply for this job.' And I said, 'I really don't want to.' He said, 'Well, you're going to and that is all there is to it!' So I applied for the job and surprisingly got it, and I have been teaching at the medical school ever since."

Not every arm had to be twisted, however. Two of Foster's most tireless supporters were doctors Ralph Dunnigan and Bill Buckingham — both UND grads. They opened the small Capitol City Clinic in the Sixties, later merging with the mid-size Missouri Valley to become the Mid-Dakota Clinic, chief rival of Q&R. Mid-Dakota developed a working relationship with St. Alexius, the smaller hospital in Bismarck.

"When I heard there was going to be a family-medicine residency program established in Bismarck, it certainly interested me," recalls Dunnigan. "Dr. Buckingham was to be the director of the residency program and we worked very well together. The whole program seemed to click right from the start. We began the residency program with the attitude that we were going to our first class, that we were all recent graduates of medical school. It is quite a thing to look around the state now and see the successful people who have passed through the Bismarck program."

A good part of their success was in developing a professional relationship with Q&R and with Bismarck Hospital.

"Dr. Buckingham and I had both come from Mid-Dakota Clinic," says Dunnigan, "and it was quite natural for physicians from Medcenter One, which was then Bismarck Hospital, to be a little suspicious of Bill and me in the area of patient care. We went through a phase when we had to actually prove we were neutral in the community. In the process of doing that, we had a great deal of help from Terry Brosseau, the administrator of Medcenter One, and Dr. Marlin Johnson, an important physician at the Q&R Clinic.

"Even though at times Dr. Dunnigan and Dr. Buckingham have been my competitors," says Brousseau, "I had to acknowledge that there were no two doctors or leaders that were more invaluable in setting up family practice residencies, not just within Bismarck but the whole system at the medical school. These two had great vision and were the most dedicated people to the program that I have come across. They had huge patient followings in their private practices, which immediately helped this family practice residency program become one of the best in the country."

Both hospitals have benefited from the presence of the medical school campus.

"We have a lot of North Dakotans who have graduated from these residency programs and many of them have stayed in the state, not just in Bismarck but other communities," says Richard Tscheider, the CEO at St. Alexius. "It was a tremendous plus for the medical school to get doctors Dunnigan and Buckingham. They were both wonderful, low-keyed, positive people who had a wonderful rapport with the rest of the medical community. I think it was rather easy for them to talk to their colleagues and get participation on their part."

While the increase in the number of family practice physicians stands as a highly visible mark of the medical school's success, the repatriation of the third year and the establishment of residency programs also bolstered the number of psychiatrists in the state. The psychiatry residency was established at the behest of Dr. Lee Christoferson, Sr., the Fargo neurosurgeon and first chair of the department of neuroscience. While he ran the graduate residency program in Fargo, a clinical psychiatry sequence was established for third-year students in Bismarck under the guidance of Dr. Samuelson.

Born in Turtle Lake, north of Bismarck, Samuelson graduated from UND and spent time in the Army during the Korean War. He was discharged when a slot opened at UND's School of Medicine. He graduated in 1954 and after finishing his medical degree at the University of Cincinnati, he returned to the Bismarck area to work as a general practitioner.

At that time, in 1957, there was no psychiatrist at all in western North Dakota, and Samuelson had no intention of going into that field. However, during an internship at Marquette University in Milwaukee, Samuelson had taken part in a psychiatry rotation. There he noticed an odd fact: Many of the same people he saw during his rotation in the emergency room at Milwaukee County Hospital he saw later while working a rotation in the psychiatric ward.

"I remember seeing a woman in the ER who'd cut her throat," he recalls. "When I saw her in the psychiatric ward, she couldn't talk. You develop a feeling for that sort of thing. But not enough to make

Ralph Dunnigan

One of the first Bismarck doctors who agreed to join the local medical school faculty, Dunnigan's example paved the way for more of his colleagues to help out.

Al Samuelson

Long a part of the medical school faculty in Bismarck, Dr. Samuelson worked with Keith Foster to develop the local campus there.

you become a psychiatrist."

Back in North Dakota, however, a doctor he knew became manic-depressive. "I never felt so helpless in all my life trying to help this guy," he says. "Also as the new guy in my medical group, I was given all of the tough clients: somatic disorders, depression, you name it. I really had developed an appreciation for how sick these people were. But I realized I didn't have the tools to treat them. This is where I really made up mind to go into psychiatry."

He read a book by famed psychiatrists Karl and William Menninger and wrote them a letter. They accepted him into the Menninger Clinic, where he emerged as a full-fledged psychiatrist. He returned to Bismarck in the Sixties when the Community Mental Health Act was starting to provide states with funds for meeting shortages of psychiatrists. Samuelson was hired to administer the program in North Dakota. He also became director of the first outpatient public psychiatric clinic in western North Dakota, working with patients brought in from all over state.

After four years with the state, he started his own practice, affiliating with St. Alexius and specializing in treatment of acutely mentally ill people suffering from severe depression and schizophrenia. In the course of his long career, he also has done contract work with community organizations, treating public patients in hospitals, prisons and on the state's reservations.

"Whatever specialty you go into as a doctor," he says, "you're going to be dealing with the chronically ill, and part of your responsibility is to help stabilize them so they can lead reasonably good lives. That's what we do in psychiatry."

When he first came back to North Dakota as a psychiatrist, however, some people were suspicious. "The John Birch Society thought it was some sort of a plot," he chuckles. "One night I was invited to talk to these people about mental-health services. Subsequently I treated the brother and the niece of one of the leaders out there."

Samuelson, who has been a faculty member in Bismarck for twenty-six years, oversees third-year medical students for eight weeks each year in a psychiatry clerkship. Each student is assigned to a local psychiatrist who serves as a preceptor or mentor. To this day, he remains passionate about his specialty, and stresses the social importance of public psychiatry.

"Our prisons are becoming depositories of our chronically mentally ill," he says. "You get people who are bona fide sociopaths and you get people whose judgment isn't very good and who use drugs or alcohol. They are walking disasters. I really feel the public sector is addressing some serious problems here. But community programs have decreased and these people wind up in the court system. I feel gratified that I've made a contribution to the public here, in contrast to working in the private sector with people who aren't as sick and who have insurance. The subject of mental health is something that has to be taught to medical students. In six weeks we are not going to make psychiatrists out of them, but we hope to expose them to the basic psychiatric syndromes and pique their interest."

The Face of UND in Fargo

As the largest, most prosperous city in North Dakota, Fargo always has been an obvious target for those from other parts of the state who feel they have not gotten an equal share of taxes, attention or respect. Since Fargo has infrequently helped its image by displays of humility or forbearance, in return, the citizens of the rest of the state have for decades referred to the county seat of Cass County as "Imperial" Cass. They know all about this nickname in Fargo and they seem to cherish it, further disjointing the noses of the afflicted.

Given Fargo's relatively quick post-war development, it isn't really surprising that — through many of its doctors and most of is legislators — the city dismissed the idea of a full-fledged medical school in Grand Forks as preposterous. Beginning with recruiting drives in the mid-Fifties, most of the doctors at the Fargo Clinic came from the prestigious Mayo Clinic in Rochester, Minnesota. For many of those doctors, the Mayo way of training was the only way. The relatively unheard-of concept of a community-based medical school, as proposed in Grand Forks, struck many Fargo doctors as makeshift and hopelessly second-rate.

The influx of these specialists from the Mayo Clinic helped the Fargo Clinic — aligned with the Lutheran St. Luke's Hospital — to outgrow its rival Dakota Clinic, which had a working relationship then with the smaller, Catholic St. John's Hospital. At one time, it was suggested that the two clinics combine forces to establish a facility rivaling Mayo. But, according to C. Warner Litten, who for years ran the Fargo Clinic and served as a key opponent to a four-

Richard Olafson

A colleague of Lee Christoferson, Olafson was an early and enthusiastic supporter of the expansion of the medical school. He later served for 19 years as dean of the Fargo campus.

year medical school in the state legislature, the marriage could never have happened.

"One of my docs came in one day and said to me, 'I'll tell you one thing, you'll never see the day when I go to St. John's to deliver a baby.' That's the way they felt in 1950."

The Fargo Clinic would eventually become large enough to merge with St. Luke's and become the present-day three-hundred-bed MeritCare Health System. St. John's, and later Dakota Hospital, disappeared. Today, the smaller Dakota Clinic is part of the seventy-four-bed Innovis Health System.

While there were doctors at the Fargo Clinic supportive of The School of Medicine — the intensely loyal George Magnus Johnson, for one — political reality in those early expansion crusades of the Seventies pushed the School into an alliance with the Dakota Clinic. Ted Harwood had served for years on the board of the Dakota Clinic, making that association more logical, but also perhaps explaining some of the anti-medical school energy coming from the Fargo Clinic.

Tom Johnson credits Dr. Dit Wentz, the Dakota Clinic director, with key support for expansion. Dakota took in fourth-year students for clinical training, and later third year students, although Johnson says there were rough spots when it came down to who was really in charge — the clinic or the School of Medicine.

In the late Seventies, when the family-medicine residency first set up shop in Fargo, a sensitive turf issue developed. "The community didn't really like it being the University of North Dakota School of Medicine, because of NDSU," says Dr. Robert Jordheim, a long-time internist with the Fargo Clinic. "And it had to be located originally at a dormitory on the first floor at NDSU, but it was basically hidden on campus."

To resolve such issues and build a better relationship not just with the Fargo Clinic but also with doctors statewide, the School of Medicine turned to Dr. Richard Olafson. A partner in Lee Christoferson's TNI, Olafson was a neurosurgeon respected by doctors in both clinics in Fargo. He was the fourth dean to run the Fargo AHEC campus — succeeding John Magnus, who had been a Tom Johnson favorite.

Born in Drayton, Olafson was encouraged to enter medicine by his family doctor. In the fall of 1955 while a student at UND's two-year school, Olafson realized that the symptoms of panhypopopituitarism following the clipping of a Berry aneurysm —

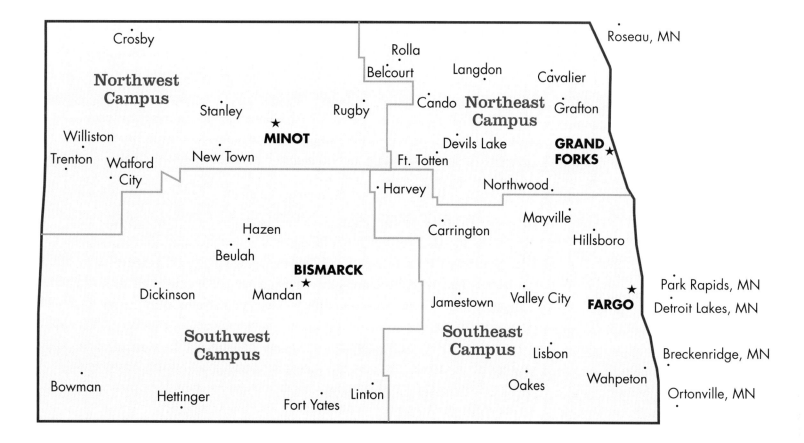

Crosby

Northwest Campus

Williston
Trenton
Watford City
Stanley
New Town
★ **MINOT**

Rolla
Belcourt
Langdon
Cavalier
Cando
Rugby
Northeast Campus
Grafton
Devils Lake
Ft. Totten
GRAND FORKS ★
Roseau, MN

Harvey
Northwood

Hazen
Beulah
BISMARCK ★
Mandan
Dickinson

Carrington
Mayville
Hillsboro

Jamestown
Valley City
FARGO ★
Park Rapids, MN
Detroit Lakes, MN

Southwest Campus

Southeast Campus
Lisbon
Breckenridge, MN

Bowman
Hettinger
Fort Yates
Linton
Oakes
Wahpeton
Ortonville, MN

a defect in the cerebral artery — being discussed in his comparative anatomy class were very much like those that had caused his father to fall ill. Olafson mentioned this to his father, who was a patient of Lee Christoferson. After Olafson got a medical degree from the University of Pennsylvania, he studied neurosurgery at the Mayo Clinic. Christoferson then recruited him to TNI, although Olafson said there was never any doubt he would return to North Dakota.

"I really felt socially obligated to return because of what the state had done for me," he says. "I figured I owed something back."

After nearly twenty years as a successful Fargo associate of Christoferson's, Olafson found that a narrowing of his spinal canal was limiting his ability to perform as a neurosurgeon. At about that time, Tom Johnson asked him to consider a career change and to become the Fargo dean.

"He put his whole heart into it," says Johnson. Nothing less was required. The repatriation issue was running into fierce resistance in Fargo, and Olafson quickly learned that his new career had much to do with being a salesman.

"My job was to sell the third year to doctors and legislators," he recalls. "A lot of people discouraged us."

He spent little time in his office. "I spent a lot of time going to surgical grand rounds, to orthopedic grand rounds, to pediatric seminars, always showing that the university was there," he says. "I became the face of the university. I was an established practitioner

Four campuses
When the Area Health Education Center grant was funded in 1973, the state was divided into four regions — Bismarck, Minot, Grand Forks and Fargo–that became campuses of the medical school. Other locations on map are locations where student training takes place.

The First of Many Times I Gulped

My father was a country attorney and later became a state official and a judge whose work I admired a great deal. But I spent my formative years at the knees of my uncles, who were the founders of the Johnson Clinic in Rugby, North Dakota. They were my father's brothers. Olaf Walter Johnson was president of the State Medical Society and a great pioneer character. He always had a joke and everybody loved him. He liked to be different and people still remember him. His brother, Christian G. Johnson, was just the opposite. He was quiet, philosophical, dogged in his love for medicine. He cared little or nothing about the income that doctors derive from their practices. His delight was serving the community and knowing everybody in the community. He knew people far and wide. He was a hero in World War II, a colonel, and when he came back to Rugby, he carried that idea of service to his community.

So those were my mentors. When I was sixteen years old, my father

(continued on next page)

with a good track record who'd had good results. I got along with people. I was not a TNI doc anymore, not a Fargo Clinic doctor. I was the university. Everywhere I went, I was university. I'd never been identified with anything as large."

Once the legislature approved repatriation, Olafson established a network of doctors and hospital administrators in Fargo and across the state. He held educational sessions, then structured committees that put together a five-year program to ease in the third-year students. The first ten third-year students were admitted to the program in 1982, with twenty the following year and thirty after that and so on.

Olafson, in fact, transformed the job of campus dean from academic advising and administrating to serving as a buffer in the political arena. His old partner Christoferson assisted him in cementing positive relationships with doctors statewide.

"We needed to see that we met not only with the movers and shakers to promote the school, but also with detractors so we could find out what the real reasons were that they objected to the school."

One of the key relationships developed under Olafson was the association between the School of Medicine and the Veterans Administration hospital in Fargo. In Grand Forks they knew that for a community based school of medicine to survive and flourish, the VA needed to be integrated with the School and the medical community .John Vennes got the connection going in 1974 with the $12 million grant to create a dean's committee. It set up an internal medicine residency at the Fargo VA, which, in those days, had a large, two-hundred-bed inpatient facility. This arrangement was ideal, considering the agreement the school had made with the state at the passage of the 2-1-1 plan, not to build a teaching hospital nor establish a freestanding clinic, nor compete with practicing physicians in the community. Thus, the VA hospital became the principal teaching site not only for internal medicine residents, but also later for the family-medicine and psychiatry residency programs.

"It was a site where we had pretty much free rein," says Olafson. "We were able without any restrictions to put our students in. They felt they could do more innovative work at the VA, and in some respects that helped move some of the local practitioners to say, 'Gee, if they can do that with public patients, why can't we do it with our patients.'"

That reputation became important later when the VA changed its emphasis from inpatient to outpatient, cutting the number of beds in half. "When the third year was repatriated from Minnesota," says Olafson, "we had to move more into the community. We needed more clinical sites than could be offered at the VA. We had to make a stronger marriage with the hospitals in Fargo — Dakota Hospital, St. Johns, St. Luke's and Dakota Heartland — so that the teaching base could be expanded."

Minot, the Mouse that Roared

The rugged citizens of Minot, anchoring the northwest quadrant of North Dakota, always have had a sense of humor about the challenges of withstanding their bracing winters. Minot is not the end of the earth, they say, but you can see it from there. To outsiders uncertain about the correct pronunciation of the city's name, locals have long offered the helpful poetic mnemonic: "Why not Minot?" And when it turns out that many outsiders decide to remain outsiders, the locals cheerfully supply the rationale: "Freezin's the reason."

In Minot, they style their town as the Magic City — a reference to a dramatic growth spurt back in the early part of the Twentieth century. They also like to bill themselves as the fourth largest city in North Dakota, although they are realistic enough to understand that others may simply view them as the smallest of the four "big" cities in the state. That mixture of braggadocio, optimism and real-world savvy has worked well for Minot when it comes to state politics.

In the early Seventies, when talk ran high of a community-based school of medicine, Minot's doctors and legislators saw the future of healthcare and also saw that if they did not act forcefully, they would not be in it. Led by the crusty Brynhilde Haugland and speaker of the House Jim Peterson, the Minot delegation led the way very early on in support for medical school expansion.

"Minot has always had some tremendously strong political interest in the medical school," says Dennis Lutz, M.D., the Minot physician who chairs the medical school's department of obstetrics and gynecology. "We had a group of legislators who realized if they weren't supportive, Minot could be squeezed out. They saw it as a positive for the community."

Local doctors like Dick Larson in nearby Velva also voiced enthusiastic support, and when Tom Johnson became dean he quickly felt the pressure from Minot's medical community.

"I got some advice when I came here from Duke Huntley, a surgeon in Minot," he recalls. "Duke sat me down on one of my

Home, at last
For years the Minot Family practice Center operated out of obscure rented quarters. In Spring 2005 a brand new building was completed, giving Minot residents a more official UND School of Medicine presence.

first visits and said, 'Tom, let me tell you something. You can develop a traditional school in Grand Forks and you can develop your school in Fargo, but if you don't include Minot, buy yourself a big comfortable chair to sit in, because you'll be sitting there looking at four walls.' In other words, you had better keep the northwestern part of the state, Minot, involved in the School of Medicine."

From the early days of the AHEC grant, Minot was viewed as a likely location for a regional campus of the medical school. During the tenure of John Vennes, a family practice residency was established in Minot in the Fifth Avenue Medical Building, then operated by St. Joseph's Medical Center. At the time, Minot was served by two main hospitals — Trinity and St. Joseph's. The Family Practice Center moved into a Trinity building after five years or so and later moved to a neutral site in the old Midwest Federal Savings & Loan building. Just recently, the Family Practice Center moved into its own brand-new building.

Through most of its early years in Minot, the Family Practice Center was supported financially by two hospitals. In the late Nineties, Unimed — successor to St. Joseph's — ended its connection. Trinity ultimately became the sole sponsor, and has remained so after taking over Unimed in 2001 to become Trinity Health Systems.

The consolidation has not only helped the community, says

Trinity Health Center's president, Terry Hoff, but makes for more efficient medical student training.

"One of the things that has been commented about by people from other areas," he says, "is that we don't have a whole bunch of everything, we have a little bit of everything. If you look in the emergency room, you don't get ten gunshot wounds a night, but you get a couple a summer or hunting season more likely. There is a wide variety of medical cases to see and learn from and this consolidation just makes things better."

Hoff, who majored in accounting at UND and graduated magna cum laude, joined Trinity in 1970. He has been president of Trinity Health Center in Minot for the last nineteen years and remembers well those early days of having residents suddenly appearing in the corridors of the hospital.

"Obviously, there were some issues with the medical staff," recalls Hoff. "First off, in the sense that, 'What are we going to let these guys do and what are we going to not let them do and how are they going to be supervised? Those questions created a fair amount of consternation. And, of course, there was also a little bit of concern from the nursing staff about, 'How good are these guys and do we have to take orders from them when they aren't even real doctors?'"

Hoff, who is a member of the Greater North Dakota Association, the Minot Area Development Corp., as well as a board member of Blue Cross/Blue Shield, notes that the organizational days of the Minot campus in the early Eighties were a time of great change in healthcare across the country.

"The changes created some uneasiness," he says, "but as time went on, I think matters worked out very well, certainly in our support of the medical school. I think the presence of medical students makes the whole organization better, as it forces those professions to redefine what their role is and what the role of others is. And that is good for healthcare."

Hoff says he has a good working relationship with the medical school, "built on trust. We don't have a lot of written documents. From the medical-student perspective, it works really smooth, and from my perspective I hardly know they are here. I see these guys walking in the halls with white coats on and I think, 'Who are these guys?' Then I look at their names and know. The student program just really works very well. I firmly believe in the value of having teaching programs within the medical community. It keeps the staff sharp and up-to-date and it helps them to continually redefine their

Dennis Lutz

The medical school's longest serving chair, Dr. Lutz has headed the department of obstetrics and gynecology since 1986, appointed to his post by Tom Johnson.

role and that permeates out into the rural areas."

Hoff notes that both residents and students do rural rotations, which helps the local physicians they work with maintain strong contacts with rural communities.

He says Trinity also works with the medical school and the residency program in the area of continuing education — not just for physicians but allied health professions — which upgrades the skill levels for staff in those areas. "You can't put a dollar-and-cents value on it," says Hoff, "but it has a tremendous value to not just this community but the whole region."

During those start-up years, the same two determined doctors who had advised Tom Johnson not to ignore Minot were the recruiting force behind the selection of the first head of the local family practice residency. He was Bob Hankins, M.D., a 1948 graduate of the two-year school. He was involved with the North Dakota Medical Association from the time he started his practice and ran the education committee, among others. When he later ran for office and became the Speaker of the North Dakota Medical Association's House of Delegates, he was a prominent supporter of expansion.

"Dick Larson and Duke Huntley came to me and asked if I would be interested in heading the residency program in Minot," Hankins recalls. "I said, 'Well, I have no administrative experience at all, I just practice medicine.' They said, 'We will get a director and you can be associate director because North Dakota needs North Dakotans.' So, I considered that and came up and looked the place over and it looked pretty good. They did have a director hired, so I agreed to come on as an associate director. Then, before we could start, the director they hired bowed out and I was told I could have the whole thing. They convinced me that I would have lots of help in Minot and that the Minot community was sold on the concept of having the residency program here."

The program thrived for a while, but fell on hard times in the early Nineties. To the rescue came Dr. C. Milton Smith, a Montana native and a 1969 graduate of UND's medical school. He practiced briefly in North Dakota, before relocating to a practice in Montana for several years. He moved to Fargo when his daughter became ill and needed specialty care. After eight years there, he was in the process of moving back to Montana when Ed James, the dean of the medical school at the time, and Clayton Jensen, the chair of Family Practice, paid him a visit.

"They came to my house and begged me to take over the program in Minot," Smith recalls. "The place was in very bad shape. It had lost its accreditation and there had been talk of closing it. But the community got up in arms. They wanted it here."

"They came to my house and begged me to take over the program in Minot," Smith recalls. "The place was in very bad shape. It had lost its accreditation and there had been talk of closing it. But the community got up in arms. They wanted it here."

Smith went reluctantly to Minot for a look-see. He had never been into academic medicine and enjoyed being a hands-on, rural country doctor. What changed his mind was the plight of the family practice residents he met: If the program closed, they would be cast adrift.

"I saw the pain in those residents' eyes," Smith says. "And I thought, well I'll come up and try to do something." That was more than thirteen years ago. Before long, Smith had turned the program around, it regained its full accreditation and he found out he liked academic medicine after all. That is because, he says, he has been able to train his residents "to see themselves as physicians and not gatekeepers. They put the patient first."

Smith instills his graduates early with his own philosophy of doctoring. "I view medicine as a very simple, straightforward thing," he says. "You've got a box, which is the environment where you see your patients. The line going through the middle of that box is the medical problem. On one side you have the patient and on the other side, the doctor. Together you work inside the box to solve the problem. You do it one patient at a time to the best of your ability."

With a solid reputation as a clinician and the force of his personality, Smith was able to recruit local doctors to serve as family practice faculty. Most important, he says, he was able to establish a good working relationship with Trinity Health Center.

"I get a lot of strong support from Trinity's administration," says Smith. "We're able to do a lot of things in the hospital. We're training people to go into rural medicine, so we put a big emphasis on obstetrics." In fact, he says, the Family Practice Clinic now does about half of all obstetrics cases in Minot.

"We also stress the emergency room," says Smith. "If you're going

John Vennes and Tom Johnson
At a recent alumni reunion, former dean Tom Johnson returned to UND and found time to share some memories with his colleague John Vennes.

to be in a rural setting, you've got to do ER work well. You're out there by yourself and what happens in the first hour often determines the outcome of a case. We have a very strong focus on that."

Much of Smith's work has been with Native American communities. His program has trained several Native American doctors with whom he maintains a close relationship. He works closely with the Turtle Mountain Reservation, headquartered in Belcourt, which often sends patients to the Minot Family Practice Clinic. He has a strong connection to the Fort Berthold Reservation headquartered in New Town, where he is in the process of developing an OB-GYN rural health fellowship program.

While Minot citizens know the Family Practice Center well, many do not necessarily connect it with the University of North Dakota or its School of Medicine.

"I think people are glad we have a residency program because that's where they access their direct health care," says Dr. Lutz. "It's a place to go and be seen by doctors, and even though they are doctors in training, they are supervised. I don't know that it's viewed necessarily as being the medical school. That may change because we've never had a free standing building and we have just opened our brand new Family Practice Center. I think people may, for the first time, identify it more strongly with UND."

Lutz has practiced in Minot since 1979. He was raised in

Montana but since that state has no medical school, he had to leave home for his training — by way of Cornell, the University of New Mexico and the Mayo Clinic. "But I wanted to come back west," he says, "and Minot had a need. Having the medical school here was a real plus."

Almost since his arrival, Lutz has been involved in the clinical faculty at the School. In the mid-1980s, the chair of the school's department of OB-GYN departed and a national search began for a replacement. Several times solid candidates were located, but when they took a look at North Dakota, they backed out.

"The hardest element of my job," says Tom Johnson, "was recruitment. We would fly to Minnesota or Chicago and interview people there. They'd come out for a visit. A guy might get all excited about it, then he'd go home and his wife would say, 'I'm not moving to North Dakota! You can move there.'"

But if it was hard recruiting just to North Dakota, it was twice as hard getting people to Minot, says Lutz.

"We have good quality of life and natural resources here," he says, "but we also have six months of winter, three or four of which can be fairly brutal. A lot of people have left because they don't like it or their spouses don't like it. Without people who grew up here and have family ties, we'd be at the very bottom of the recruiting chain. But this is a good place to make a livelihood. You don't have fifty orthopedists or fourteen neurosurgeons. You can be one of maybe a handful of people in your specialty. So you are going to be busy clinically, which translates to income. I think that's how people are recruited."

In 1986, when Tom Johnson hired Lutz to fill the vacant chair, the only seeming drawback was that Lutz did not live or work in Grand Forks with the school's other administrators.

"Actually," he says, "it has helped me as chair not being in midst of all the day-to-day rumor mill that goes on in Grand Forks. By not being on those campuses, I've been able to keep the university out of the fray of competition. You don't think about it, but if I'm in Grand Forks, I have to see patients and therefore compete for patients. I'd have to be with one clinic or another. I've always enjoyed a good association with all OB-GYNs in the state and it's because I'm not competing with them."

The focus of the OB-GYN department is providing third-year students with an eight-week clinical introduction to the specialty. The program is conducted on the Fargo, Bismarck and Grand Forks campuses, with the curriculum coordinated by Lutz.

"We try to give them good role models," he says, "to show

I'll Pick Medicine

Well, I had a special friend at the time: my wife. We were both born and raised on a farm. She was not interested in having a farmer husband, so I had to pick a professional career. It just so happened that I had pneumonia during the winter of 1948 and the following year, appendicitis. Both times I was hospitalized in Rugby and encountered Dr. O.W. Johnson and Dr. C.G. Johnson as well as Dr. Ted Keller, who was Reed Keller's father, and Dr. Fox, who was a younger member of the group at that time. They were an inspiration. I thought, well, I'll pick medicine, and so I did. From then on, I was focused to that goal.

Donald McIntyre, M.D., class of 1957, earned a medical degree at the University of Pennsylvania in 1959 and practiced in Rugby.

students what's good about the specialty. If we get people interested we try to devote our resources in fourth year to helping them get a good residency program." Lutz also offers a one-month elective in obstetrics and gynecology through his office in Minot.

Currently, twelve to fifteen percent of every class chooses obstetrics and gynecology, about twice the national average. "Our students compare very favorably with other schools," says Lutz. "We have some students who are as good as any student in the United States."

In fact, it is not the turning out of good students that is the challenge in Minot, but, rather, it is finding enough local physicians to take part in their education.

"Because we're a smaller community with a smaller hospital, we have a smaller contributing faculty or volunteer staff," says Martin Rothberg, M.D., an assistant dean of the medical school and director of the Minot campus. "We don't have a lot of physicians in each specialty. We have one heart surgeon, one rheumatologist, one dermatologist, one pulmonologist, one nephrologist. In Fargo, you might have sixteen nephrologists. If a lot of students want a rotation in this or that, we need to find medical staff to give them the opportunities they need. It can be a challenge, but we pretty much rely on ourselves here and so far we've been successful."

Rothberg's success in persuading his colleagues to take part is not surprising, since he himself was recruited to Minot from out of state. A cardio-thoracic surgeon, he came to North Dakota about thirteen years ago from Nebraska. He began teaching family practice residents and medical school seniors and he helped start an intensive care rotation.

"The family practice residency program here really does fill a need in the community," he says. "It's not just that these students are getting an education here. We don't have enough primary care providers in this part of state. The community needs that program. We have residents who are learning but also taking care of patients. They provide a real service."

Tender, Loving Care in Grand Forks

While Tom Johnson was making headway with doctors outside Grand Forks, earning their trust and convincing them to become teachers at the regional campuses, he was finding it more difficult wooing physicians back home. Some local doctors resented that he never attended Grand Forks' third district Medical Society meetings,

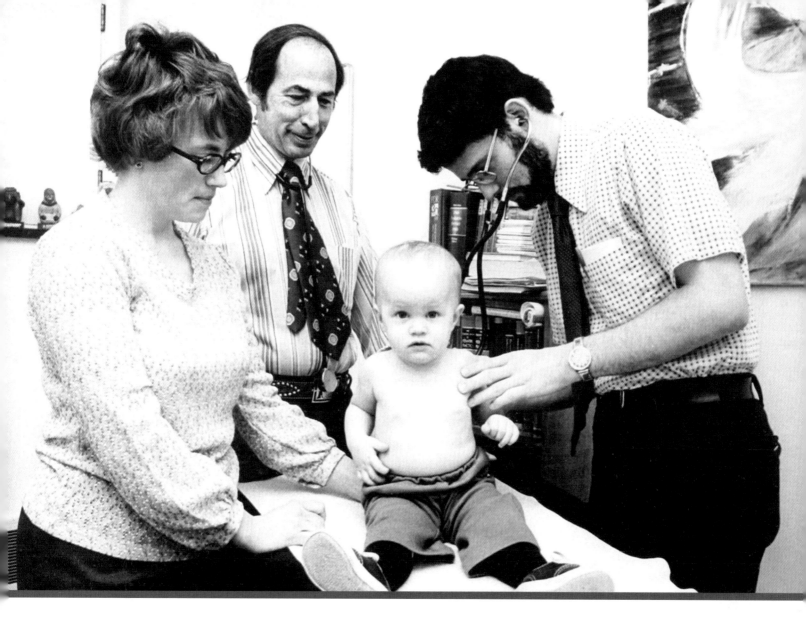

The watchful eye
This 1976 picture depicts Dr. Thomas Schafer observing 4th year medical student Francis Rash examining a baby while Mom looks on.

seeming to prefer the political environment of Fargo and Bismarck.

"From what I've heard others say, he would spent more time in Tioga, North Dakota, talking to one physician than he would walking across the street to the Grand Forks Clinic and talking to a lot of physicians," recalls Dr. Casey Ryan, the president of Altru. "Maybe people felt a little bit slighted in the sense that for all you're doing for the medical school, the dean needs to have a little more presence with the group right in town."

Johnson was not unaware of those feelings, says long-time Grand Forks urologist Dr. Kenneth Helenbolt. "I don't know just why, but I think he sensed that Grand Forks was kind of anti-medical school," says Helenbolt. "At one time he told me privately..., 'You are one of the people we can get along with who seems to like the medical school. The rest of them want no part of it.'"

Today, Johnson says that he deliberately put distance between himself and the Grand Forks physicians as part of a strategy to keep from being viewed elsewhere in the state as overly identified with Grand Forks.

"I did it by design, considering our limited resources and accreditation," he says. "First of all, I felt the leadership of the Grand Forks Clinic wasn't all that friendly. And the United Hospital

Walter Wasdahl

For 23 years between 1961 and 1984, Wasdahl chaired the department of pathology at the medical school. Plainspoken he was known for eschewing lectures in favor of hands on clinical work and getting students to think for themselves.

was standoffish. They both had real (and legitimate) concerns about the development of a traditional medical school (like in South Dakota), where you would have people in the medical school in competitive practice with the local physicians. It was the whole town-gown issue. I chose to involve Bismarck rather than Grand Forks in the third year. It was to avoid turmoil in the ultimate setting up of a school of medicine that was supposed to involve the VA in Fargo as well as the whole state. Watching other new statewide medical schools develop, I'd become convinced that most of your problems are at your home base. We had enough problems getting the school funded, established and accredited. Not involving Grand Forks (in the third year) was designed to avoid problems and to save our energy for bigger battles. Of that, I am guilty."

Even so, Dr. Rodney Clark, another long-time Grand Forks physician, does not believe there were more than a few skeptics among local doctors back then. Today, he says, "The physicians in town are proud of all the residencies, because we're all involved."

Clark distinguishes between opponents of the medical school and those who raised serious questions. The most prominent of the latter was the late Robert Painter, M.D., a former president of the state Medical Association and former member of the State Board of Higher Education.

"Bob Painter was for the medical school," says Clark. "At meetings, he would say, 'Could I ask a question?' and he'd bring up very important points that always led to progress."

Painter was instrumental in combining St. Michael's and Deaconess hospitals to become United Hospital, the forerunner of Altru. He also played a key leadership role in establishing the medical park complex in Grand Forks.

"Bob Painter is one of the reasons I got interested in medicine," says Ryan. "He was my physician growing up, and when he was dying I was his physician. He was a wonderful person. Nothing was ever done by him for any reason except that it was the best way to do it and in the best interest of the patient and the medical school. He was truly a leader."

In the days when the School of Medicine was a two-year institution, most doctors in the Grand Forks Clinic also were associate professors. For example, Clark, an OB-GYN specialist, gave three lectures a year to second year students on diseases of the vulva.

Once a month, Clark, Dr. Wally Nelson and Dr. Dick Leigh would leave their clinic offices to meet with Wasdahl at the School of Medicine. He had set up a pathology lab on campus and received tissue samples on slides from doctors across the state. "Wally would pull all the slides of interesting OB-GYN stuff," says

Clark, "and we'd spend a couple hours in the evening going through all of them. It was informal. That's what Wally Wasdahl was like. There was no town and gown problem between the clinic and the university."

In those days, Wasdahl — who later became chair of the department of pathology — worked under Dr. James Cardy, the department's founding chair. Under Cardy, the department developed a pathology residency long before the four-year school was established. Art Saiki and Wasdahl did much of the teaching.

"The pathology residency in this town was a big thing," says Clark. "If you had a surgery case, you always went down to the university and looked at your slides the next day. There were always people in the department, a doctor or a resident who would look over your slides with you."

When Deaconess and St. Michael's merged into United Hospital, pathology students gained much of their experience there. Today, the School of Medicine houses most of the faculty, and most doctors practicing at Altru Health Systems — where the name Wally Wasdahl is still revered.

"My perspective on medical education and how medical education should be taught was really adapted from how Dr. Wasdahl taught me," says Dr. William Newman, class of 1972, a long-time diabetes specialist who is now assistant dean for veterans affairs at the school and chair of the department of internal medicine. "Dr. Wasdahl would never really reveal too much. When I went through medical school, a lot of the curriculum at UND and other medical schools was what I called the regurgitation-hurdle approach. In other words, you remembered a great deal of information, you regurgitated it and then you were over a hurdle and went on to the next set of things. Dr. Wasdahl never took that approach. Dr. Wasdahl asked you to take what you knew, put it together from what you saw in front of you and reason to a conclusion. Now this was very uncomfortable for me, but it was an extraordinary education. To have to sit there with those slides with Dr. Wasdahl on the other side of the microscope, and tell him what I thought, perhaps revealing that I was on the wrong track, was not a comfortable experience. But some of the best lessons in life come from being uncomfortable. An adage in medical education states that unless the students sweat, they don't learn, and I agree with that. Obviously, you can have it too severe, but it never was with Dr. Wasdahl. It always was a learning experience that you had to invest enough so that you maximized the return from that learning experience."

Even when he was a student at UND, Wasdahl impressed. "We all marveled at him. Whenever there was an exam coming up the following morning, the rest of us would be up until 2 a.m. and Wally seemed to be all settled down by about seven in the evening," says Dr. Robert Jordheim, class of 1952. "He would come around and say, 'What are you worried about, this is simple.'"

Wasdahl did not change his style when he became department chair.

"He invigorated all the people he worked with," recalls Jean Holland, an emeritus professor in the department. "He caused people to develop their own initiative and work in their own way to get the best of what was available there. I really benefited a lot from working with him. For example, when cytogenetics began to come to light, he said, 'I don't believe this.' So I had to grow some cultures to show some chromosomes for cytogenetics, and he was just wild and thought it was wonderful. He was a great guy to work with."

In 1976, five years before repatriation, an OB-GYN residency began in Grand Forks, although it was short-lived. Located in United Hospital, it was headed by Dr. Preston Dilts and trained three residents a year in a four-year program. Dilts, who later became chair of the OB-GYN department at the University of Michigan, left after two years. The department went through two other short-term chairs and had developed a decent faculty when the University of Texas opened its own OB-GYN residency program at Lubbock. It hired away three doctors, including the chair, dealing the program a blow from which it could not recover. The residency ended abruptly, stranding several residents in the middle of training — one of them was Dr. Michael Brown, who eventually finished his training elsewhere. He later moved back to Grand Forks, was elected mayor and remains a strong supporter of the School of Medicine.

The fits and starts were painful at times but most remember them today as elements of the classic storming, forming, "norming" and performing cycle any organization goes through on its road to success. In the words of Rodney Clark, "It took a lot of tender, loving care to get this medical school where it is."

By 1988, eleven years after Johnson took over as dean, the School of Medicine had emerged from its long shakedown cruise in one piece. "Tom Johnson," says John Vennes, "is the person who redesigned the medical school such that the third year now offered clerkships and the school could now be characterized as a complete medical school."

Somewhere, Harley French is smiling.

"Tom took a school that had been created on paper and he actually made it work," says Dr. Dennis Lutz. "What Tom Clifford was to UND, Tom Johnson was to the medical school. He knew what he needed to do. He knew what had to be done. He was the right person for the medical school at the time expansion occurred. He was always friendly, always available if you had question. He got the school up and running."

In 1988, Johnson surprised many when he announced his resignation. He was heading back to Michigan.

"I remember asking him why he wanted to leave," recalls Dr. Hank Slotnick. "He said, 'Well, I just don't have the fire in my belly anymore.' I didn't understand what he meant at that time, but I do now and I think that I can't do anything but admire him for both recognizing that and knowing when to act on it gracefully."

It was time. There was nothing more to it, says Johnson.

"I said when I came that there is an eight-ten-twelve rule. After eight years, you think about getting out. After ten years, you get out. After twelve years, they kick you out. I think there's a lot of truth to that. I was there eleven years. I had accomplished what I went there to do. We got the third year back and the school was established."

In fact, Tom Clifford and others were so satisfied with the stability of the school that they felt it was time to start thinking about a different kind of expansion.

"The next step was to build buildings," says Johnson. "I'm not much for building buildings."

That challenge would fall to his successor. During Johnson's last days as dean, John Vennes asked him him how he would like to be remembered. "He indicated that he hoped that he had made a difference," Vennes recalls. "He really did make a difference."

But not just with the bigshots.

"The best reward I ever got was on my last day," says Johnson. "I walked into my office and on my desk was a yellow pad. In a scrawl it said, 'Dr. Johnson, we will miss you.' It was signed, 'Lee, your janitor.'"

Lois Steele

The first director of the Indians Into Medicine program in 1973, Steele left after a year to earn her medical degree. When the director's post came open again, Tom Johnson named Dr. Steele to her second tour of duty in 1980.

Indians into Medicine

One of the most innovative programs in the history of the School of Medicine — one that has had a lasting impact on the medical education of hundreds of young American Indians across the country — came about almost by accident.

It happened in 1972 when Dr. Robert Eelkema was in Rockville, Maryland, visiting the campus of the National Institutes of Health.

Eelkema, then the Chair of the Department of Community
Medicine at UND's School of Medicine, went to the NIH to
investigate grants to fund the expansion of the medical school from
two to four years. He was successful in that he learned of the AHEC
program — Area Health Education Centers — that eventually would
fund the initial stages of the school's expansion.

As he was leaving that day, he walked with Doug Fenderson, his
AHEC contact with the Bureau of Health Manpower. As Eelkema's
luck would have it, Fenderson was a North Dakota native.

"I was on the parking lot of building 31C at NIH," recalls
Eelkema, "when Doug Fenderson mentioned that he was just
starting a minority program as part of the AHEC program. He
had just appointed a director and it was George Bluespruce."

It turned out that Eelkema, who has an uncanny knack for
knowing key people in key places at key times, was a classmate of
Bluespruce at Berkeley while earning a master's degree in public
health. He immediately contacted Bluespruce and got the go ahead
to apply for a grant to fund the medical training of American
Indians at UND.

Eelkema and his close friend Gary Dunn, at that time a consultant
to the medical school, went to Dunn's Grand Forks apartment and
began brainstorming the grant. Dunn's wife Nancy sat at the
typewriter, taking down their ideas. They envisioned a program that
would help students on reservations with science and math training,
and would pay for their training as doctors in the medical school.
As Nancy Hepburn Dunn typed up their final grant, she looked at
the title they had given the program: Indians Into Medicine.

"How about we just call it INMED?" she said. They liked the
catchy title and so did George Bluespruce and the NIH. At that
time, the federal government had done away with its program of
drafting doctors and assigning them to health facilities on
reservations. It meant there was an even more critical shortage of
doctors on reservations than before.

INMED was funded by NIH in 1973 and continues to this day.
The program has awarded medical degrees to 116 American Indians,
representing one out of every five Native American doctors
belonging to a federally recognized tribe in the country. The
program survives on federal grants, with minimal costs picked up by
the university. Over time, it has expanded to train Indian students in
nursing, clinical psychology and other health services careers.

While INMED today serves as a national model, it went through

Summer visitors

This group of Lakota Oglala Sioux high school students was part of a 2004 summer program at the medical school sponsored each year by the Indians into Medicine program. From left, front row: Jessica Janis, Charity Wilson, Desirae Blacksmith, Twila Yellow Horse; Back row: Dallas Nelson, Wylie Janis, Aaron DuBray, Ida Clarke.

some difficult growing pains. As well intentioned as the program was, the school did not really consider the vast cultural differences between potential medical students growing up on a reservation versus students from a non-Indian background. That disparity became evident early on in the unexpected lack of interest among young Indian students in pursuing a medical career.

"It turned out there was no role model for these kids on the reservations to become a doctor," says Judy DeMers, the associate dean for student affairs. "There was nobody to say, 'You really can do this.'"

In fact, the only doctors most Indians had known were those supplied by the Indian Health Service, doctors who either were white or foreigners and who left as soon as their obligation was fulfilled. This was the challenge facing INMED's first director, Native American, Lois Steele.

"Lois was a go-getter and a hard-driver," recalls one of her students, Dr. Richard Luger. "She was a commander. She had a good sense of humor and seemed to have a good relationship with the students." Steele soon left the program to enter medical school herself. Once she had earned her M.D. degree, Tom Johnson hired her for a second tour as INMED director.

One of her key moves early in the program was appointing Jim Claymore, a member of the Sioux Nation, to the Tribal Advisory Board. Claymore had just gotten out of the Army and was living near Fort Yates when Steele invited him to come to Grand Forks to discuss INMED.

"Several of us came up and it turned out we were the nucleus group to develop the program itself," he recalls. "I became very much involved. We had never had any real professional people, i.e. lawyers, doctors, etc., on the reservations. The biggest thing that I wanted to do was to try to get our kids interested in a profession and have a great deal of pride in themselves. I see so many youngsters who have a great deal of potential but they often fail to realize it fully on the reservation."

Claymore became not only a charter member of the Tribal Advisory Board, he eventually chaired it for more than two decades. The toughest time of all, he says, was at the very beginning when a good deal of energy was spent defeating a political movement to shift the program to Oklahoma.

"Then the hard part was to get it started," he says, "to go out and talk to the people in the reservation about the programs themselves. One question that would come up immediately was, 'How many doctors do we have now?' That was after the first year or two and it takes seven or eight years to do this, so it was pretty difficult to get across to them that it takes time. Everyone thought we should have doctors immediately. I was very happy when our first doctor graduated from the program. At last I could say 'Yes, we have one, and we have this many more in school.'"

It did not hurt Claymore's stature with the tribes that he could claim a famous pedigree. In 1876, when his grandfather, Harry Kingman, a full-blooded Sioux, was ten years old, he stood on a hill with other Indian children and women watching the battle of the Little Big Horn unfold. Harry watched the combined Sioux and Cheyenne force wipe out the infamous Indian fighter George Armstrong Custer and his Seventh Cavalry regiment.

Later, Harry was sent to school "out East," says Claymore. "He was interesting enough that they sent him to Harvard to deliver some speeches. He learned what was happening on the outside, the white world, and when he came back to the area, he had different jobs on the reservation. He was a cattle inspector, a carpenter and he ended up being the last civil service judge that they had on the

Cheyenne River Reservation in South Dakota."

It is where Claymore was born. He grew up well aware that "with reservation life, the initiative was taken away from us and we depended upon the federal government for a lot of things. That was the hardest part, trying to sell the program to the Indian people, who had the feeling that it takes a smart person to do that. It does, but the point is we had people smart enough."

Eventually, as more and more Indians graduated from the program and returned to reservations to practice, they became visible role models for others.

> **He was raised on the Belcourt Reservation and as late as high school had no interest in medicine as a career. His father encouraged him to become an auto mechanic or heavy equipment mechanic.**

"I think it is probably one of the most significant programs that we run," says DeMers. "I really believe we need to produce Indian physicians if we are going to work toward solving some of the problems on the reservation. A lot of extremely good Caucasian physicians have served in reservation hospitals, but they tend to have some difficulty in relating to the culture. And often those that can relate to the culture aren't particularly well accepted by the Indians as individuals and the tribe in general. I think if we are really going to see continuity of care on the reservation, we need to have Native American physicians who are comfortable there."

Dr. Richard Larson, an INMED graduate who works on the Belcourt Reservation, says the program is an ideal model for stimulating interest in rural medicine.

"The best way to get doctors back to rural areas is to recruit them from rural areas," he says. "I have a hard time visualizing people from the cities working in the small towns of North Dakota unless they are actually from the area."

Larson's mother is a registered Chippewa. He was raised on the Belcourt Reservation and as late as high school had no interest in medicine as a career. His father encouraged him to become an auto mechanic or heavy equipment mechanic.

"I was working hard in high school and getting fair grades," he recalls. "One day in November of my junior year, Alma Wilke, the INMED high school recruiter, introduced herself and told me about the INMED program and its association with the University of North Dakota School of Medicine. Right away, I thought that might be something I would be interested in. She signed me up for the summer institute program and after that it was all uphill."

Today, Larson is a respected physician at the Turtle Mountain Reservation hospital in Belcourt. The rationale behind INMED is not only that reservations have too few American Indian physicians and health professionals, but that healthcare has been substandard for too long. For example, according to Jim Brosseau, M.D., Eelkema's successor as chair of the Department of Community Medicine, it is only in the last few years that the prevalence of diabetes among Native Americans has been recognized.

Brosseau, a member of Awakening the Spirit, the Native American initiative of the American Diabetes Association, speaks regularly before meetings of the Indian Health Service and knows first-hand of the need for physicians on reservations.

"Fifty percent of adult Indians over the age of forty have diabetes," he says. "One hundred years ago, Indians had the same genetic structure, but their diets were vastly different. Now, they are extremely sedentary and their diets are poor. Obesity is widespread."

Thus, with the need more apparent than ever, the INMED program recruits into summer enrichment sessions Indian students from junior high school through professional school level. Each session is geared toward bringing students up to speed in the sciences and guiding their career choice in medicine and health services. With such a system in place, the program no longer has trouble filling its classes each fall.

Chapter 8

CHAPTER EIGHT

Building on Success

DOCTOR HEMPLER'S WHISTLE

In 1988, as the School of Medicine began scrambling to find a new dean, its brand-new completeness as a four-year institution of medical training looked perfectly respectable on a doctor's diploma. The physical reality, however, was another story.

In its eighty-three-year existence to that point, the School of Medicine had essentially occupied two buildings. The first was Science Hall, built in 1902, three years before Melvin Brannon founded the School of Medicine. It is where Harley French and Art Saiki kept the faith for decades through thick and mostly thin times. In 1949, the school moved into the brand-new Medical Science Building, erected and quickly expanded with funds supplied by the mill levy. Another mill-levy product, McCannel Hall and its two-floor expansion were built next door to Medical Science between 1956 and 1962 to house the new rehabilitation hospital. When the hospital's mission separated from the university in 1973 and it moved to the new medical park, the university used McCannel to house the student health service.

In 1976, the two hospitals in Grand Forks — Deaconess and St. Michael's — merged to become United Hospital, operating out of the St. Michael's building on Columbia Road. A few years later, when United was in the ongoing process of shifting from the old St. Michael's building to its new site in the medical park — where it would become Altru Health Systems — it provided space in St. Michael's as it opened up to the medical school.

Previous page:

Taking shape
From the air, looking southeast, one can see the dramatic changes over the years to what was once the old St. Michael's Hospital. Expansion has added the Karl Christian Wold Biomedical Information Research Center (at right), the Ed James Research Facility (at left), the biomedical research facility, lower left corner. Out of view is a new neuroscience research center.

This was part of an unusual agreement hammered out by Tom Clifford when United first purchased St. Michael's from the Sisters of St. Joseph. Clifford not only was president of UND at the time, he was a member of the United board and a great friend of those Sisters. He negotiated a $3 million sale price for St. Michael's, which went a long way toward providing the Sisters with desperately needed pension funding. Clifford got Bob Jacobson, United's administrator, to agree that if United should ever leave St. Michael's, its board would sell the hospital back to the university for the same $3 million.

"Of course, Bob kept his word," says Clifford, "and the university bought it back for $3 million and it appraised at $11 million at that time, so we really appreciated that. That was the kind of cooperation that we had that made expansion possible."

In the original plan, United was to build its new hospital on property adjacent to St. Michael's. That move, though, would have limited the medical school's future ability to expand. At about that time, the Grand Forks Clinic, which was behind the United merger, purchased land that is now the medical park, giving the medical school room to grow.

Gradually, the administrative offices of the school moved into the old St. Michael's Hospital building, although the basic science departments and the medical library remained two long blocks away in the Medical Science building. The St. Michael's offices were known as Med Science North and the rest of the school was Med Science South.

By the time Tom Johnson completed the expansion of the medical school in the early Eighties, it became apparent that more space was needed and that the school's functions ought to be centralized.

"It was evident that our facilities were not up to speed," says Randy Eken. "We had inadequate lab spaces and teaching facilities."

Clifford had been talking about building new facilities at the St. Michael's site. Long before that, when talk of expansion was first heating up in 1972, Clifford made it clear that new facilities were not a primary objective in developing the larger medical school. Budget conscious politicians feared that an expanded school meant costly construction. Those fears eased somewhat when the university said it saw no need to build a new hospital. In fact, Clifford in those days made it clear UND was not looking for any new facilities.

But by 1988, the need could not be ignored. The new four-year school was facing an important accreditation by inspectors of the Association of American Medical Colleges and the American Medical Association, who would not look kindly on cramped and outdated facilities. The trick was going to be finding non-state money to build what the school needed. That was the challenge facing whoever succeeded Tom Johnson. What they needed was a fundraiser, a builder.

Clifford named the Chair of the Department of Surgery, Dr. Edwin James, as the interim dean and to the committee charged with finding a permanent successor to Johnson. James was an impressive man. He had spent his career as a military surgeon and had earned a national reputation by the time he arrived in North Dakota from West Virginia in 1975. Considered an intellectual by his peers, James wrote a text on surgery that was used by a number of medical schools, including UND.

"Ed was a real different personality," says Judy DeMers. "He had a typical surgeon's personality and I don't know for sure what that means, except he was very organized and had very definite ideas on how he looked at things." John Vennes agrees. "He had the mentality of a surgeon. There is the job to do, let's get it done, what's next? There was never an element of doubt in his mind."

Which is not to say that James was a fireball, says Tom Johnson. "Ed was a plodder. I mean, our getting a surgery residency, I never thought it would happen. But plodding old Ed, in his methodical way brought these bigwigs in surgery in here to do guest lectures and such. He really deserves the credit for that residency."

As a member of the search committee, James agreed not to become a candidate for the deanship himself. But on the last day for submitting applications — after he had seen who had applied — James abruptly put his own name into the mix.

"That started a real controversy," recalls DeMers. Two of the applicants for the job, fellow faculty members, accused James of unethical behavior. At the very least, protocol had been violated. But it all amounted to nothing for James had one great advantage: Tom Clifford liked him. And when the smoke cleared, Clifford had named James the new permanent dean of the School of Medicine.

"Ed James already had the presence," notes Dr. Casey Ryan. "He was chair in the Department of Surgery, he worked as an active, operating surgeon and he was a leader. He built his following the old-fashioned way, as a clinician. And then he became the dean."

In the early going, some saw James as dictatorial and difficult, because his personality and style compared unfavorably to their memories of good old Tom Johnson. "Being retired military, he was abrupt and could be very rigid," says Lavonne Johnson, James's long-time secretary. "But he was very personable after you got to know him."

One stark contrast to Johnson was in his brisk approach to legislators.

"He often said, 'Things ought to go this way because this is what I said and I'm the dean,'" recalls DeMers, a veteran of the state House and Senate. "He was the ultimate authority. His approach to

Edwin James

Though his untimely death to cancer kept him from seeing the final results, the aggressive building program begun under Dr. James turned the medical school into a modern, state-of-the-art facility.

the legislature was, 'You just tell them I'm the dean and that I said so.' I said that doesn't really work out there."

But like Johnson and Tom Clifford, James was especially good at giving people enough rope.

"He recognized that each chair needs to put their own stamp on the department," says Dr. David Antonenko, who succeeded James as chair of surgery. "He wasn't a micromanager. As long as the job description was carried out for the department — teaching, research, education of residents, interaction with the governing structure of the school — he left you alone."

"The best way to describe him from my point of view is: He was an enabler," adds Dr. Wayne Swenson, the director of the Bismarck surgery clerkship. "He was just a very exciting person to work with."

But a man not totally predictable, says Dick Davison, the retired executive director of the State Board of Higher Education. He remembers James as a man who played his cards very close to the vest.

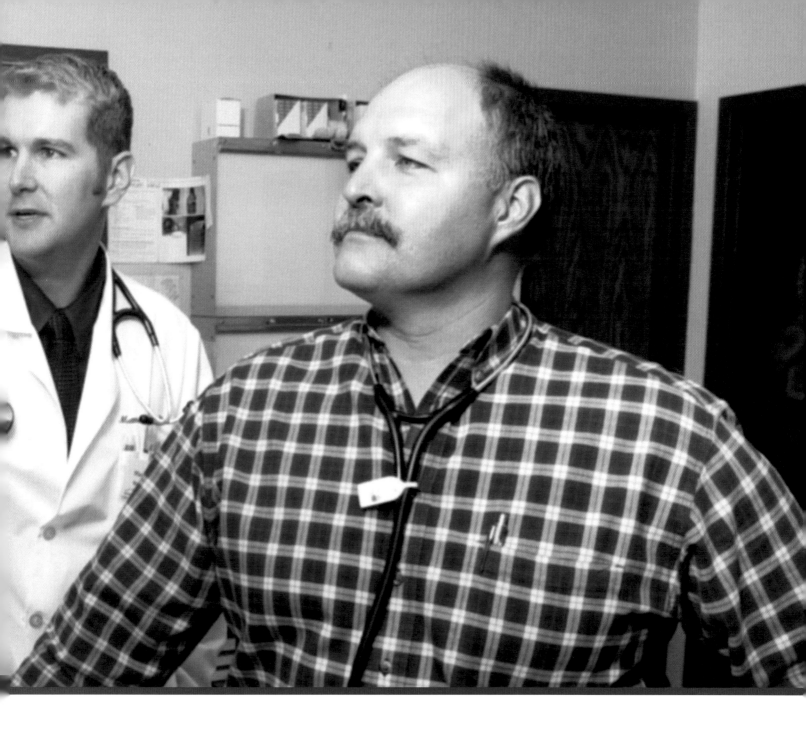

"He had a great stone face," says Davison. "He knew what he wanted to happen, but he never told anybody. I would have lunch with him and then we'd go for a ride and talk about the medical school and about him and about where it was going and such. And he had a very good mind, but you couldn't always tell what he was thinking. We sat on the bridge one time out by Oslo or Manvel, talking about the beauty of the Valley, about the medical school and about him and his life. We talked about family and such, and I know that Ed knew what he wanted done, but I never found out directly."

But if James had trouble articulating grand philosophical visions a la Tom Johnson, he had no problem at all in dreaming up a nuts-and-bolts building program that was aggressive and breathtaking in scope.

"Dr. James developed a vision to build 140,000 square feet of new space," says Randy Eken. "I personally thought we were a little crazy at that time. Dr. James wasn't as dynamic as some, but he was very smart and persevering, strong-willed and believed in the need for construction."

The watchful eye
Dr. Rob Beattie, right, consults as his then-student Matt Schaefer (Now Dr. Schaefer, Class of 2003) reviews an X-Ray in offices of West Regional Medical Center in Hettinger. Schaefer was part of ROME program training doctors for providing rural health needs.

I Met a Girl

I was simply a country boy in the Thirties, in the Depression. My family had lost their money and I needed an education, so I started at North Dakota State. We students had all kinds of problems getting enough to eat and going to school, but at the end of my second year, I met a girl and I couldn't see her being on the farm. I'd always had an inkling about going into medicine, so I switched in the third quarter and I started pre-med at UND.

James Mahoney, UND class of 1941, finished his M.D. degree at Northwestern and for many years practiced in Devils Lake.

The James plan was to build a new basic science building and to utilize the existing St. Michael's structure. As that idea was put forth, James then decided the school needed to replace its outdated library with a modern bioinformation center — also designed as an adjunct to the St. Michael's building. Combined, the two projects would cost about $15 million, of which the school had not a penny on hand.

"I don't think anyone thought there was a chance that the building project he dreamed of could be accomplished," says Dr. Roger Sopher, the former chair of the Department of Pathology. "But Ed was a classic surgeon. Surgeons in a lot of ways are medical Marines. Their main tactic is a frontal assault. Ed knew what he wanted and knew how to get there. One was advised to stay out of his way."

Behind the building dream was not simply the desperate need for more working space. As a brand-new four-year school, the university knew it had to recruit some top-flight talent to maintain the reputation of its basic science program and to staff the new clinical departments. If the school hoped to compete for the best researchers and clinicians — especially given the undeserved reputation of North Dakota as a remote outpost — it needed modern laboratories and a dynamic sense that growth was part of its mission.

"He wanted to make this a premier teaching institution," says Antonenko, "but, in addition, it had to be a premier research institution. I think it was with that vision that he set up the funding drives and was able to politically get people to support the program."

James threw himself wholeheartedly into the work of raising the needed capital. His efforts led him in two directions — one into the somewhat familiar world of private philanthropy and federal grants, and the other into uncharted territory: the alumni's untested generosity.

As far as hunting down available federal money, the university had a strong ally in Quentin Burdick, (the late senior U.S. senator from North Dakota and a key member of the powerful Appropriations Committee). Happily, Burdick's chief of staff in Washington was Dr. Mary Wakefield, a former faculty member at UND's College of Nursing. Wakefield earned a Ph.D. in nursing before entering the political arena, first as Burdick's chief of staff and later as Senator Kent Conrad's. (She since has returned to North Dakota and is the medical school's associate dean for rural health.) And it certainly didn't hurt that the head of Burdick's most recent reelection campaign was none other than Judy DeMers, the Associate Dean for Student Affairs.

"Senator Burdick was always a really good friend of the medical school," says DeMers. "We went out to D.C. and talked to him and he indicated that he would like to do something, especially since I had helped out with his last campaign."

Because Burdick had strong ties to the U.S. Department of Agriculture, it was decided to couch the request for funds as a USDA-sponsored rural health initiative. Burdick submitted a bill to that effect, while back in Grand Forks the School of Medicine's Center for Rural Health became very involved in writing the justifications for the funding. The bill ultimately passed, giving the university about $10 million in federal money to build its basic science center. The state spent not one cent on the structure.

Landing the grant made it easier for the school to approach the alumni to raise the $5 million needed for the bioinformation center. Even so, there was uncertainty at the start of the campaign. Never in the history of the School of Medicine had its graduates been approached for contributions. Would they respond? Did they care?

Earl Strinden, the long-time political force in the state legislature, was the head of the Alumni Association at the time. He remembers the energy put forth by James in pressing the appeal to the alumni.

"He was so focused, such a hard worker and delightful person," he recalls. "We had meetings all around the nation with the alumni, and we also had some wonderful alumni leadership."

One of those loyal alums was Strinden's brother, Dr. Dean Strinden of Williston, who played an essential role in stimulating interest in the drive. Earl Strinden also gives a good bit of the credit to Bonnie Sobolik, the tireless Alumni Association staffer in Grand Forks who coordinated the entire campaign.

"It took a lot of time in small planes and automobile trips around the state for everybody to get reached that needed to get reached," recalls Randy Eken. "It is not easy to get a check out of somebody's billfold, but Dr. James was certainly up to all of that."

"From a standpoint of fundraising," adds Antonenko, "Ed was as good as any I've seen in many years. He definitely put the school before himself."

James and Earl Strinden also followed up several leads to private funding during the drive, including one to the family of Keith Wold, of Boca Raton, Florida, heirs to the Johnson & Johnson estate. After their visit, the Wolds donated half a million dollars to the bioinformation center fund. Combined with the $4.8 million contributed by the alumni, the School of Medicine had its new bioinformation center.

The first of the two buildings to open was the Basic Science Center. It might have been called the Quentin Burdick Science Center but for one tragic fact. At Christmastime in 1992, Ed James complained of severe headaches. When he did not respond to pain

Donald Hagen

A 1961 graduate of the medical school, Donald Hagen entered the Navy and rose to become surgeon general in the mid Eighties.

LITTLE SATELLITE ON THE PRAIRIE

It's been forty years now since a young doctor named Jerry Sailer drove into the small, southwestern town of Hettinger, North Dakota, and reveled in its back-of-the-moon invisibility.

The reason he went there was the same reason so many doctors kept staying away. "It was," says Sailer "the most medically isolated place that I knew of."

Strangely, those qualities in this town of thirteen hundred just miles from the South Dakota border were what already had attracted Sailer's UND classmate, Dr. Paul Retzer, to Hettinger. "When we arrived we found it was a triage kind of medical system with hardly any technology and no support staff," Sailer recalls. "I had this dream that we could develop a medical system that was kind of like an urban medical care system in a rural area. Paul was willing to take a run at that."

Sailer was not your usual physician. He was smart enough, after graduating from UND's two-year medical school in 1959, to be accepted at Baylor University in Houston, where they saw big things ahead for him. But when he told them he was applying for a rotating internship in Duluth, Minnesota, after getting his medical degree, the assistant dean sent for him.

"He said, 'You know, we have had you ticketed for academic medicine and would like you to apply to either Johns Hopkins or Harvard in some kind of residency program. Why in the world are you thinking of taking a rotating internship in Duluth, Minnesota?'

"I said, 'I want to do general practice in a small town someplace in North Dakota.' He

said, "You mean you have wasted your education at Baylor? If you want to be a missionary, why don't you just go to South Africa and forget the whole thing?'"

Sailer, though, ignored the insult and persisted in his dream to practice rural medicine with a capital R. It may be that not many dreams end in Hettinger, but where others saw barren prairie and a lack of amenities and culture, Sailer saw only the chance to serve a population that had nobody to care for them.

He and Paul Retzer did take a run at making it work in Hettinger, and forty years later the results of their hard work stands as one of the truly unique medical systems in the country. The West River Regional Health System in Hettinger is a thoroughly up-to-date thirty-bed hospital with a staff of more than a dozen idealistic doctors — most of them UND grads — who, like Sailer and Retzer, eschewed the fast lane for the vast lane.

But wait. That many docs and all that shiny, expensive medical equipment to treat thirteen hundred people? Therein lies the secret to Sailer's success. It did not take him and Retzer long to realize that if they wanted to treat patients, they had to go out and find them. So early on, they started driving thirty and forty miles out and back every day to small towns where they set up offices. Sailer used the term satellite clinic to describe them, the first use ever of that term in medicine.

Soon, those satellite clinics were branching out up to ninety miles away from Hettinger, covering about twenty-thousand square miles — a territory larger than five of the Eastern states. It includes five counties in North Dakota and three in South Dakota, and while there are only about twenty-thousand people in that area, it has been enough so far to generate enough income to have in-house CAT scans, a radiologist, a surgeon, internal medicine specialists and a large staff not ordinarily found in such a small town. There have been times when West River purchased new equipment before clinics in Bismarck, the state capital, the closest big city to the northeast.

"Originally, it was very difficult," says Sailer, "as people weren't used to it. We started trying to do complete evaluations and take care of sicker people than had been done here before. It was slow to start but began to grow."

As it did, the irony of some advice given him by his father was not lost on Sailer. "My interest in medicine as a career stemmed somewhat from my father's suggestion that if I became a physician, my clients would come to me. If I became a lawyer, I would need to go to my clients."

But it was not just the advice of a well-meaning father that seemed to go against what Sailer was doing.

"The medical wisdom at the time I started was that the satellite clinic system wouldn't work," says Sailer. "I went and talked to a group of physicians I knew and respected in larger places and I said, 'Why couldn't we do this in rural America?' The answer I got all the time was that it wouldn't work. 'Well, why wouldn't it work?' I wanted to know. The answer: 'Nobody does it!' They were content to practice the science of medicine only in a setting as it had always been practiced. I guess thinking in terms of systems, I have never been satisfied to just zone in on the details. I want to see if we can do something about how the whole system works."

Luckily, several other doctors have had the same itch. New physicians are very carefully recruited to Hettinger to make sure that their temperament fits the small-town mindset, but that their skills are of the big-city caliber. Over the years, the clinic has served as a special supporter of the School of Medicine. Not only are the majority of its physicians graduates of UND, but Hettinger serves as a main training facility for students interested in rural health and family practice specialties.

"We felt that we could bring medicine to communities that didn't have any," says Sailer. "The other side of the enterprise was that we could develop economically enough so we could afford to get technology and hire laboratory people, therapists, technicians and technologists that we would not otherwise have had."

Reed Keller

It was said that the brilliant, energetic Dr. Reed Keller was one of a kind. Keller chaired the department of medicine and according to Tom Johnson was "the best doctor in North Dakota."

medication, he went to the Mayo Clinic and found out in April 1993 that he had a very aggressive brain tumor. Though he tried chemotherapy, the cancer was too far along. James died in February 1994, shortly before the Science Center opened.

"He was absolutely committed to the building program," says Dr. Clayton Jensen, the man who replaced James for two years as interim dean. "Unfortunately, he didn't get a chance to see the end result. But he left a legacy. The concept of cluster rooms and the bioinformation learning center really made it possible for the changes in curriculum that have occurred today. He laid the groundwork."

When the Basic Science Building opened a short time later, it was named in honor of James. An irony, perhaps says Judy DeMers. "I do think that Dr. James would have been the first to say, 'No, it should have been named for Quentin Burdick.'" While not everyone agrees, no one disputes the contribution of Ed James.

"Ed brought the medical school to a single location," says Vennes, "where it has modern labs some good technology, and a good library to attract good scientists. He wasn't here to see the completion of it but he sure left his mark."

As for Dick Davison, who could never seem to get James to be specific about his overall vision, the literal shape of the school today says it all.

"Tom Johnson was the implementer, the healer, the man who spread the good gospel of the medical school and healthcare," he says. "But Ed always wanted to talk about buildings. Ed was the builder."

One of Ed James's closest associates in the School of Medicine was a man almost exactly his opposite. Where James — according to Johnson — was "quiet and sleepy," Dr. Reed T. Keller was practically born in the fast lane. His father, Dr. Ted Keller was a partner in the well-known Johnson Clinic in Rugby. Dr. George M. Johnson, nephew of those famous Rugby Johnsons, remembers Reed Keller well.

"Reed was one of a kind. He was always doing these daring new things. He once went up in his father's airplane — he was dangerous as hell as a flier; he had no fear — and this one day he parked his father's Piper Cub in the branches of a cottonwood tree. He was always hell-raising."

But he also was brilliant. He graduated number one in his UND class and transferred to Harvard to earn a medical degree. He published early and often in the prestigious New England Journal of Medicine, and when he joined the faculty at UND in 1973, he was the youngest professor of medicine in the country. That year, Keller became the first full-time chair of the department of medicine.

"Reed built a fantastic internal medicine residency," says George

Johnson, "the graduates of which are still sprinkled around the state. But then, he just dropped it because he decided he wanted to do more practice."

As an internist, Keller had a strong following. "Reed was probably the best physician in North Dakota," says Tom Johnson. "He was smarter than hell, but he was a terrible administrator. He was also a very funny guy. I loved being with him. But I really can't characterize him because he was so many things."

Sometimes those many things carried a positive and negative rolled into one.

"He had a manner with patients that I have tried to emulate since I met him," says Dr. David Theige, the internal medicine residency program director and associate professor of internal medicine. "He had a way of making personal connections with people upon first meeting them and convincing them that he really cared. He also was a brilliant diagnostician. We used to have a conference in our residency program that we called Chairman's Rules. It was a sort of stump-the-professor session. Reed would come down once a month or so and we would have a patient waiting for him in a conference room. One of the residents or students would present the case and Reed would then have an opportunity to talk to the patient and do an examination, if he wished. And then he would, off the cuff, discuss the case. We worked very hard to try to stump him and never succeeded. One of the cases, I remember, it took Reed about thirty seconds to figure out."

But, says Theige, "He had another side to him. He did a lot of partying and wild things that were hard for me to figure out. I always had a hard time fitting that side of his personality with the other side."

Like Gene Cornatzer, Keller was a hyperactive man. "I'll never forget the first day that I met Reed Keller," says Dr. William Newman. "What I noticed most was that he couldn't seem to stand still. But it was clear he was obviously an extraordinarily intelligent, articulate, motivated individual."

Dr. Wally Wasdahl, who introduced Keller to Newman that day, remembers him as "an unrelaxed person, pacing like a caged lion, all the time walking back and forth. Yet I haven't seen any department chairman of medicine that impressed me any more."

Then there is the odd memory of Randy Eken, the associate dean of finance who did not know Keller well, but approved his expense accounts in those days. "One day I got a request for reimbursement from Reed for a quarter," he says. "It was for a tip. I don't know if it was meant as a joke or not. But I'll never forget that, this doctor who drove a Porsche, asking for a quarter. I took a

Excuse Me, Doctor

I went to St. Luke's Hospital in Fargo. I can remember very well one experience I had in the operating room. We had the opportunity to hold a retractor in the operating room, which I did for a long time. I can't remember the surgeon's name, but I inadvertently put my foot on his shoe during a surgical procedure. I said, "Excuse me," and he looked at me very gruffly and said, "That's all right, I've been walking on them for fifty-five years." That was the end of that experience, and it discouraged me from going into surgery."

Jon Tinglestad, M.D., class of 1958, became a pediatrician.

quarter out of my pocket and paid it myself."

The Porsche played a central role in the legend of Reed Keller and almost personifies him. He often bragged about being able to drive between Grand Forks and Fargo faster than anybody. One day, coming back from a visit with a friend, Keller lost control of his car. It rolled over, skidded and rolled over again. His friend suffered a crushed trachea and was rushed to a hospital. Keller, however, seemed fine and unhurt. He went home, but that night his wife, Mary Ann, a nurse, found him sweating profusely. The pupils of his eyes were wildly eccentric and he could not be wakened. Rather than take him to a Grand Forks hospital, she had Keller rushed by ambulance to Fargo, where neurosurgeon Robert Johnson was waiting.

In the ambulance enroute, Keller went into cardiac arrest. As he was brought into the emergency room of the hospital, a doctor who knew Keller remarked that he was dead. But then Dr. Johnson, the neurosurgeon, appeared. Without wasting a second, he cut open Keller's swollen head on the spot and removed a large clot of blood that was killing him. Four weeks later, Keller was back to work, bragging not only of being D.O.A., but also of a curious fact discovered by the Highway Patrol, which investigated the wreck. The skid marks they found were the longest ever recorded on a North Dakota highway.

"That was Reed Keller's life," smiles Dr. George Johnson.

The former dean, Tom Johnson, says Keller would unashamedly use his accident to his advantage.

"We got along well, but I got mad at him so many times because he wasn't a very good administrator. He was like an old farm dog, who you'd holler at and he'd roll on his back and look at you with his tail slowly wagging. Reed would say to me, 'Now, remember, I'm brain damaged.'"

In fact, Keller was just as savvy as ever. But he was also a heavy smoker. When he began to have gastric problems he did the unthinkable for most doctors but typical for Reed Keller: he performed his own gastric biopsy, putting a tube down his throat and collecting a tissue sample. Without telling anyone, he sent it off to a lab, but marked it "John Doe." Two days later, according to George Johnson, the results were delivered to Keller's secretary. She told Keller, "John Doe has stomach cancer." Keller's reaction was deadpan. "Yeah," he said. "Okay."

"I saw Reed three weeks before he died," says George Johnson. "He got himself out of his deathbed. He was all jaundiced and looked like a walking cadaver. He drove to Fargo to go to the internal medicine office to prove that he could do it. I came out of the building at 5:30 in the afternoon and saw him standing on the corner. He looked like a ghost who had already gone to the Great Beyond. I walked toward him and I said, "Reed...," and he interrupted. He said, "Dammit, I'm still here."

Dr. Theige has a similar memory. "Just a few days before he died, I was wandering through the building and found that Mary Ann had brought him into the office for an hour or two. He was quite ill and weak, but when he saw me he beckoned me into the office. He spent some time showing me the X-rays and pathology slides from his own cancer. It was something to listen to. He told me that his last wish was to do a grand rounds based on his own case. I really miss him."

Ed James died about a year after Reed Keller. By then, in 1993, the university and the School of Medicine had lost many of its most loyal and hardworking stars. Tom Clifford had retired as president after twenty-one years. Dr. Robert Fischer, Gene Cornatzer and John Vennes also had retired. The new president of the university, Kenneth Baker, was in the process of finding a new dean for the medical school and, in the meantime, looking for someone to act as interim dean.

Vennes remembers paying Baker a visit and offering a bit of advice based on his own experience.

"I said 'I think you need an M.D. as interim dean. Have you considered Clayton?"

Baker listened as Vennes outlined the career of his close friend, Clayton Jensen. He was born in the small town of Stanley, North Dakota, which might have been considered a really small town if it were not so close to Vennes's home town of Zahl. Jensen graduated from the UND medical school in 1956 and earned his medical degree at Bowman Gray in 1958. For the next twenty-five years, he was a much loved family doctor in Valley City, with a brief hiatus in 1975 working at the medical school with Vennes and Ed Donatelle, the first chair of the family medicine department.

He already was recognized as a leader of the effort to convince the state's doctors to support a four-year school. As a result, he was known and respected by doctors in every corner of North Dakota. When the 2-1-1 program began, Jensen helped develop the family practice curriculum for fourth-year medical students and helped set up the family practice programs in Minot and Fargo. He became the first director of the Fargo Family Practice Center.

Later, Jensen returned to private practice and spent another ten years in Valley City, participating as a preceptor for medical students during their family practice rotation. In 1985, Johnson recruited him to return to the School of Medicine. Two years later, he became chair of the Department of Family Practice and later took on the

From an F to a B

I had a very good time in my junior year at UND. I was living the good life. I was blowing physics off. Dean Robinson called me in and it really woke me up. I wasn't going to get into medical school unless I did well. I told my mom the problems I was having and she said, "Who created them?" I became a serious student. I regained focus. I did nothing but study physics for a solid week. I raised it from an F to a B plus.

Richard Olafson, M.D., class of 1957.

added duties of Dean for Clinical Affairs. In addition to dramatically boosting interest among students in the family practice specialty, Jensen played an unusual role in bailing out the department of neuroscience from an awkward situation.

The Bush Foundation and the Northwest Area Foundation had given the neuroscience department a grant to develop a program for teaching the prevention, control and treatment of AIDS to the Native American population. But the program was foundering. Tom Clifford, who was a member of the Bush board, had received complaints from several Indians that university investigators were offending tribal custom with clumsy questions about sexual behavior.

Clifford, who had always maintained good relations with the North Dakota tribal leaders, asked Ed James to have the Department of Family Medicine take over the grant. Jensen was the ideal person to handle the issue. During his thirty-two years as a member of the active reserve of the U.S. Public Health Service, Jensen logged quite a bit of time working with Indians on reservations in North Dakota and in Washington.

In this case, Jensen brought each of the community health representatives from the state's reservations to a meeting in Bismarck. He gave them the floor and listened for two hours to their heated complaints. Jensen asked how the program should be restructured to make it successful. Ideas poured forth, the grant was completely rewritten and the program achieved its goal.

After listening to Vennes, Baker began checking with others who echoed the Vennes recommendation. Baker had been on the verge of appointing Tom Norris, the executive associate dean at the time, to the interim post. Norris, however, held a Ph.D., not an M.D. So Baker named Jensen the interim dean, a post he held for the next two years.

"Clayton was the perfect person to walk in behind that brainstorming Ed James," says Harvey Knull, dean of the graduate school. Judy DeMers concurs. "Clayton is very soft-spoken, very kind, yet he can be tough as nails."

These were years when the buildings begun under Ed James were completed, giving the school an entirely new look and feel. Jensen, though, was not in his office very often. He continued to commute from his home in Fargo during his tenure, occasionally sleeping overnight in an office. But he spent most of his time traveling across the state — he logged fifty thousand miles a year by air and automobile — to meet with doctors and community leaders across the state.

"I saw it as my job to bring all the clinical resources around the state into the fold rather than having them feeling isolated out there," he says. "I tried to act as a facilitator. I visited every community hospital at least twice a year and every single doctor's office that had a student in family medicine. I was a conduit between the medical school and the family doctor. I think that is important. If you are going to have the support of the physicians, hospital administrators,

Adventures in the Classroom

I remember microbiology. I remember when we had to draw blood from each other and look at each other's slides in pathology. I fainted, fell flat on the floor.

B. Varberg, M.D., an orthopedic surgeon, class of 1961, practiced in Minot.

hospitals, you make a concerted effort to make sure they know what is going on and that their contributions are valued."

During his tenure, Jensen had an opportunity to work closely with his colleague John Vennes on several innovative projects. They developed the Med Star system that set up an electronic distance-learning capability in community hospitals and doctors offices throughout the state. Tapping into the system, doctors and hospital staff could access continuing education programs from the medical school, "a fairly effective way to get teaching out around the state," says Jensen.

Another venture involving Jensen and Vennes in the early Nineties since has developed into a significant research arm and enhanced the medical school's national reputation.

It all began with the late Lee Christoferson, Sr., the brilliant Fargo neurosurgeon who in 1974 became the first chair of the medical school's Department of Neuroscience. Christoferson had always dreamed of putting neurology, neurosurgery and psychiatry together in an academic environment. In developing his department, he started a residency in neurology that was short-lived. But the residency he got off the ground in psychiatry took hold and continues successfully to this day.

Christoferson believed deeply in research. In the mid-1980s he

The big dig
Dean Ed James, M.D., breaks ground for a new research facility adjacent to the old St. Michael's hospital structure that is now the core of the School of Medicine. James died before the building was completed. It is named in his honor.

Reluctantly, I Followed the Course

My father was in World War II, and his division was constantly in combat for three years. He hated it and it really affected him. Looking back, I can see that it really sapped his strength. He was content to just stay home and let the world go away. He and my mother pinned their hopes on their kids. My mother said to me, 'Jim, when you grow up you're going to be a doctor.' She told my brother Jon, 'You're going to be a lawyer.' He's a lawyer today and I'm a doctor. When I was a senior in high school, I applied to go to Michigan State for engineering. I had a National Merit scholarship. My mother said, 'Jim, I thought you were going to be a doctor.' I realized then that she was serious. Reluctantly, I followed the course. But all through medical school, I had serious reservations. I got married my second year in med school, and my wife Jolene was very supportive of what I was doing. When I got into my residency in internal medicine, I went to the Marshfield Clinic in Marshfield, Wisconsin, a small town of twenty-five thousand. I met two doctors there, George Magnin and Ben Lawton. They were very heroic, just doing their job taking care of people. They had dedicated their lives to that. That's when I knew I was in the right field.

Jim Brosseau, M.D., class of 1968, is a long-time internist in Grand Forks who chairs the department of community medicine.

created the Neuropsychiatric Research Institute, which is best known by its initials, NRI. Christoferson set up a board of directors that included the movers and shakers of Fargo, including the president of North Dakota State University. It also numbered the president of UND and others from Grand Forks associated with the medical school. One of those members was John Vennes.

NRI was a completely private and independent entity at the time. During the first few years of its existence, there were rumblings of discontent in the medical community that scientists and not medical doctors, were in charge. The institute was soon having trouble both winning cooperation from doctors and attracting top-quality scientists. At one crisis point in 1992, NRI found itself without a director. Tom Clifford, a member of the board, and Christoferson approached the recently retired Vennes and asked him to take over as the interim director of NRI. Find a way, they told him, to make it a vital part of the Fargo community. Vennes agreed on one condition: his entire salary be donated to the fund for the new bioinformation center.

Vennes then began a nationwide tour of similar research institutes, concentrating on programs in Colorado, Pennsylvania and Delaware. Applying the logical scientific method to his inquiry, Vennes found a common element in each institute that played heavily in its success. Each had a strong alliance with a medical school or a hospital. NRI had neither. Vennes came back and proposed a simple solution: NRI needed to develop an association with the School of Medicine.

The School worked out a unique arrangement in which the chair of the Department of Neuroscience — a medical doctor — would also serve as the director of NRI. Half of that salary is paid by the institute and half by the school. In addition, all of the professionals employed by NRI would also have appointments in the medical school.

"The affiliation with the medical school made it a lot easier to attract scientists who were used to academic backgrounds," says Dr. James Mitchell, the nationally recognized psychiatrist recruited in 1996 by Jensen's successor, Dean David Wilson, M.D., to head both NRI and the Department of Neuroscience. "Not having an academic appointment was a concern to people. That's why they didn't come before."

NRI scientists not only teach students things like research methods and design, but also perform statistical analyses for different researchers across the state. Of course, a primary function is original research.

"A lot of my work is trying to increase the amount of clinical research in the Red River Valley," says Mitchell. "Other than a few limited areas, there hasn't been a lot going on. In conjunction with the medical school, the institute is now beginning to bring federal research dollars into the state as well as some measure of prestige."

In fact, NRI has become one of the top five research groups in the world studying the problems and treatments of eating disorders as well as the genetics behind the disorder. Mitchell recently received leadership awards in research from the Eating Disorders Research Society and the National Eating Disorders Association.

"It's clear that eating disorders have a very high heritability," says Mitchell, "among the highest of any psychiatric disorders." NRI is part of two multi-centered research groups across the country — funded by the NIH — who are analyzing data related to the eating disorder problems from eight hundred families. The project is collecting DNA samples from these families and storing them in special laboratories so that researchers in the future who want to study the genetics of anorexia will not have to spend time and money collecting samples.

Another focus at NRI is the development of state-of-the-art treatments, especially for low-income patients with little or no health insurance. These treatments are based on counseling techniques rather than simply medications.

"Counseling techniques that have been shown to work for most people are not being widely utilized," says Mitchell. "The average psychologist who goes to graduate school tends to be taught very little in the way of 'manualized' (standardized) techniques. If I'm a psychologist, I may tend to do whatever I usually do with whoever walks in the door. And it may not be the best treatment for that person. But we now know that highly skilled, manual-based approaches, which are not easy to learn, are far more effective than just generic psychotherapy."

The average person suffering from bulimia or anorexia, says Mitchell, tends to be put on antidepressants. "But we have an eight-session behavioral package that works remarkably well. If you follow people long term, the disorder doesn't come back. It's far less expensive than a year's cost of medication. But most counselors don't know how to do it."

One area Mitchell's group is exploring is the use of telemedicine to deliver psychotherapy to patients who live in remote areas. They also are experimenting with getting data from patients who carry hand-held computers, allowing scientists to study their behavior more in depth. The computers also are programmed to take patients through certain exercises when they get into problem situations.

The success of the NRI-UND connection in the last eight years has not been lost on the Fargo medical community, which has become closer to the medical school than ever.

"This is part of the maturity of a medical school," says Dr.

I Was Having a Good Time

I was born in Risippi, just east of Dickinson, and grew up on a farm. My mother is a Christian Scientist, so I didn't think about medicine at all. I went to North Dakota State University and got a master's degree in organic chemistry. It was during that last year that I realized how much I detested organic chemistry. I decided to switch into medicine because I thought it might be a better field. I went up to Grand Forks for my interview with Dr. Hamre — Mr. Tough Guy — big, old, stoic, aristocratic, long-nosed individual. He looked at my transcript and said, "You did terribly!" I was on scholastic probation twice my freshman year in college, but I had all A's my last year in the natural science courses. He said, "What were you doing?" I said, "Well, I was having a good time." I was playing jazz piano and working with a local band in Fargo to earn a living and go to school. I was getting by on personality. It doesn't work. Anyway, he looked past that. I took the MCAT examination and was admitted to the medical school as the last alternate that year with a man named John Wallerius, a very good friend who was a seven-foot center for the University of Minnesota basketball team. The first day we got this bag of bones to memorize and from then on, life was a glorious experience of fun. I have always had fun with medicine. It was a great privilege to be there.

Wayne Swenson, M.D., class of 1959

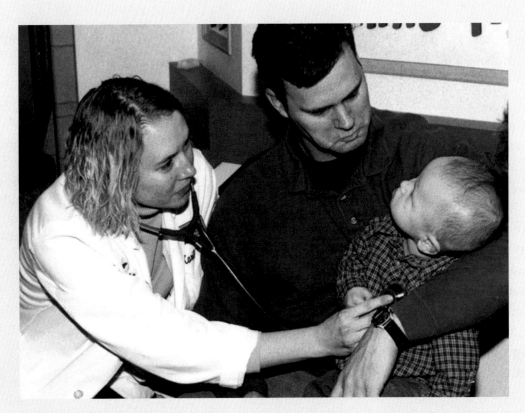

Getting the beat
Karilyn Avery, M.D, a UND medical student when this photo was taken in 2002, administers to a father and his baby in the Altru Child Evaluation Program in Grand Forks.

Roger Gilbertson, the CEO of MeritCare, Fargo's largest hospital and healthcare system. "The hard work John Vennes did as the interim head of NRI in bringing various people together paid off. Clayton Jensen, as the dean of the public medical school created a relationship with a private institution — which is not easy for a state-run institution — I give them both a lot of credit."

As an inheritor of that legacy, Dr. Mitchell can point to the work of doctors Sharon and Richard Wilsnack and their internationally acclaimed research on alcohol-related problems among women as an example of how his department of neuroscience focuses on the brain in a biopsychosocial sense — connecting brain function, mind and behavior in a more comprehensive approach.

Sharon Wilsnack, Ph.D., a clinical psychologist, and her husband Richard Wilsnack, Ph.D., a sociologist, have earned an international reputation for their research on gender and alcohol. Since 1980, they have conducted a federally funded longitudinal study of women and drinking — the only such study ever attempted. Funded by the National Institute on Alcohol Abuse and Alcoholism (NIAAA), the Wilsnacks have been able to conduct intensive follow-up interviews every five years with their subjects — drawn from a large adult sampling across the United States.

Their study has expanded to include the work of researchers from dozens of other countries. In fact, in 1993, the Wilsnacks founded the International Research Group on Gender and Alcohol (IRGGA) whose thirteen original researchers from the United States, Poland and Sweden have been joined by more than one hundred researchers from forty countries.

The common questionnaire they devised has standardized information gathering on the drinking habits of women and men. With it, the UND couple started Gender, Alcohol, and Culture: An International Study — or GENACIS, as it is known — which investigates alcohol behavior in nearly forty countries. The Wilsnacks have secured funding for these projects from the NIAAA and also from the World Health Organization, the European Union and the Pan American Health Organization.

They have found, says Sharon, that early research on gender and alcohol was male-dominated, "There has always been a huge stigma about women drinking. You find it in every culture and historical period. That lack of visibility allowed women to keep those problems hidden."

And in too many places, adds Richard, men's hazardous drinking is regarded as normal behavior. "Men don't try to get help," he says. "There's an attitude of acceptance: that's what men do. On the other hand, women's abuse of alcohol is considered so deviant that those women are likely to be punished or their families and spouses want to keep them hidden. Because women's problem drinking is treated as abnormal, a lot of women don't get treatment."

Sharon is a member and chair of the subcommittee on college drinking of NIAAA's National Advisory Council on Alcohol Abuse and Alcoholism. She and Richard published a book in 1997 on gender and alcohol.

"The most important step will be to take the findings of this research and make a difference in the world," she says. "Our gender and alcohol project has gotten a lot of attention. We're waking up to alcohol as a global problem."

Both Wilsnacks are full professors in the School of Medicine and had a hand in shaping a new curriculum instituted under Dean Wilson in recent years. "We are very pleased," adds Sharon, "with the medical school's awareness of how important this research is. We talk to students about how you can identify alcoholism in medical practice. That's been a positive thing."

Chapter 9

CHAPTER NINE

Doctor Hempler's Whistle

When H. David Wilson, M.D., flew into Grand Forks in 1995 to interview for the position of dean of the School of Medicine, it was not the storied weather or the supposed remoteness of the state that gave him pause.

It was the sign out in front of the school. Not only was the sign hard to read, it was confusing — even disappointing.

It was posted in front of the old St. Michael's Hospital on Columbia Road, which, with the Ed James additions, had become the new, centralized home of the medical school. Yet the sign was positioned in a way that made it difficult, if not unsafe, for a passing motorist to read. One had to be exactly parallel with the sign to puzzle over what it said:

Med-Sci North
Physical Therapy

Everyone in the medical school knew what it meant, even if the sign was incorrect. The name Med-Sci North was meant to distinguish it from Med-Sci South, the headquarters of the basic science departments two blocks away in the old Medical Science building. But basic science had already moved into Med-Sci North's brand-new addition.

Wilson, a long-time pediatrician and academic standout at the University of Kentucky, was aware of Tom Johnson's folksy repatriation of the third year, and

Previous page:

H. David Wilson, M.D.
In his ten years as dean of the UND School of Medicine and Health Sciences, Wilson has overseen changes as large as installing a revolutionary curriculum and as small as erecting an easier-to-read and more accurate sign in front of the school.

of the energy Ed James had put into getting the four-year school into modern facilities. All that was done and the university now was casting about for someone to pull everything together and move on to the next level.

Yet in sharp contrast with all that newness stood this tired, outdated sign in front of the largest building in Grand Forks — a 300,000-square-foot labyrinth with more than one hundred rooms on each floor. The sign out front gave no clue that exciting changes — the transformation of raw students into learned professionals — were taking place within those rooms. It seemed to Wilson to reflect an ambivalence in coming to grips with the future, a certain comfort level with the status quo. He knew that medicine was in the grips of the greatest period of change in its history — some of its own making, some not. Clinging to the status quo could be as deadly as any disease. Wilson sensed that if he was to lead the School of Medicine at the University of North Dakota into a new millennium, he was staring then at his challenge in microcosm.

Indeed, his hiring surprised many faculty members. Dr. Richard Olafson, the neurosurgeon and long-time dean of the Fargo campus, served on the search committee that selected Wilson, an outlander, over two very well-thought-of North Dakota doctors.

"During the search process," says Olafson, "a number of people felt we should have a North Dakota dean. In that process, I went and lobbied very hard — I spent a very emotional hour with Ken Baker, the university president at the time — to hire Wilson. David was needed. He was bringing new ideas. He was quiet but had a lot of steel and backbone. He could stand up to some of these people who felt, 'We're very happy where we are. We continue to do what we do, and we don't need innovations or new ideas.'"

Impressed with such a recommendation, Baker hired Wilson. He was not the warm and fuzzy Tom Johnson, nor was he the politically untouchable Tom Clifford. Like Ed James, though, he knew what he wanted and, going James one step further, he knew how to articulate it.

"He is the most academic of the deans we've had," says Dr. Dennis Lutz, chair of the department of obstetrics and gynecology. "By that I mean he comes as a professional educator. That means he has a little more global view of education. We've had a visionary builder. We had a person who got the structure in place. Now we have a professional educator who was a clinician and who understands where we're headed."

That there would be change under Wilson's tenure became

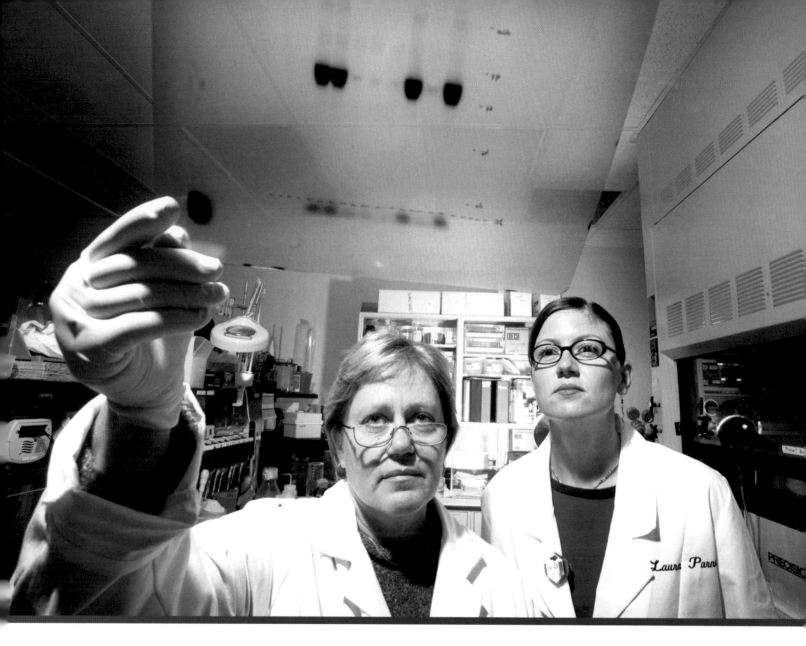

quickly apparent. "I'm a forceful person," Wilson admits. "I try to be nice. I vow to be fair. I have strong opinions and usually voice them."

Very soon after his arrival, the Med-Sci North sign was gone — replaced not merely by a new sign, but a new name for the entire school. Since the days of Melvin Brannon it was known simply as the "School of Medicine." But Wilson grasped early on an important reality. Skeptics were prone to take the budget for the medical school and divide it by the number of doctors who graduated each year, then complain that it was a lot of money to spend on just fifty-seven degrees (the school now awards sixty-two annually). If the budget were divided by the total number of medical students over four years, however, the result would be different. In fact, besides the sixty-two doctors that graduate each year, there are today 859 students in the first three years of medical school or in other academic programs — from doctors in residency training to occupational therapists. There are more than sixteen hundred undergrads earning credit hours at the medical school toward degrees in nursing, teaching and science, and another eleven thousand-plus medical professionals taking courses through continuing medical education.

Showing the way
Associate Professor Roxanne Vaughn, Ph.D., shown analyzing a type of X-ray film used to detect radioactive protein. Observing is Laura Parnas, a graduate student from Argentina.

Who we are
One of Dean Wilson's first acts was to expand the name of the School of Medicine to reflect the diversity of medical specialties being taught within its walls.

Wilson thought the school needed a name that reflected its broader mission. He proposed to university President Baker that the name be changed to "School of Medicine and Health Sciences." Baker, fearing that doctors would resent it, said no. Undeterred, Wilson conducted a study that showed doctors did not mind at all. Baker relented and the change was made. The new sign, lit up at night, is perpendicular to Columbia Road so that passing motorists know exactly what that building is all about. A few years later, Wilson asked John Vennes to organize a fund drive among alumni, which raised $300,000 to build a modern entrance and foyer to the building. It was named in honor of alumni favorite, Dean Ted Harwood.

"Now," smiles Wilson, "people know where and what we are."

Wilson attended to one other bit of piano tuning before getting down to the more involved and less visible issues he saw facing the school. He posted on each door leading into the medical school building a card containing these words from the late Supreme Court Justice Louis Brandeis:

What is a Profession?

A Profession is composed of a body of knowledge, a substantial portion of which is derived from experience.

A Profession is responsible for advancing that knowledge and transmitting it to the next generation.

A Profession sets its own standards ... and cherishes performance above personal rewards.

A Profession is directed by a code of ethics, which includes the moral imperative to serve others.

"I've been worried for some time," says Wilson, "about the profession of medicine. I think medicine is at risk of losing that status of 'professional' in the next twenty-five years if we're not careful. All too many physicians today have sort of forgotten that medicine is a service. We are here to serve others. We are not here to just make money. We need to remember that society grants us this status and society can take it away. Medicine has become in many cases very much about technology and tools and procedures. If we're not careful, we forget that the object is to take care of people. A lot of doctors have lost the connection of why we're in this."

Wilson's own connection is as simple as a whistle. His father was a funeral director in southern Illinois who had wanted to be a doctor but did not have the money for the education. His mother was a nurse. Wilson remembers amused doctors allowing him, as a curious young boy, to snoop through the drawers in their desks during office visits. But mostly he remembers those childhood times when he was sick in bed with measles or whooping cough and waiting for Dr. Hempler to arrive.

"He was a well-trained, skillful general practitioner, the person my parents turned to when my brother or I was sick," he recalls. "He was kind, smart and could do things to make you well. I could tell when he arrived downstairs because he whistled as he climbed the stairs. He was an inspiration. From the time I was five or six, I said I wanted to be a doctor. I never deterred from that."

Most people who knew him in those days, however, would have bet money David Wilson would become a veterinarian. His father and his funeral-home partner bought a farm and began raising purebred Angus cattle. Young David took to not only riding horses and handling farm chores, but also working closely with the local vet, pulling calves, taking blood specimens and even doing some artificial insemination.

"Everybody just assumed I'd be a cowboy doctor," says Wilson. "Instead I became a pediatrician."

This, after spending high school in a military academy where he grew to like the disciplined life. Then, after medical school at St. Louis University and residencies at the University of Kentucky Medical Center, he spent two years in the Navy practicing pediatrics.

"I have always liked children and related to them," says Wilson. "Little kids do neat things. Some people can't stand a crying child. I can tell if a child is crying because he's hungry or her diaper is wet or because they are in pain. The former, I don't worry too much about. The latter, it's my job to try to figure out why the pain is there and make it go away."

A lot of doctors, he adds, don't like pediatrics because they can't stand the parents. "But you just have to understand: No directions come with these children," he smiles. "And doctor literally means teacher. So you're teaching these parents how to take care of their child. I enjoyed all of that."

That belief in teaching helped sway him to try his hand at academic medicine. After his Navy years and a fellowship in infectious diseases at the University of Texas Southwestern Medical School at Dallas, Wilson began a twenty-two-year career at the University of Kentucky. He served as vice-chairman of the Department of Pediatrics at the College of Medicine and later as director of admissions. He ultimately rose to associate dean for academic affairs. In 1988, he was named a fellow of the American Council on Education, a highly competitive, national leadership program. He served his ACE fellowship year as an assistant to David Roselle, the president of the University of Kentucky.

In the meantime he also was a general pediatrician, an infectious-disease consultant and, for eight years, in charge of the pulmonary clinic responsible for eighty children with cystic fibrosis.

"I loved teaching," he says, "loved my practice, and enjoyed clinical research." It was during those years as a clinician, he notes, that he developed a philosophy about professionalism among doctors and the critical need for a human connection between doctor and patient. During his residency training, he recalls, he was caring for a young boy named John nearing death from leukemia. He saw John's attending physician distance himself from the boy. In the later stages of his illness, the doctor rarely entered the boy's room, whereas Wilson relieved John's exhausted mother and sat with John when he died.

The experience would have a lasting impression on Wilson's view of not only how a doctor should behave as a professional, but of how a doctor should be trained in the first place.

"Many physicians deal poorly with the dying and avoid the situation," he says. "I believe they experience a feeling of personal failure. I also believe many personally fear death and are rarely present for patient and family at the time of death. I promised myself after John's death never to distance myself from patients when the going got tough, and to do everything I could to assist to the very end. It takes courage, but I personally believe that is one of the responsibilities of being a doctor."

A second similar episode, this one closer to home, reinforced the point. Wilson's father had developed terminal thyroid cancer. On his visits, Wilson met his father's oncologist, who seemed competent, he remembers, although not especially compassionate. In fact, during one visit, Wilson realized his father was in great pain but was not prescribed any pain medication. He insisted the nurse call to make sure adequate pain medication was ordered. Later, when his father was near death, Wilson arrived at the hospital and found him in agony. Nurses had not administered morphine. Wilson got them to act and his father was able to relax and die peacefully.

"I promised then," he says with resolve, "that we would do a better job teaching medical students and residents about pain control and care of the dying."

In fact, the restructuring of the entire curriculum has been one of the hallmarks of Wilson's tenure at North Dakota.

"The students here are terrific," he says. "Many are farm kids who come here bright-eyed, humanistic and altruistic. I would hope that we nurture that, that we don't beat it out of them. I think in many medical schools, unfortunately, they come in really nice people, and you meet them six years later and too many of them are hard and calloused. They're kind of angry about the process. In many places, the first two years are almost drudgery. We have to be careful. These are young, impressionable people and it is our responsibility to work hard to maintain their goodness and their altruism and their human side, so that we send them out to be humane doctors."

To that end, and with Justice Brandeis in mind, Wilson added to his new curriculum a symbolic change in one of the school's longest traditions. It used to be that upon graduation, UND's medical students would go through a ceremony in which they recited the doctor's Hippocratic oath. They still do, but now Wilson instituted another

Beulah's doc
After Aaron Garman, M.D., class of 1996, finished his training, he established his practice in the small western North Dakota community of Beulah. Garman is holding his daughter Isabel in this 1999 photo.

A Good Fit
In the first week of their medical school experience, students receive their white coat in a special ceremony where they also recite the Hippocratic oath for the first time. Dean Wilson, shown with Joshua Knudson, class of 2008, believes the ceremony impresses on students the responsibilities they face as medical professionals.

ceremony at the very beginning, as well. After the first week of classes, the parents and families of medical students are invited back to the school for a special event. A speaker gives a talk about what it means to be a doctor and Wilson delivers a combination pep talk and warning.

"I tell them this is not the same old, same old," he says. "You are different from this day on. I'm going to treat you like colleagues and I expect you to behave like colleagues. There's a higher standard we're going to hold you to. We expect you to behave in a professional manner. We will nurture you and we will watch you closely. And if you're unprofessional, I'll boot you out of school."

At this point, students put on their white coats for the first time and recite the Hippocratic oath.

"I have a moral obligation to the public," says Wilson, "to make sure the people we send across that stage at graduation are people we trust to go out there and not only be smart enough to be good doctors but be professional enough to do the right things. I tell students, you're in the most treasured profession of all. People will share with you their innermost secrets. You can learn a lot about humanity if you keep your eyes open and reflect on the people you see and the things you deal with. For me, every day as a doctor has been a glory. And I worry for a lot of people who get mixed up in the business of medicine for the money they can make. And they miss the real joys of helping other human beings."

It is not uncommon at a medical school for a new dean to revamp the curriculum to suit his or her vision. Typically, changes involve the types of courses taught, a shift emphasis from one science to another or the addition of new clinical specialty courses. Notable curriculum changes have occurred at UND's School of Medicine during the terms of Harley French, Ted Harwood and Tom Johnson. But the changes under Wilson are so profound that the curriculum at UND has become a model of which other medical schools have taken note.

The change is based on a shift in educational philosophy. Under the traditional curriculum, medical education is divided between the first two years of basic science courses and the last two years of more practical hands-on clinical training. The basic science courses always were taught in the didactic method — with a teacher giving a series of lectures on one aspect of science, such as anatomy, and students cramming that information and taking an exam. Then it was on to the next block. Given that students often took several blocks at once, the life of a medical student was an exhausting marathon of cramming, with the biggest challenge, sometimes, trying to stay awake during tedious lectures.

Clinical training in the old system did not begin until the third year. Students rotated through various "clerkships," watching and occasionally assisting medical doctors for three months at a time as they dealt with patients in specialties such as obstetrics or internal medicine. Fourth year was set aside for more specialized clinical training based on a student's particular interest.

"The problems with the standard clerkships are that they were relatively fixed," says Dr. David Antonenko, former chair of UND's Department of Surgery. "The teaching in many respects has been Socratic. Rather than student-centered, it has been faculty-centered. That was great for some of the students, but it was terrible for most of them It was terrible for the group that is in between the lower third of the class and the upper third, and was really boring for the upper third of the class. Most students really didn't learn well in that situation."

Such learning systems, common in most medical schools throughout the Twentieth Century, were known as Flexnerian, after Abraham Flexner, whose curriculum reforms in the early part of the century helped standardize medical school training. The great disadvantage of the Flexnerian model was that the basic science and the clinical concepts never quite came together in students' minds

The Exciting Thing About Science

A word that I always emphasize in every lecture is serendipity. "Blind luck," some people would call it, but many discoveries are made by accident. If one has been thinking long enough and working hard enough, one might come up with something another might just pass by. You understand what it means because something clicks. Serendipity. Just by the fact that you see this and subconsciously put it all together in your mind, you get new insight. Most of the major discoveries had serendipity as a component of the experience. I emphasize that always. It's a big thrill when that happens. It's one of the exciting thing about being a scientist: I kept a notebook at the top of my bed so that when I woke up in the middle of the night with a wild thought, I could quickly write it down. Sometimes they looked pretty silly in the morning, but sometimes they were the best thoughts I ever had.

Robert Nordlie, Ph.D., is the former chair of the department of biochemistry and molecular biology.

until they were out of medical school and into a residency program. Real-world circumstances forced them to start thinking about everything simultaneously.

Wilson, like many of the older faculty at UND, trained under that very system. He thought its rigors were unnecessary, though, and could cause student burnout and cynicism. Worse, such rigors were counterproductive to the mission of graduating humanistic, professional doctors. But he had already seen how a change in philosophy could alter the result. At Kentucky, as associate dean of the medical school, he was charged with revising a very similar Flexnarian curriculum.

"I said we're going to wipe the slate clean and start all over." He got practicing doctors and faculty involved to devise a new curriculum that was more patient centered. Wilson believes that experience had much to do with his selection as UND's dean.

Though some faculty members at UND were skeptical of Wilson's proposed change, he identified a group of supporters and formed a study group. He is quick to point out that the curriculum that resulted, which has been in place at UND since 2000, is not his but that of the faculty who designed and implemented it.

"I had some ideas and some of those are incorporated," he says. "We got permission from the academic council to move forward. It took several years of planning. We went to other schools, we read about every curriculum in North America. It's been a joy."

The core of the new curriculum is a system of problem-based learning and it begins the very first day of medical school. On that Monday, students are handed a paper case history of a specific patient.

"They don't know half the words," says Wilson. "They say, 'What does this mean?' and they write it on the board. And a group of seven or eight students and a faculty facilitator work through the case together."

On Wednesday of Week One, they get a little more information, such as some lab results. "All this time," says Wilson, "they're thinking, learning. Trying to figure out the connections. Maybe they decide this sounds like heart disease or lung disease. And they do a lot of reading on all the potential diseases they think might be here."

Wednesday is when they share that information with their teammates. On Friday, the patient they have been studying appears in front of class with a doctor. Not only have medical students traditionally not seen patients until their third year, they have not seen real doctors either. But now a physician talks to them about

Pathology research lab
Seema Somji, Ph.D., research assistant professor, cultures human normal and malignant cells.

the case and how the diagnosis was made and what treatment was instituted. At that point, the students get to talk to the patient.

The rule, says Wilson, is that they ask any questions they want, such as, What did you think when they told you that you had breast cancer? How did you feel when you had the miscarriage? What did you think of the medical treatment? How much did it cost? What would you change about this? How did it affect your family life?

"It puts the human face on all this," he says. "I tell people that when I was a med student I spent the first two years learning about diseases that affect people. Here, we spend the first two years learning about people who happen to have diseases. I think it helps keep the humanity there, keep the focus on people. These are not theoretical cases. This is a living human being who could be in their office. After two years of this, I will tell you, they're already pretty good doctors. The challenge of medicine is to try to maintain that connection to people. That goodness."

Each week in the first two years, students get a new case that they discuss three times a week in small groups with a faculty member. "It has just been an absolute hoot to sit in with a small group of students and watch them attack a case and see how they are learning to think," says Dr. Roger Sopher, former chair of the department of pathology. "I would say that puts them six to eight months ahead of people who were in the old curriculum."

Faculty members are assigned to each student team for a block of ten weeks. They act as a "coach on the side," says Wilson, rather than a "sage on the stage." Their job is to ask probing questions, offer suggestions, supply information and make sure students address

Judy DeMers

Judy DeMers has worked as an administrator at the medical school since 1977. The associate dean for student affairs and admissions at the School of Medicine and Health Sciences, DeMers is also a nurse who served for eighteen years in the North Dakota House of Representatives and Senate.

the major objectives of the case. Students study the cases, decide what they do not know or understand, make assignments to themselves and, during the meetings, teach one another. During the week they study everything essential for understanding the biochemistry, anatomy, microbiology-immunology, physiology, pharmacology, pathology, psychosocial and economic aspects of the patient, the family, and the disorder. There are still some lectures and labs that go on every day, but the patient case is at the center and the lectures and lab experiences are chosen to complement the case.

The basement floor of the medical school has been remodeled so each student team has an individual study room available twenty-four hours a day. Following each block, the students are remixed into new teams, ensuring they learn to deal with many different treatment styles and opinions. "We believe this approach teaches students how to learn in an active mode rather than by passive memorization," says Wilson. "The learning is in the context in which it will be used in medical practice."

As in any program that does away with a traditional system, the new curriculum had skeptics among the faculty. Many wondered how well a student could actually learn in such a system. Would students learn as much as in the old didactic approach? Would they be able to pass their exams? How would their scores compare nationally to those of students in other medical schools?

Some worried that borderline students might not adapt to a system that placed more responsibility for their learning on their own shoulders. As David Antonenko says, "It is easier to sit through lectures if you have always been a passive student."

But along with that added responsibility is a built-in system of student support for each other. "They teach each other a lot in these small groups," says Dr. David Theige. "The wisdom in the collaborative system is that students will help one another to progress to the next stage while maintaining their love of learning and love of medicine."

In fact, since its inception, says Dr. Sopher, students who tended to struggle with the old curriculum are doing much better with the new curriculum. "I think it might be that they are learning in a more holistic fashion," he says. "They can see the big picture and then go and fill in the details."

Among the supporters of the new curriculum is Altru's Dr. Casey Ryan. "Dean Wilson has been a very good dean for the medical school," he says. "The new program for educating students is an outstanding step in the right direction."

University President Dr. Charles Kupchella agrees.

"We're absolutely parallel in our thinking of how this should go," says Kupchella, who came to UND from Southeast Missouri State University but earlier in his career spent several years as a cancer researcher in the medical school at the University of Louisville.

"When I first went to Louisville to teach and do research, I was appalled at how little attention medical school faculty paid to how you get somebody to learn — how you actually affect learning and measure it," says Kupchella. "It was because they didn't have to think about it. Every student who came to the medical school probably had a 4.0 index. The faculty figured they could just prop somebody in front of a room and have him spout facts for an hour. The kids would absorb it and pour it back on paper when it came time to take the exam. And yet it didn't seem to be generating the kind of doctors who were humanists, who could relate to patients as people."

Making the change at UND, however, meant more than simply changing philosophy. Faculty members, especially basic scientists, had to reorient completely their professional lives to make the new curriculum work.

"In the past," says Sopher, "our basic scientists would have, say, four lectures to give and then they were done with the curriculum until next year. They could get back to their research. Now, if you're going to facilitate a group of students, you're tied up for a period of ten weeks. It does demand a lot of faculty time."

Faculty members — both basic science and clinical — went through extensive retraining to get ready for the new system.

"I am one who does not like change," admits Dr. Lloyd Bakken, "but I have adapted to it because unless you change, you will not survive. Change is the nature of things. A lot of the changes in medicine have forced us as physicians to be better professional people. It has forced the best-of-the-best to be best; those who have been too lazy and don't want to adapt to change will be left behind. Perhaps that is the price we have to pay to move forward."

Moving forward is exactly what the new curriculum has the school doing, says Associate Dean Judy DeMers.

"Twenty years ago we were somewhat of an adolescent, in ways," she says. "We were very secure in basic science kinds of things. Our clinical approach was just developing on a trial-and-error basis. We were looking for our niche. I think with the curriculum changes Dr. Wilson has instituted, we really found our identity. We do this very

Scoping it out
Gene Homandberg, Ph.D., chair of the department of biochemistry and molecular biology, oversees the work of Danping Guo, left, a research specialist, and Lei Ding, a graduate student from the People's Republic of China.

well. Our students' test scores are as good or better than those of students around the country and often better."

DeMers also has seen positive results in her daily contact with students. "I don't see the stressed-out students I used to see," she says. "They don't have to get caught up with taking multiple courses at once and taking exams every five days, like in the old system. Most students say they wouldn't want to go to school under any other system."

While increased scores are certainly the benchmark for proving the system works, not inconsequential are some hidden benefits.

"Many students in the past were tired, unhappy and anxious to get away from basic science learning, instead of anxious to see it at work in applied medicine," says Wilson. "We are seeing students at the end of the second year excited about learning, happy, confident and self-directed. This is a total change from medical education in the past. I believe they will appreciate better what it is like to be the patient and, therefore, be more compassionate, communicative physicians."

While Wilson's curriculum changes have dramatically reshaped the inner dynamics of the School of Medicine and Health Sciences, his scholarly emphasis on research has had a lasting effect as well.

"He has been a champion of hiring faculty who are good scientists," says John Vennes. "He has put key individuals into departmental positions who have the kinds of leadership abilities to attract funding and research."

In fact, the research emphasis has modernized the school, says Dr. Roger Gilbertson, the CEO of Fargo's MeritCare Health System, the state's largest hospital.

"I think what Wilson has brought to the medical school is somewhat of a hybrid model," he says. "It was a community-based medical school that was all clinical — fundamental basic medicine that they teach students and residents and so on. But he came in and said, 'I'd like to have some element of an academic center here.' So, he brought people in at the basic science level that did research and they've been very successful at acquiring a fair amount of research dollars. He's been very successful in recruiting some very high-level people. I think that's part of the maturity of a school. Now, are we going to be an academic medical center? No, but do we have enough academics in this thing that give some renown to the school? Some prestige? And enhance the product? Absolutely. This idea of fostering some scholarly activity on the part of people in training in medicine is absolutely the right thing to do in terms of where the medical school is going."

President Kupchella agrees with Gilbertson. "For most of its history," he says, "other than a few pockets of acclaimed research, the medical school has not had what you would call a national reputation. But the faculty are starting to build that in areas like neuroscience and translation research, and soon in other areas. They are doing the kind of work that brings national visibility."

Leading the way in that research effort is one of Wilson's prize recruits. Manuchair Ebadi, Ph.D., a nationally-known researcher in Parkinson's disease, came to North Dakota from the University of Nebraska in 1999, and brought with him nearly $5 million in grant funding from the NIH. In fact, his enthusiasm for going after grant monies has created a new culture of research among his colleagues.

Only a few years before Ebadi arrived in Grand Forks in 1999, the School of Medicine and Health Sciences had less than $300,000 in pending grants. As chair of the department of pharmacology, Ebadi recruited five researchers who, among them, brought in more than $10 million in outside funding. Between 1999 and 2004, the medical school realized more than $71 million in grants and contract awards. "When I got here, people weren't doing research," says Ebadi. "I told them if you are in a university setting, research is what you do. It caught on. They applied for grants and got them."

Now associate dean for research and program development, Ebadi says the school will receive $28 million this year alone in outside grants. That includes a $3.9 million grant he secured from the Office of National Drug Control Policy to bring the first microPET, hot lab and cyclotron to North Dakota. There are only a dozen such devices in the country, and none in the Midwest. The cyclotron will be used to study the effects of cocaine, alcohol and other drugs on brain function.

To house the two-hundred-ton cyclotron, Ebadi, with the help of Senator Byron Dorgan, won a $4 million grant to erect a neuroscience building adjacent to the School of Medicine and Health Sciences. He plans to use this Center of Excellence in Neuroscience for further deep-brain research, including studies on Parkinson's disease, whose incidence in North Dakota is unusually high. Ebadi, who has published seven books, including the recent "Parkinson's Disease" with Ronald Pfeiffer, M.D., of the University of Tennessee, says the illness affects people in agricultural states and people who live longer — both markers of life in North Dakota.

For his efforts, Ebadi has won the Thomas J. Clifford Faculty Achievement Award for Excellence in Research. Kupchella named

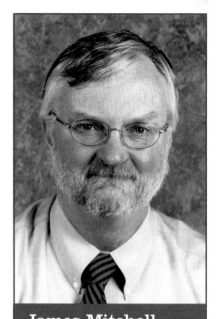

James Mitchell

Recognized nationally for his research into eating disorders, Dr. Mitchell, a psychiatrist, chairs the department of neuroscience. He also directs the Neuropsychiatric Research Institute in Fargo.

Clayton Jensen

After the death of Ed James, the university in 1993 appointed Jensen as interim dean. A respected family doctor, he was chair of the department of family medicine. He retained that post during the two years he served as dean.

him a Chester Fritz Distinguished Professor of Pharmacology.

"It's our obligation and our mission to generate new knowledge as well as to transmit it," says Kupchella. "We've been derelict — or underfunded — in failing to support research enterprise in years gone by. But when NIH recently doubled its budget, we were positioned well to ride that escalator. North Dakota is the second ranked state now in the percent of grant-money gains. We've had a five hundred percent increase in funding from the NIH."

In fact, Kupchella and Wilson have worked closely on the university's strategic goal of reaching $100 million annually in sponsored research. A third of that is expected to come in through environmental and energy research, says Kupchella, a third from various other programs and a third from the School of Medicine and Health Sciences.

It's a tall order, perhaps, for a small university. Ebadi, who serves on several national review committees for grant agencies, admits it is difficult to land a grant if you are not from a big-name university.

"If the grant application comes from Harvard or Hopkins," he says, "everybody takes their hat off. It has to be good. If it's from a small school, they hold their nose. That prejudice is there. But, outstanding universities attract outstanding scientists who submit outstanding proposals. And we have recruited outstanding scientists."

Even so, the emphasis Wilson has placed on research has been questioned by some who fear that the medical school is diluting its simple mission of turning out more doctors for North Dakota.

"Lately, because we're so successful in research now, some have said, 'Has the dean changed the mission of the school?'" says Wilson. "But no. Our first and most important mission is to produce doctors for North Dakota. We're not only producing really good doctors, though. In addition we're also doing research."

And for good reason, says Dr. James Mitchell, the man Wilson recruited away from the University of Minnesota to chair the department of clinical neuroscience and also head the Neuropsychiatric Research Institute (NRI) in Fargo.

"Those of us who do clinical research feel strongly that if you have an active research program, you improve patient care," he says. "You attract people at the cutting edge of their field. You're able to provide patients the newest therapies. I know there's resistance to research around the state. Part of that resistance stems from the fact that people have simply not been used to doing research."

For years, clinical faculty members have acted almost as volunteers, drawing a stipend or a modest part-time salary rather

Ribbon-cutting

A host of VIPs assembled in 2004 for the ceremonial ribbon cutting for the new neuroscience building adjacent to the medical school. From left are Grand Forks mayor, Dr. Mike Brown; North Dakota Governor John Hoeven; Board of Higher Education member, Kayla Effertz; U.S. Senator Byron Dorgan; UND Vice-President Peter Alfonso; Dean David Wilson; UND President Charles Kupchella; Associate Dean Manuchair Ebadi.

than the full salary paid to faculty at traditional schools. Wilson, however, expects that for whatever pay they draw, even clinical faculty members should be willing to become involved in research efforts that would translate into usable clinical therapies.

"We do a fair amount of research on the clinical side," says Altru's president, Dr. Ryan. "It's good to have interaction between the medical school and the practicing clinicians. That is easy to talk about but harder to bring about, whether you're just going over to the medical school and giving a one-hour lecture or being involved in a research project with them. It just takes commitment. People who do both practice and research have to have a lot of energy. Those are the people you want to get, but it is not always easy."

Some have argued that research is not the proper role for a medical doctor. Mitchell, who is a clinical psychiatrist as well as a researcher, says such comments reflect a classic resistance to inevitable change.

"I don't think we're a good-old-boy kind of school anymore," he says. "I don't think we're doing each other favors just by being on the faculty. David has made it very clear that there are expectations for people's productivity. I think it should be that way. If you are not carrying your own weight in terms of academic accomplishment, it is time to go home. Medicine has got to change. The field is evolving so rapidly. We all have to be willing to change."

"There's been just a huge sea change here," adds Dr. Sharon Wilsnack, Mitchell's colleague in the department of clinical neuroscience, who, with her husband Dr. Richard Wilsnack, has conducted groundbreaking research into the epidemiology of gender-based alcoholism. "It's not so much a question of do you support research. It's more like, if you're not doing research, what's wrong with you?"

After all, says Mitchell, the point of medical research is to find usable solutions to problems. For example, without his research into eating disorders, "People wouldn't have access to these new therapies we've developed because they were not being widely disseminated yet. A lot of patients in that age group are poor or have limited health insurance."

Ultimately, says Richard Olafson, one of Mitchell's Fargo colleagues, research enhances one's skill as a clinician. "Your practice is going to be so much more exciting if you can interact with a researcher. Our patients will be so much better off. But it's change and change is painful."

Until 1948, the dean of the School of Medicine was an invisible figure to state budgeters in Bismarck. Harley French might have been a revered figure on the UND campus, but he never really got a chance to leverage his reputation before a legislative budget committee. Before 1948, when voters approved the mill levy, it fell to the president of the university to defend the budget of the medical school along with the budgets of all the other schools under the UND umbrella. Thus, the medical school never really had a face or a personality in Bismarck.

The mill levy not only gave the School of Medicine its own dedicated chunk of state money, it gave sudden visibility to the person who held the title of dean. Now the dean had not only to present and defend the budget, but to present and defend himself as an individual those legislators could trust. Almost overnight, the job description of dean expanded to include an essential skill: political schmoozing. Some deans, of course, have been better at it than others.

Ted Harwood never was really at ease in the political arena, but legislators generally liked him because he was humble and respectful and was as fiscally conservative as most of them. Tom Johnson they loved because they all wanted to be just like him or, knowing that was impossible, they wanted him to like them — a total reverse of the expected role. He was such an entertaining man of the people that he got pretty much what he wanted when he wanted it. On the other hand, though legislators respected Ed James as a surgeon, they bristled when it seemed he was talking down to them or treating them as subordinates. In truth, he suffered mightily as the man who followed the unfollowable act of Tom Johnson.

As for the two interim deans between Ted Harwood and David Wilson, both Clayton Jensen and John Vennes were easy men for legislators to like and to get along with. Both have sterling reputations as medical man and scientist. Both also had broad support across the state among doctors and politicians. Vennes built a quiet reputation as a sensible and sensitive man during the years he stumped the state for expansion. Jensen, the fatherly family doctor from Valley City, likewise made many friends and few enemies during his years crisscrossing the state and talking to fellow doctors about expansion and the family practice residency.

Enter David Wilson, a horse of a very different color than any who had run the race before him. He was affable, but not a good old boy. He had been a cowpuncher in an earlier life, but came across as something of an intellectual. Like Tom Johnson, Ed James, Ted Harwood and Harley French, he was not a native North Dakotan, yet unlike them, some viewed him as an outsider. Most important, unlike Johnson, James, Harwood and French, he had not been brought in from without to repatriate, build, expand or hold the fort and make do. He was hired, instead, to lead the medical school on to a distinguished future, perhaps the most open-ended assignment handed any dean in the school's history. Even so, he arrived with very specific ideas of what needed to be done and, seizing the initiative, he set about doing them.

"In some places, the department chairs run the show and the dean is a figurehead," says Dr. Mitchell. "There's lots of politics between departments and fighting over resources. Here, David is always very upfront about what's going on. He's also a person who is in charge. He makes most decisions himself, after he's well informed. He's very self-directed. He has his own game plan and pushes it forward, but he's very straight with everyone about what he's going to do."

"Straightforwardness" characterizes this dean's approach to legislative relationships much better than the term schmoozing — a word that does not quite fit the traditionally formal Dr. Wilson. Many who have seen him in action in the political arena say the "upfront" approach goes over well.

"I think you have to have a tremendous amount of political savvy in that job and that is what Dr. Wilson has," says Richard Tscheider, CEO of St. Alexius Medical Center in Bismarck. "He has the temperament to carry on a cordial relationship with people and yet get the job done. That ability is something most physicians don't have the temperament for."

Adds Vennes, "He has been careful to learn who the legislators are. And he's always inviting people to come see the medical school." One politician who has frequently taken Wilson up on his invitation to visit the campus is John Hoeven, North Dakota's governor.

"He's very professional," says Hoeven of the dean. "He gets along well with people. He has a challenging job, but he's progressive and he has the school moving forward and doing new things. I'm excited about what they are doing."

Hoeven bases his opinion less on politics than on simple observation. "Whenever I'm at the medical school, at some point I sit in a room with students. They are so excited about being at UND and so high on the quality of the school. The pride they have and quality of education they feel they get — to me that speaks volumes."

What most legislators hear even louder is the sound of money coming into the state through the various research projects Wilson and his faculty have engineered. Again, that outside money not only buys research, it creates jobs and boosts the North Dakota economy.

"About seventy percent of research grants go to pay people," says Wilson. "They buy cars, they rent houses, they buy houses, they pay taxes. They increase the wealth of North Dakota. They increase our quality of life, too. We are importing some very bright people who are going to make really good citizens for our state."

He also has managed to hold total increases in state support of the medical school budget over the last ten years to about $800,000 — from $29.4 million in 1993-1995 to $30.2 million in 2003-2005. At the same time, he increased revenue from outside sources by almost three hundred percent. Ten years ago, the state's portion of the medical school's revenue was almost fifty percent. Today it is less than twenty-five percent, with more than a third of the school's revenue now coming from grants and contracts. The mill levy, which once was the entire basis of the medical school's annual operations, now accounts for less than three percent of the annual budget.

Many legislators like also that Wilson has maintained powerful connections to the world outside North Dakota. He is a member of the executive council of deans at the Association of American

Medical Colleges, and a member of the American Medical Association's Council on Medical Education. Wilson just finished a term as the AMA's representative to the Liaison Committee on Medical Education, which accredits all medical schools in the United States and Canada.

"I get to associate with the best deans in the country," says Wilson. "The dean from North Dakota has never been on these councils before. I feel like they know where North Dakota is now. They know me. I've engendered a certain amount of reputation that is good for the school, and I bring back ideas that I think will help make us better."

Wilson's ease in working with political groups has carried over into another critical arena — that of developing working relationships with the state's hospitals where much of the clinical training of students takes place. Roger Gilbertson, the CEO of MeritCare Health System in Fargo says he was immediately impressed by Wilson's style.

"He was an easy person to relate to. We connected right away," he says. "I thought he had the same values that were important to me. He had passion for education and excellence that I certainly admired. So we sat down and said, 'How can we make our collaboration work better?'"

One problem area involving Fargo was the state of the internal medicine residency there. It had lost its direction after the death of Reed Keller and had lost its accreditation. In talks between Gilbertson and Wilson, MeritCare agreed to resurrect the residency program and take it in-house, where it has regained its former elite status.

"With that," says Gilbertson, "we said we need to be partners." He and Wilson tackled a sore point that often exists between many hospitals and nearby medical schools — the fear that doctors might be competing with the hospital for patients.

Doctors who were part of MeritCare also served as part-time faculty at UND. The medical school kept a percentage of each patient fee earned by its faculty to pay for its costs. But the system muddied the lines of responsibility and accountability, says Gilbertson.

"I'd say David understands how this community-based medical school can work better. He understands that the medical school must be viewed not as a competitor within the medical community, but as an adjunct to their life in medicine."

Under the new system, MeritCare does the billing for all patient care and contributes to the university part or all of certain faculty salaries.

"We eliminated that financial competition, which was a negative

Life as a Med Student

All schools were the same when my generation was starting out. Everything was pretty didactic. Do I feel I gained a lot from that? To be honest, no. I'll tell you what I did gain. This was some fifty years ago. I remember when Ed Haunz, an internal-medicine physician from Grand Forks, would come to the school and lecture. Once he brought a lady out who had hypothyroidism — no thyroid function. I still remember her. He spoke a little about her physical condition and then he had her kneel on a chair as he tested her ankle reflexes with his reflex hammer. Generally, an ankle reflex comes back quite quickly, but hypothyroids are very slow. I still remember seeing that ankle jerk the foot, going out like this, and very slowly returning — one of the classic signs of hypothyroidism. I always said I would never forget it and I never did. Sometimes I would be checking for that and a colleague would say, 'Why are you doing that?' and I would say, 'It's a classic sign. Ed Haunz showed us.' To this day, it is buried in my brain. The didactic lecture part was fine, but I couldn't clearly relate it to a patient. And Dr. Wilson is now utilizing this teaching method as Dr. Haunz did. That's to me how medicine should be taught. That's how you remember."

John Graham, M.D., is a member of the class of 1952.

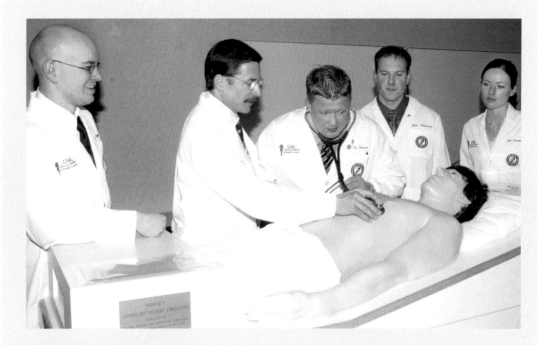

Listening to Harvey
A group of medical students led by Jon Allen, M.D. (second from left) practice listening for sounds of the heart with "Harvey," a sophisticated cardiac simulator. From left: Ryan Hegge, Allen, Chad St. Germain, Justin Reisenauer, Jill Lindelow.

factor in allowing teaching to flourish within the organization," says Gilbertson. "So, I'm very supportive of the medical school."

After ten years, the combination of Wilson's straightforward approach with those outside the School of Medicine and Health Sciences and his adherence to his own game plan within has finally put distance between himself and the memory of his predecessors. "Dr. Wilson's style is different from that of Tom Johnson," says Judy DeMers. "He's a much more formal person. But he fits what the school is now. Or the school fits him."

DeMers, who has worked for four different deans, sees subtle changes in Wilson. Early on, she says, many of the people he recruited were top clinicians with solid connections but not necessarily academics.

"I think we are seeing much more of a balance," she says. "I think he recognizes that Kentucky and North Dakota are two disparate schools. When he first came, he talked about Kentucky as a model. Now he has gained the perspective that North Dakota is a unique place and there are some things that you can import and other things that you have to do your own way."

For instance, she says, "I don't think we will ever be a school where all of our clinicians will be academicians. It just wouldn't work or be appropriate for this setting. I think he recognizes that, too."

What has not changed, she says, is his grasp of the initiative. "He does have a vision of how to move the school along to where he wants it to go. Sometimes the conflict is that not everyone shares that vision."

More than once Wilson has challenged search committees with that vision. "He has great faith that he can recruit almost anyone to this school, given the time and energy," says DeMers. "And he's done it."

She knows, because she chaired a search committee looking for a dean of academic affairs. The committee brought in three people, all of whom Wilson rejected. The search was restarted and Wilson refined even further the qualities he wanted in that person. "It was a long process," says DeMers. "It took three years, but we got the kind of person we wanted."

"I've learned," says Wilson, "that it often takes me two years to find the right person for a department. You think you've got to get this spot filled, and somebody comes along and they look like they're okay and the temptation is to say okay. But I won't do that. I say, 'Not good enough, keep looking for another year,' until I find someone of the quality and attitude that we need in North Dakota. Somebody who understands the way we teach."

Once, after rejecting the candidates proposed by a committee searching for a new chair of the department of pharmacology, Wilson began sifting through the applications of those who had not made the final cut. Among them he found that of Dr. Manuchair Ebadi, then of the University of Nebraska, who had 350 published papers and three large grants from the NIH.

"What about this guy?" he asked. The reply: "He's too good. He won't come here." Wilson ended up bringing Ebadi to Grand Forks and hiring him.

"He works seven days a week," says Wilson. "He's the most productive person on the whole campus. He knows how to move the agenda along and I give him a lot of credit for where we are. That's why he's now my associate dean for research. But we almost lost him because we didn't have a high enough opinion of ourselves."

Just as Tom Johnson learned, Wilson knows that recruiting top talent to North Dakota is a challenge.

"People just think its too damn cold to ever live here," he smiles. "I tell friends, number one, it's no place for wimps. Number two, I like the winter here better than I did in Kentucky. Winter is terribly cold, but you don't stay bundled up all the time. I go pheasant hunting out to western North Dakota in the fall. We go to the hockey games in the winter and we get out and do all the winter things. The days are usually sunny and it's beautiful outside — snow-covered, bright and shiny. Here, you learn to embrace winter."

Chapter 10

CHAPTER TEN

Trump Cards and Second Opinions

To ask a doctor today for an opinion on the future of medicine is to invite either an unfettered oratory on the marvels of modern science or an impassioned sermon on the dangers of not seeing the forest because the trees keep getting in the way.

Usually, it's a little of both. Of course, the great forest that contains within its boundaries all the promises of medical science was once only dreamed of territory, just as the Great Northern Plains once were unknown and a subject of conjecture. As the Twentieth century unfolded, medicine and North Dakota more or less grew up at the same time and now it seems undeniable that the future of one is entwined with that of the other.

The hearty pioneers who endured daily privations to raise family and preserve community in North Dakota were savvy survivors who prized their health. They may not have known much about the emerging science of medicine, but they did know that to keep surviving they needed not necessarily medicine, but medical people to help them. Just as no one else was going to plant their crops for them or raise their cattle and feed their families, they knew they literally had to cultivate and harvest their own doctors.

What is evident now about the days when Melvin Brannon opened the School of Medicine at the University of North Dakota is that the future of medicine in 1905 was not microbiology or biochemistry or sand filters or vaccinations or boiling water and a clean scalpel. It was not

Previous page:

Doctor moms and their daughters
In the fall of 2004, three women grads of the UND medical school had daughters enrolled in the school at the same time. From left are Jessica Miller and her mother Brenda Miller, M.D., '95; Jill Lindelow and her mother, Jan Bury, M.D., '90; Michelle McCann and her mother LaVaun McCann, '87.

the forest at all, but the individual saplings that needed nurturing. The future of medicine in 1905 North Dakota, quite simply, was people.

Can the same be said today, a century later?

Listen to what an old country doctor out in the small western prairie town of Williston, North Dakota, has to say about that. For decades, Dr. Dean Strinden, class of 1948, was a well-known figure in Williston, a man who headed the school board in addition to practicing medicine. He also is a doctor whose involvement in medical politics played a vital role in winning support for a four-year school of medicine in North Dakota. Retired now, and enjoying life, he speaks with a hint of mischief in his eyes.

"One of the things we hear frequently, because of the enormous changes that have taken place in medicine," he says, "is that the golden age of medicine is over."

He is right. Almost since the days of Dr. Henry Wheeler, someone or other has been decrying the end of medicine's good old days.

"I remember when I was in pre-med, just out of the Army after World War II. I had some allergy and I saw one of the older doctors here in town. He was a wonderful old doctor who looked like a man who should be a doctor. He asked me what I was going into and I said pre-med. He put his feet up on his desk and leaned back and he said, 'You know, the golden age of medicine has passed.'"

He pauses for dramatic effect.

"This was back in 1950," says Strinden, "before polio vaccine, before heart transplants, before you put new hips in people and transplanted a kidney. There hasn't been a single branch of medicine that hasn't seen enormous changes for the better since then."

There is little doubt, he says, that the science of medicine, as always, is changing for the better. The trouble, he says, is that it takes more than a scientist to dispense it, no matter how golden the age.

"The human being hasn't changed any in centuries," says Strinden. "We still have the same body we had thousands of years ago. The needs of people haven't changed. My point: You can't substitute the art of medicine with the science of medicine. They have to go together. You have to have a feeling for people. They aren't test tubes and they aren't machines; they are human beings. We have gained enormously by all the changes in science, but in so doing, we have lost some of the humanity, which goes with being a good, rounded physician. I would remind you that before a surgeon was a surgeon, he was a doctor. Being the doctor should always come first."

That prescription certainly fits the symptoms as described by more than a few of his colleagues and classmates.

Rural Medicine

Sometimes I think that every general internist should spend some time in a rural community because there you learn to be a lot more self-reliant trying to work through the problems rather than immediately getting a consultation. I see sometimes in the bigger system that people do a lot more triage and don't want to spend the time solving the problem. One of the other nice things about the rural practice is that you are the expert and you get to do everything. You go as far as you can and then refer them on. That is the neat part of being in a rural practice. There is a lot of camaraderie in that you know everybody in the clinic. You know them well and you know their patients well.

Rhonda Ketterling, M.D., class of 1979, is an administrator at MeritCare Health System in Fargo. She practiced for several years at the Johnson Clinic in Rugby.

"Doctors are losing a little bit of their touch with patients.
It is patient and machine, instead of patient and doctor."
–Dr. Edward Hagan

"We are not as independent a group of critters as we were at one
time. Our practice is shaped every day by administrators, politicians,
and by those who hold the purse strings."
–Dr. Al Samuelson

"I think so many of our young doctors think they work for
the insurance company rather than for the care of people."
–Dr. Clay Klakeg

"Sometimes I will present a particularly bothersome case and
students immediately talk about fancy X-rays and labs. I say, 'Have
you examined the patient? Have you looked at the patient?'"
–Dr. John Graham

Brothers in medicine
Drs. Kevin and Kelly Longie of
Tioga, N.D., shown here as
students studying a slide
containing cancer cells, were
the first set of twins to graduate
from the School of Medicine
and Health Sciences INMED
program. They received twin
degrees in 2005.

Symptoms, of course, imply a disease or a condition requiring
medical attention. But too often, it is the disease that gets the
attention, not the patient.

"Patients are no longer 'Mrs. Jones,'" laments Dean David
Wilson. "They are 'the appendectomy in 504.' We put ourselves at

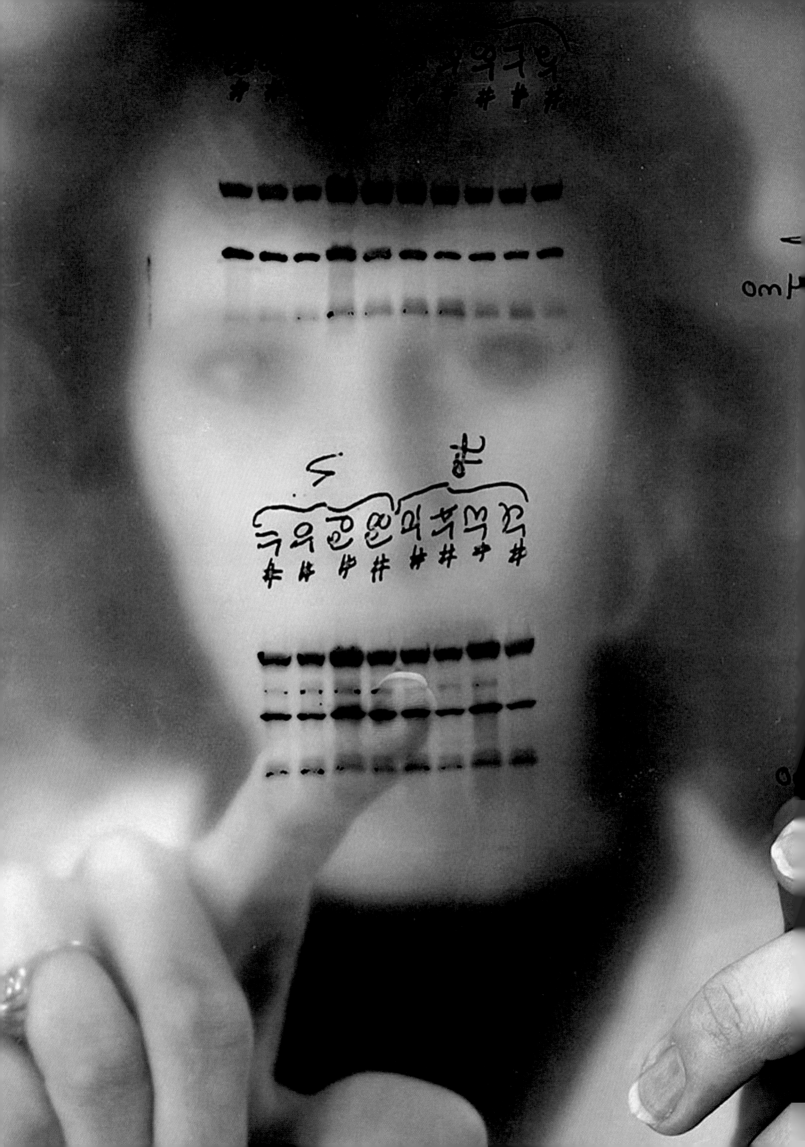

Mysteries of DNA
Holly Brown-Borg, Ph.D., an associate professor in the department of pharmacology, physiology and therapeutics examines a western blot of proteins.

great risk if we don't put our patients first, and if we don't sacrifice our own comfort for the good of others."

Fortunately, in a sparsely populated state where individuality is prized and young people often are raised with a sense of duty and sacrifice, Wilson's ideas have not been a tough sell. And as more and more doctors trained in North Dakota emerge into the world beyond the Red River of the North, more and more outsiders are impressed with their grasp of what is important.

"Invariably," says Wilson, "I hear back from Michigan or Iowa or Johns Hopkins: 'Your students are very well educated ... hardworking ... compassionate ... please send us more.' My job is to get them to come back to North Dakota."

That used to be a lot harder because so much of medical-student training took place out of state. By offering its own degrees and its own residency programs, however, the School of Medicine has found a reliable way of channeling local talent back into the state's healthcare system. Those graduates who leave the state for residencies and training not provided by the school may still decide to settle elsewhere. But the same sense of sacrifice that made them want to become good doctors in the first place often impels them to come home.

"If we are going to have a stable medical staff in North Dakota, we are going to have to train our own people who are accustomed to living here and who enjoy living here," says Strinden. "With their roots in the ground, they are going to stay. To me, those are the most compelling reasons to spend the money needed to support the school."

In one hundred years, those compelling reasons have not changed. But a whole panoply of additional reasons have made themselves known — perhaps equally pressing rationales for a medical school that have become increasingly apparent as society becomes more sophisticated and more disconnected from its simple past. They put the concept of "the future of medicine in North Dakota" in a light that was not available a century ago.

For instance, although in urban areas families with disabled children have access to support networks and social programs to gain emotional as well as medical help, in rural areas, families are often too isolated to gain information and comfort from others with similar problems.

While there is federal money available to help local communities create programs to solve such issues, the skills, contacts and practical understanding to penetrate the daunting government bureaucracy are often underdeveloped in small towns. Until recently, for example,

Why I Became a Doctor

My father was a physician. He had come from Canada and was practicing family medicine and OB in Devils Lake. He was always sort of a hero to me. In fact, my nickname was placed on me when I was about six by a janitor. He called me Little Doc. I guess I always tried to imitate my father. Sometimes when you live that closely with a professional you realize that is what you want to do. I would go to the hospital and go to the office and was always kind of tickled when he would discuss some things with me.

John Graham, M.D., class of 1952.

most ambulances in rural North Dakota — often operated by small clinics or volunteer fire companies — had no external defibrillators on board for use in the event of cardiac arrest, even though federal monies were available for such equipment.

A century ago, the idea simply was to get doctors — humanistic or otherwise — to settle in the scores of tiny rural towns across the state. That need still exists in many small towns, but less tangible shortages and gaps in healthcare in those remote areas often transcend what one or two or even a handful of doctors can do. In fact, the biggest concern in many places about the future of modern healthcare is not rising costs, hard-hearted insurance companies or unfeeling doctors. Rather, it is a fear that, for them, there is no healthcare future.

Such problems became clear to Wilson when he took over as dean. In his early deanship, he simultaneously headed the medical school's Center for Rural Health while he searched for the right person to run it. In terms of delivering compassionate doctors to rural towns, Wilson enthusiastically supported the ROME program — Rural Opportunities in Medical Education — aimed at producing doctors trained specifically for practicing general medicine in small towns. Medical students enrolled in the ROME program spend much of their clinical training in the third year working through various specialties in a single rural setting, such as at facilities in Hettinger, Jamestown, Williston or Devils Lake.

Yet Wilson found vexing the vacuum of responsibility for tending to the other less visible healthcare needs of rural communities. He realized he needed to extend the compassionate reach of the medical school itself into those areas of North Dakota where healthcare needs go beyond, simply getting a doctor to move there.

To tackle such problems, he knew, required the gathering of information and data so that sensible strategies were developed, clear channels of responsibility established and available funding collected and efficiently used. He perceived it important enough that he made rural health one of three key areas of research on which he wanted the school to focus. Two of those areas have been discussed in earlier chapters — educational research that has led to the ongoing development of a learning-based curriculum, and focused scientific research such as Dr. Ebadi's work in neurodegenerative diseases.

"I knew we could not be all things to all people," says Wilson, "and that we needed to focus our limited resources for research. But we're the most rural state in the country to have a medical school and we ought to be one of the nation's leaders in rural health."

To make that happen, he spent four years trying to convince Mary Wakefield to come back to North Dakota from the fast-lane world of Washington politics. Wakefield grew up in Devils Lake and graduated from the University of Mary's School of Nursing. She eventually earned a Ph.D. in nursing and was a tenured professor at UND's College of Nursing when Senator Quentin Burdick offered her a job as his legislative assistant for health. She went East in the late Eighties and eventually became Burdick's chief of staff. After Sen. Kent Conrad succeeded Burdick, Wakefield joined his staff and eventually led it as well. She then taught at George Mason University in Virginia and ran its Center for Health Policy Research and Ethics for six years.

At one point, during Wilson's recruiting efforts, she admits she asked herself, "Why am I doing this in the D.C. area when I'm from North Dakota? Gosh I could do a lot of the same things back there."

And so she has. Dr. Wakefield, now an associate dean, and director of the Center for Rural Health, has transformed the once tiny office with its eight staffers into a whirl of thirty-two analysts, policymakers and field workers. Her staff regularly visits small towns across the state, meeting with rural hospital and nursing home administrators, nurses, community leaders and local citizens. The hosts learn what the medical school offers in the way of services and the Center finds out what are the current and emerging rural health problems.

"This medical school is about producing doctors for North Dakota," says Wakefield, "but it is also about helping improve the quality of healthcare services, of getting access to healthcare, of looking at insurance issues for patients. It's connecting families to other families that have disabled children. We work at the community level around very specific issues — like kids with disabilities — all the way through to working on health care finance issues through the Medicare program."

Drawing from her developing community contacts, Wakefield has identified four areas of need where her office, through research and the use of her prolific connections in Washington, has been able to make a difference.

Performing basic health services research. Wakefield's staff regularly collects and analyzes a variety of health-related statistics in rural areas. They found in a survey of rural emergency room usage, for example, that a large percentage of users did not have classic emergency needs. Many used the emergency room for oral health problems, suggesting a previously unidentified need for dental

Mary Wakefield

An associate dean and the director of the Center for Rural Health, Wakefield has transformed the once tiny office with its eight staffers into a whirl of thirty-two analysts, policymakers and field workers.

services in some areas. Her staff also found a large number of people with worker's compensation claims directed to an emergency room by an employer rather than to a local clinic. The difference in costs for such treatment often is passed on to taxpayers.

Community service program development. The problem of the defibrillators was quickly solved when Wakefield's office secured federal funding to provide two hundred sets of paddles to ambulances in rural North Dakota. The Center identifies such needs by performing ongoing community-health assessments. It found that many patients in Langdon, for example, drove all the way to Grand Forks for medical services rather than use the local hospital. That was hurting the local hospital and destabilizing the infrastructure of medical care in the area. In such cases, Wakefield's staff conducts focus groups to identify the real needs of residents and to help community leaders find solutions.

Policy analysis. Recognizing that there often are gaps between state and federal public-health policies, Wakefield's office applies its rural research findings to informing local and congressional politicians about the real needs of the area. Her office has contracted with the state to designate health-profession shortage areas and medically underserved areas in North Dakota. As a result, two-thirds of the state was officially designated as a health-profession shortage area — information passed on to congressional representatives.

Education. Wakefield's department offers outreach training to rural health care providers on how to "work the system" more efficiently. For example, providers learn to write better grants to ensure they take advantage of all funding available.

"I bring knowledge of where money is and where to find the legislative support," she says. "Too many academic researchers are clueless about the value of research, beyond getting it published in an academic journal. That's just the beginning for us. We communicate directly with our congressional delegation."

One of her key missions is improving access to healthcare for rural communities. That means more than finding them a doctor. "They require so much more than that," she says. "If you don't have a community that knows how to retain that provider, good luck. If you can't help that community access National Health Service Corps providers, good luck. We do some of the matching. We track where the community needs are and we advertise with our medical residents and let them know where the needs are."

Her office often helps the thinly staffed state health department

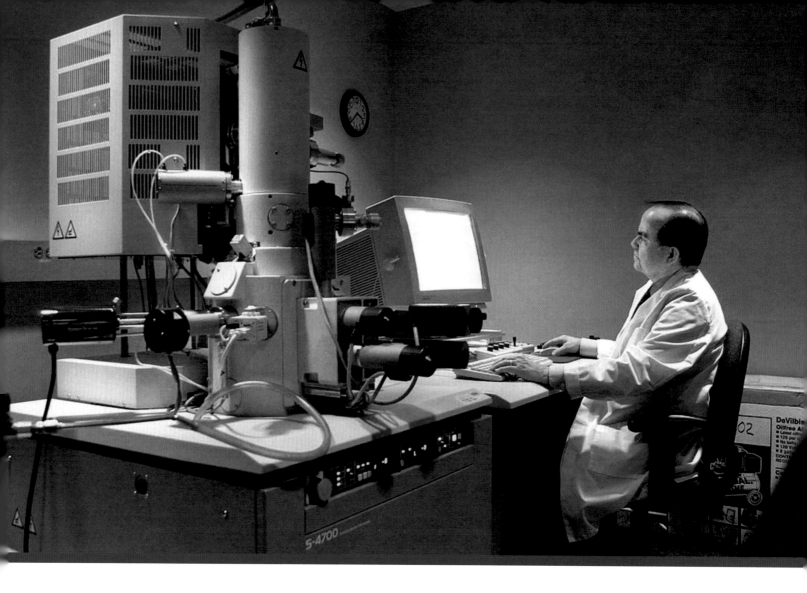

write grants and it even performs such number crunching tasks as analyzing all ambulance claims for North Dakota in order to compile a rich database on who pays for what.

"Without this office, you'd ask where these services would come from?" says Wakefield. "I can't think of another place that could get those dollars. There's just not another entity to do it. The thing is, we're doing it in an objective way. We're not a special-interest group. We're not the Medical Association. That gives us a standing when we go out and talk.

Wakefield's office has done so well helping local communities that it was asked by the U.S. Department of Health and Human Services to be a co-sponsor of its Rural Assistance Center. This is a Web site (www.raconline.org) funded out of the HHS Office of Rural Health Policy that serves as what HHS calls an "information portal" for rural communities and others that have problems attaining healthcare. Wakefield's office will help, for instance, a healthcare provider in Alabama cut through the red tape to hook up with the correct federal agency to get funding for a rural community.

"It's brought tremendous visibility to UND and North Dakota and this medical school," says Wakefield.

The Center for Rural Health also is the home for the National Resource Center on Native American Aging — a collaboration with

Not your father's microscope
Chair of the department of anatomy and cell biology, Ed Carlson, Ph.D., works at one of the medical school's scanning electron microscopes.

After the hunt
Dean H. David Wilson, right, and John Vennes, medical school colleagues and frequent hunting partners display the fruits of their turkey hunt in a recent outing in the Badlands of western North Dakota.

UND's Office of American Indian Student Services.

"We're the only repository of information on Native American elder healthcare needs in the country," says Wakefield. "It's never been quantified. We've got data now on over 130 tribes across the United States to help them develop an infrastructure to deal with their problems."

Thus far, she has been able to do all of that and finance ninety-three percent of her own office operations with grants and outside funding.

"We're bringing in money like crazy," Wakefield says, "to try to maintain and strengthen the rural healthcare infrastructure wherever and whenever we can."

The importance of that infrastructure which benefits from the medical school's aggressive support and the initiative of regional healthcare systems cannot be understated.

"We are in a region that is growing older and less populated," notes Terry Hoff, president of Trinity Health Care System. "But growing up as a farm boy in Parshall, I know how critical access to healthcare is to the rural areas. We had a physician from Mohall who called us up and said, 'Your helicopter saved my father's life.' I talked to our family practice physician in New Town and she told the story about folks that were in the casino and one of them wasn't feeling well. As they were driving out of town, they saw our clinic sign. They came in to get checked out and the person was having a heart attack, so they quite literally saved that person's life. If rural healthcare isn't there and we don't as a center support that rural system, a lot of people are not going to have the quality of life and health they should."

When David Wilson became dean ten years ago, one of the nagging concerns in the back of his mind was a worry that every dean since Harley French has had to deal with: Would the state legislature one day withdraw its support for the School of Medicine? Would politicians finally decide it was just too expensive to have a medical school in North Dakota?

Certainly, the bulk of the political opposition to the medical school had long since died down by 1995. Nevertheless, it seemed as if there always was one legislator or another who was elected on a budget-slashing platform and immediately boasted he would save taxpayers a lot of money by shutting down the medical school. Time and again, school officials jumped through hoops held high by such crusaders, trying to justify its existence once again.

If it seems ludicrous that such a possibility still existed so recently, consider that when Charles Kupchella was hired as president of UND four years later in 1999, he, too, heard the constant threats.

"You still had people talking about, 'We need to get rid of that medical school,'" Kupchella recalls. "There was a new member of the State Board of Higher Education. He was kind of a maverick. He had not even been on board when he was quoted as saying that this was something he wanted to do. Quickly he came to see what everyone else sees: When you can point out that half of the doctors in the state graduated from your medical school, then you have to ask, 'Would we have that many if it weren't for the School of Medicine?'"

As for Wilson, he says he took the job "As a leap of faith. You never know if you're making a big mistake." When he arrived, to make matters worse, then President Ken Baker was not getting along well with the legislature. "He was a bright guy," says Wilson, "but in his first dealings with the legislature, he did not do well."

Wilson stepped carefully into the North Dakota political arena, always sure to wear conservative suits and ties to budget hearings, and to stress his farm-boy heritage in Illinois. He might look like a doctor, but he made sure legislators knew he had once shoveled grain and manure and raised cattle like many of them, and now hunted pheasants and turkeys each fall with Dr. Vennes.

But even though Wilson's demeanor has seemed to resonate with legislators during his tenure, the larger question remains. When can

Tending to tummy
Alyssa Hoverson, a student when this photo was taken, was a ROME student, training for the practice of medicine in rural areas. Hoverson earned her medical degree in May 2005.

the School of Medicine stop looking over its shoulder, a la baseball legend Satchell Paige, in fear something might be gaining on it?

"I don't think the opposition to the medical school is anything like it was," says Kupchella. "I think people credit the medical school with giving the state the best healthcare available anywhere in the United States."

Former State Senator Judy DeMers concurs.

"I think the medical school is here for good," she says. "The people who took it as a real issue are long gone. They never won any of those battles. The economic impact on the state has been proven. Now it is more or less taken for granted in the legislature that we're going to support the school."

That does not mean there will not be the occasional political maverick, but it probably means empty cans won't make as loud a noise as they used to.

"The legislature will always be somewhat skeptical about the medical school simply because we gobble up a lot of tax dollars," says Bismarck psychiatrist Al Samuelson. "But we have never had any trouble justifying that to the taxpayers in the end. All citizens in the state want their kids to be doctors. There is always that dream: their child is going to become a doctor and they want opportunity for her or him to do that. That is as important as having medical care available to them."

In fact, the tiny town of Turtle Lake, where Samuelson grew up, has produced four UND-trained doctors, all of them still practicing in North Dakota. "I believe the only reason I am a physician is that the UND medical school was there," says Samuelson.

At any alumni gathering, that testimony is heard again and again.

"I was fortunate to be accepted into medical school," says Dean Strinden, "because I was not necessarily a good student. I worked hard, but I wasn't the brightest light on the hill, as they say. Had I not gotten into school here, I'm sure I never would have gotten into medicine. I owe a lot to the School of Medicine."

But what if the unthinkable were to happen?

"If we didn't have the medical school," says Dr. Casey Ryan, CEO of Altru Health Systems, "there would be a ripple effect as it relates to the recruiting and placement of physicians in the state of North Dakota. It would have a negative impact on our ability to recruit other physicians in the state. I think it would be bad news for North Dakotans and I'm always disappointed when you hear people try to break it down into a dollars and cents issue in the state legislature."

It was not until 1914, nine years after its founding, that the School of Medicine at the University of North Dakota graduated its first female student. She was Solveig Sigrid Gislason, who went on to practice in Edina, Minnesota.

Gislason was the only female in her class, a common situation for many years for the few female medical students who matriculated through the school. Today, more women than ever are entering medicine. At UND, half of the students admitted as freshman are women.

Until very recently one had to believe that a female student possessed special qualities to be able to make it through a male-dominated faculty and student body, as well as in a profession in which women doctors often were looked down upon by their male counterparts.

Here are glimpses from female UND med students of three different eras showing the hard-earned but relentless progress women have made in staking an equal claim to the chance to become a doctor.

Thank You, Roy Bach

I was born on a farm in North Dakota in 1916. I rode horseback ten miles a day to high school. It was kind of cold sometimes. I missed one day when my folks wouldn't let me go because there was a bad storm.

My mother didn't approve of my going out into the world alone. She thought I was too young. I went to the Benson County Agricultural and Training School. The boys mostly learned agriculture and the girls learned home economics. In addition to that, you could take a few additional subjects called a college-preparatory course.

I did both and then got a scholarship to Concordia College in Moorhead the first year. The scholarship amount was based on your grades the first semester and I got all A's, so I got a $150 scholarship, which was a lot of money in those days. That was only for that year, though, and we didn't have any money to pay for tuition the next year. It was cheaper to go to the North Dakota University, so I did.

I had always liked science. In high school I helped out the science teacher, Roy Bach, and he and his wife were friends of mine. After my sophomore year, I talked to him with the idea that I was probably going to teach or do research as lots of women did in those days if they weren't secretaries or clerks. He said, "Why don't you go into medicine?" Well, I hadn't really given that any thought because I had very little connections with a doctor.

Our hometown doctor, whom I only saw when I got a smallpox vaccination, was stone deaf and I didn't know any others. You know, we didn't go to the doctor much in those days. There had never been any doctors anywhere in our family. My mother always thought I could do better, I could never do anything well enough for her. I was the valedictorian in my high school class but she never praised me very much. That wasn't her nature. My parents were Norwegian and they didn't go in much for that sort of stuff. My dad thought it was all right for me to become a doctor, but neither of them ever got very excited about it.

I must credit my high school biology teacher with my going into medicine. He had wanted to go into medicine himself and had taken some pre-med courses, but then the depression came along and he had to go out and teach for a living. That is how Roy Bach became a high-school science teacher and I guess I was kind of his alter ego.

I started by washing test tubes at the medical school in Science Hall. I was sort of under the tutelage of Dr. Saiki. He thought maybe I could do something better than wash test tubes, so he had me making media for test tubes and so on and so forth. Eventually, I worked in his department and learned how to cut slides. At that time, the University of North Dakota was a state laboratory for pathology, since many of the hospitals didn't have much of a pathology lab, so they would send in their specimens. After I had worked with Dr. Saiki for a while I would describe the specimen and would cut sections and make slides. I continued to do that during medical school.

After I finished medical school, I called my mother — they were still living on the farm. I wasn't home yet, but it was near springtime. She told me the newspaper editor in our town had asked her if he could interview me and write a story about me. I think there were only three of us from high school who went to college as most of them went to work on the farm. She said she couldn't see much point in that, because I didn't even have a job yet, so he never did come out.

Eva Gilbertson, M.D., graduated from the School of Medicine in 1939, the only woman in her class. She earned her medical degree at Temple University in Philadelphia, and then completed a radiology residency at the Mayo Clinic. She eventually settled in Seattle, Washington, where she became the first woman in the state to have a private radiology practice.

Thank You, Robert Plum

There was a female pharmacist in Hettinger where I grew up, and I thought that was something in medicine that women could do. This was back in the late sixties when I was in high school and there weren't a lot of women in medicine. But I had a very progressive guidance counselor, Robert Plum, who took me aside one day and told me there was no reason I couldn't be a doctor. I started to think about a career in medicine then.

Like most physicians, I have a competitive side. In order to maintain my grades and to make sure that I would perform well in class, I spent a lot of my time in medical school studying. Sometimes I look back and wonder if I should have had more fun and spent less time with my nose in the books. I don't regret it, though. I think there was a different pressure in those days for women in medical school. (I want to beat that drum to death). There were eleven women in my class, which was actually quite a few as the year before there were only four. On my first day of medical school, one of my male colleagues walked up to me

and said, 'You know, you are taking a spot from a man who should be here!' At that time, I decided I would grind him into the dirt, academically. And so I did.

Rhonda Ketterling, M.D., class of 1979, worked for years at the Johnson Clinic in Rugby. She is currently an administrator at MeritCare Health System in Fargo.

Thank You, Solveig, Eva and Rhonda

I was a physical therapist. There were times I didn't feel I had control over situations, that I could make decisions. I felt I was hampered by not having the authority. I thought originally about medical school, but I had four kids. Then a little later on, I looked at actual role models, like Jan Bury (class of 1990). She has six kids. I thought, if she could do it, I could do it.

I don't recall any negative attitudes in my training. Even when I started working out in my preceptorship. But I was an older student and when you get to a certain age you just don't tolerate anything. I occasionally run into elderly patients who do not quite understand I could be a doctor. One old gentleman said to me, "Dr. Miller, you sure are a good nurse." How could you get upset about something like that? Some of those women who were students in the early years here really paved the way. Some of them had a hard time of it, but my way was smoother because of them. My practice has changed to taking care mostly of women and children. I like to focus on women's issues and delivering babies. If a man comes into the office, I say to him, "Who's your wife and why did she make you come?"

Brenda Miller, M.D., class of 1995, practices in Bismarck. She is one of three female doctors in North Dakota, all UND medical school alums who have daughters enrolled in the School of Medicine. (see photo at the beginning of the chapter) Today such mother-daughter succession is a rarity — but a welcome rarity, and given the changes of recent years, it might soon become commonplace.

Underlying these and similar remarks by supporters of the medical school is a caveat belted out in a Sixties-era song. It's about the wisdom of tearing down Paradise and putting up a parking lot. In the words of Joni Mitchell: You don't know what you've got till it's gone.

"We may have plenty of physicians right now, at least in the major centers of the state," says Terry Brosseau, former CEO and president of MedCenter One in Bismarck. "But, if you shut down the residency programs or the medical school, we can rapidly go back in a eight- or ten-year cycle to where we were before the medical school expanded. That is the lesson we have to preach. North Dakota is going to have to take care of itself."

To do that, of course, there have to be North Dakotans around to preach to. One oft-repeated rationale for the medical school is that it gives young people not only a chance to become a doctor, but a reason to see their home state as a place worth staying in to raise a family.

"We talk about maintaining our youth here and that's a critical point," says Dr. Roger Gilbertson, CEO of Fargo's MeritCare. "Even though people go off to residencies to other parts of the country, we get our fair share who return here. Yes, one of the challenges of North Dakota is trying to be self-sufficient. We have our own mill and elevator because we're pretty paranoid about Minneapolis. The nature of growth and development here is that we can't rely on somebody else to do what's best for North Dakota. The medical school has had a big role in developing the state's economy and its quality of life. It's a tremendous resource to the state and a much greater resource than most people even understand."

Fortunately, among those in agreement is North Dakota's governor, John Hoeven.

"People see that it takes resources to support the medical school, but they also see it has a positive economic impact," he says, "and we work very hard to tie it closely with our economic development efforts. The UND medical school fits in that plan and does so very directly, for example, with its deep-brain tissue research efforts and other new research programs the school is pursuing. It follows our Centers of Excellence concept, where the university interfaces with the private sector not only to teach students but to create jobs, to do research and development and to foster entrepreneurship; in the commercialization of technologies and products and services. The medical school is a big part of our economic development efforts."

Such development, of course, goes beyond providing jobs and career opportunities.

"Large corporate organizations do not move their business to a state that does not have adequate health facilities or adequate college opportunities for the kids the families are bringing into the state," says Terry Brosseau. "If North Dakota doesn't maintain those things, we will have no opportunity for future economic development."

Which is why UND President Kupchella says confidently, "This school of medicine is one of the best trump cards we have here in terms of economic development. It's absolutely a plus."

That fact, says Governor Hoeven, is not lost on the majority of North Dakotans. "I think there's a real perception throughout the state that we do have more doctors because of the medical school. And there's good support in the legislature for it because people see it fills vital medical and economic needs for the state."

If such ringing endorsements calm the fears about the future of the medical school, there are still nagging doubts about the future of medicine itself. It's not the scientific advances that worry doctors, but the way in which modern bureaucracies hampered their practice.

"One of biggest things that has happened in medicine in forty years," says Roger Gilbertson, "is going from an autonomous, independent kind of operation in medicine — where a doctor was

Medical school for the public
Ken Ruit, Ph.D., associate professor of anatomy and cell biology, describes the functions of the brain and spinal cord to some of the participants of the first "medical school for the public" lecture series, held in December 2002.

Photo courtesy of Jackie Lorentz/Grand Forks Herald

After the flood

The great flood of Spring, 1997 destroyed several buildings in Grand Forks and forced the evacuation of the city. It also did hundreds of thousands of dollars in damage to the nearby medical school. Graduation that year was held in Fargo. However, alumni donated $425,000 and the Robert Wood Johnson Foundation added another $300,000 to get the school back in operation. Homes in the Lincoln Drive area (shown here) were evacuated hours before the dikes gave way on April 18, 1997, flooding the homes with about eight feet of water.

more or less an island — to a much more complicated profession requiring a great deal of interdependency among the players. That's part of the challenge to many doctors who are trained to be independent, that coordination of care."

Yet while many doctors rail at such changes, the profession has only itself to blame, says Bismarck's Dr. Keith Foster.

"The unfortunate thing is that the physicians let the fox in the chicken coop," he says. "They said, 'Just let me practice medicine and you administrators take care of the other end.' Unfortunately, they have, and the doctors have lost control."

It is not a matter of pride over the loss of personal control, says Foster, but a larger more disturbing loss of professional autonomy.

"I saw a lady yesterday," he says, "who had a baby ten weeks ago and the baby isn't doing well. She wants to go down to the Children's Hospital in Minneapolis. The third-party payer won't let her go, and that is tragic. She is going to go anyway and spend her own money and that isn't right. Anytime somebody asks for a second opinion and you don't give it to them, you are a fool."

Terry Brosseau, past chair of the Medical Center Advisory Council, admits the current healthcare system has made the practice of medicine less desirable than it should be.

"The players in the whole insurance industry — large-employer groups and government have not realized how difficult and inefficient they have made it for physicians to practice in this day and age," he says. "I think what physicians are actually going to have to do, is become more active in changing the process of the system. Until they step out and demand that the relationship between the patient and the physician become primary again and reduce the bureaucracy and paperwork (which, incidentally, has not saved any money in my opinion but has only created additional costs) the practice of medicine on the part of the physician is going to be diminished."

Brosseau's cousin, Dr. Jim Brosseau, the chair of the medical school's Department of Community Medicine, sees first-hand those difficulties. Dr. Brosseau works with providers in various locales across the state to set up chronic disease management programs. "We take a two-pronged approach. We stress primary prevention — promoting everyday good health and healthy lifestyles — and secondary prevention with chronic-disease management." As an example, Brousseau's office recently created a statewide North Dakota Tobacco Quitline (866-388-7848) to advise smokers on how to stop.

What could be troublesome about that? "Most prevention is not covered by reimbursement," Brosseau says. "So, there's little attention paid to it. Yet, there's got to be some value placed on preventing disease. We need more efficient management of chronic diseases."

For medical students, concerns about the future of medicine are often a worrisome distraction, especially since many young doctors come out of medical school with the added pressure of up to $100,000 in student loans to repay.

"I encourage all the students I work with not to be discouraged by talk of how things are going for the future," says Dr. Richard Larson. "A lot of people are saying the golden age of medicine is over and that is not true. The amount of medical knowledge we have gained in the past ten years is astounding. We are learning so much and so fast. I tell all the students not to listen to the negatives. Medicine is a great field and I would choose it again in a heartbeat."

No matter what the future holds for medicine, says Dr. Phil Dahl of Bismarck, "There will always be a place for a good, honest physician. I think that medicine is still a great profession. I have had to spend time apologizing for the practice of medicine to previous patients and friends, and that is too bad, but somehow or another we should keep in mind that medicine is still not all scientific. There is still an art of learning to know not just the patient, but his background, his living status, what his family was like in the past, his home life, and so on. We physicians must think about treating that patient in the way we, ourselves would like to be treated. I have found out, as have many of my colleagues, that the best way to learn what it is like to be sick, is to get sick ourselves. We get a different attitude."

Graduate student research

Jon Gaffaney, a former student in the lab of Roxanne Vaughan, Ph.D., professor of biochemistry and molecular biology, works with a Brandel tissue harvester to study how cocaine, amphetamine and dopamine interact with the dopamine transporter. Studying the protein may lead to possible effective drug therapy. Jon is currently a post-doctoral research associate at the University of Wisconsin.

APPENDIX I: SOURCES

The sources of information for this centennial history of the School of Medicine and Health Sciences include the documents, articles, books and letters listed below. Much of the book's content is based on the recollections of individuals interviewed by John W. Vennes, Ph.D., and Patrick A. McGuire over a period of five years.

In addition, the authors owe a debt to several individuals without whose untiring efforts this project would not have been possible. Thanks to LaVonne Johnson, Teresa Evanson, Lori Sannes, Pamela Knudson, Victoria Swift, Joel Johnson, M.D., Don Larson, Judy DeMers, Wanda Weber and Chuck Kimmerle.

Documents, Articles, Books & Letters

"Heroic Medicine." Free Software Foundation, Inc. 59 Temple Place, Suite 330, Boston, MA 02111-1307. <http://en.wikipedia.org/wiki/Heroic_medicine>.

"Homeopathy." Free Software Foundation, Inc. 59 Temple Place, Suite 330, Boston, MA 02111-1307. <http://en.wikipedia.org/wiki/Alternative_medicine>.

"The Battle of Big Mound." American Battlefield Protection Program, National Park Service, 1201 Eye Street, NW, Washington, DC. <http://www.cr.nps.gov/hps/abpp/battles/nd001.htm> .<http://www.cr.nps.gov/hps/abpp/index.htm 1983>.

Alumni Review, The University of North Dakota, "Saiki remains Active in Medical School."

Alumni Review, The University of North Dakota, Vol. XXII, June 1947 "'47 Commencement to Honor Brannon."

Boelkins, James. "History of Pharmacology at the University of North Dakota," Published on the occasion of the centennial of the University of North Dakota, 1983.

Bowman, Robert C., M.D. "Flexner's Impact on American Medicine," University of North Carolina Medical Center. <http://www.unmc.edu/Community/ruralmeded/flexner.htm>.

Brannon, Melvin A. "Old Time Heroes of the University of North Dakota." University of North Dakota Quarterly Journal 13.4 (July 1923).

Bridston, Joseph B. "North Dakota's Medical Center Program." Booklet based on presentation of Sen. Bridston to Medical Center Advisory Committee 16 June 1951.

Briggs, Bruce T., Moorhead State University, presentation on North Dakota health care.

Burns, Paul D. "History of Obstetrics and Gynecology." Published on the occasion of the centennial of the University of North Dakota, 1983.

Clifford, Tom, Robert Eelkema, M.D., and Patrick A. McGuire. Good Medicine: How wit and guile saved the School of Medicine at the University of North Dakota. CliffElk Press, Grand Forks, North Dakota, 2003.

Cornatzer, W.E. PhD, M.D.. "History of Biochemistry Department, 1951-1982." Published on the occasion of the centennial of the University of North Dakota, 1983.

Cristoferson, Lee A., M.D. "History of the Neuroscience Department." Published on the occasion of the centennial of the University of North Dakota, 1983.

Dunkley, Susan P. "History — Department of Pediatrics." Published on the occasion of the centennial of the University of North Dakota, 1983.

Ederstrom, H.S., PhD. and Stanley J. Brumleve, PhD. "A History of the Department of Physiology and Pharmacology, 1905-1977, and the Department of Physiology, 1977-1983." Published on the occasion of the centennial of the University of North Dakota, 1983.

Eelkema, Robert C., M.D., MPH. "History of the Department of Community Medicine, 1969 to 1983." Published on the occasion of the centennial of the University of North Dakota, 1983.

Ettl, Lorraine Roberts. "History of the Medical Library." Published on the occasion of the centennial of the University of North Dakota, 1983.

Flexner, Abraham. Medical Education in the United States and Canada: A Report to the Carnegie Foundation for the Advancement of Teaching. Boston: Merrymount Press, 1910.

Floyd, Barbara, University Archivist, University of Toledo. "From Quackery to Bacteriology: The Emergence of Modern Medicine in 19th Century America."
<http://www.cl.utoledo.edu/canaday/quackery/quack-index.html>.

French, H. E. "Remarks of Doctor H.E. French, Dean, School of Medicine,
at the Governor's Conference on Medical Care and Health Service in North Dakota, July 27, 1944."

French, H. E., M.D. "A Glance at the History of Public Health in North Dakota," Read before the North Dakota Public Health Association, Fargo, North Dakota, 10 May 1947.

French, Harley, M.D. "Medical Education in North Dakota." Lancet 1936

French, Harley, M.D. "North Dakota Medicine – A 70-year Span." Lancet January 1971

French, Harley, M.D. "The School of Medicine of the University of North Dakota," Lancet, Feb. 1932

Fry, Richard B. Letter to H.E. French. 5 April 1952.

Geiger, Louis G. University of the Northern Plains: A History of the University of North Dakota,1883-1958. Grand Forks:The University Of North Dakota Press, 1958.

Grassick, Dr. James. North Dakota Medicine, Sketches and Abstracts, 1925.

Hafermehl, Louis N. "The Birth, Life and Death of Science Hall on the Campus of the University of North Dakota." North Dakota History, Vol. 69, No. 1.

Harwood, T.H. Letter to A.D. McCannel. 5 November 1954.

Harwood, T.H. Letter to A.K. Saiki. 1 December 1954.

Harwood, Ted. Letter to Judy Harris. 4 February 1977.

Harwood, T. H., M.D. "MEMORANDUM TO PRESIDENT STARCHER FROM T.H. HARWOOD M.D. Re: Some generalizations about the Medical Center." 18 October 1954.

Harwood, T.H., "History of the University of North Dakota School of Medicine." Lancet May 1960.

Documents, Articles, Books & Letters

(continued)

Harwood, T.H. Letter to Wilbur F. Potter. 6 August 1970.

Harwood, T.H. Letter to Dr. W.F. Potter. 28 July 1948.7-28-48

Harwood, Theodore. Address at the Arthur K. Saiki Testimonial Dinner. 15 December 1954.

Huntington, George. Robber and Hero, the Story of the Northfield Bank Raid. St Paul: MHS Press, 1986.

James, Edwin C., M.D. Duane F. Pansegrau, M.D., and Joan Workman, BS. "Surgery." Published on the occasion of the centennial of the University of North Dakota, 1983.

Knight, K. "Mandan Indians." The Catholic Encyclopedia.
1910. Online Edition, Robert Appleton Company, 2003.

Lind, Am. "Occupational Therapy." Published on the occasion of the centennial of the University of North Dakota, 1983.

North Dakota Centennial Blue Book, 1889. Publication of the North Dakota Secretary of State.

O'Keefe, N.J., M.D. "History of Department of Radiology, UND School of Medicine." Published on the occasion of the centennial of the University of North Dakota, 1983.

Obituary of Arthur K. Saiki. Grand Forks Herald 19 September 1980.

Robinson, Elwyn B. History of North Dakota. Lincoln: University of Nebraska Press, 1966.

Saumur, Jean Holland. "Department of Pathology History." Published on the occasion of the centennial of the University of North Dakota, 1983.

Sayre, J.L. Letter to Harley French. 18 April 1945.
Schoenbach,Victor J., PhD., Associate Professor, Department of Epidemiology, School of Public Health, University of North Carolina at Chapel Hill.

<http://www.epidemiolog.net/evolving/HistoricalPerspective.pdf>. <www.epidemiolog.net>. 1999, 2002.

Schuetz, Barb and Reed T. Keller, M.D. "History of the Department of Internal Medicine." Published on the occasion of the centennial of the University of North Dakota, 1983.

Schuetz, Barb, Reed T. Keller, M.D., and William P.Newman, M.D. "History of the Department of Internal Medicine." Published on the occasion of the centennial of the University of North Dakota, 1983; revised, 2004.

Vennes, John, Ph.D. "Department of Microbiology and Immunology." Published on the occasion of the centennial of the University of North Dakota, 1983.

Vennes, John, Ph.D. Eulogy at funeral of Art Saiki. 23 September 1980.

Vennes, John, Ph.D. "Some Light on the Past." Power Point presentation 2004.

Vicker George. "History of Public Health." <http://www.unmc.edu/Community/ruralmeded/model/history_of_public_health.htm>.

Waldron, Edward E. From House Calls to HMOs: A History of Organized Medicine in North Dakota. The North Dakota Medical Association, 1986.

Wilson, Dr. H. D. "Address to Faculty, UND Faculty Lecture Series." 26 September 2000.

Woodason, Eleanor B. Letter to John Vennes. 6 May 2000.

Wubah, Daniel A. "The germ theory of diseases," 1998. <http://www.towson.edu/ wubah/medmicro/Germ_theory.htm>.

Zoller, Jo Ann. "Family Medicine." Published on the occasion of the centennial of the University of North Dakota, 1983.

Interviews: John Vennes

Antonenko, David, M.D.; Arusell, Robert, M.D.; Bakken, Lloyd, M.D.; Barcome, Donald, M.D.; Barger James, M.D.; Brousseau, Terry; Briggs, Bruce T., MS; Buckingham, William, M.D.; Carlson, Edward, PhD; Claymore, James; Chally, Cecil, M.D.; Clifford, Tom, J.D.; Cornatzer, Gene, M.D., PhD; Creech, Lila, M.D.; Dahl, Phil, M.D.; Davison, Dick, PhD; DeLorme, Gene, JD; DeMers, Judy, MS; Dunnigan, Ralph, M.D.; Ederstrom, Helge, PhD; Eelkema, Robert, M.D.; Eken, Randy, MS; Eylands, Jon V., M.D.; Fischer Robert, PhD; Foster, Keith, M.D.; Gilbertson, Roger, M.D.; Gilbertson,Eva, M.D.; Graham, John, M.D.; Hagan, Edward Jordan, M.D.; Halvorson, Larry, M.D.; Hankins, Robert, M.D.; Helenbolt, Kenneth, M.D.; Hinrichs, Mark, M.D.; Hoff, Terry; Holland, Jean, MS; Holmberg, Conrad, M.D.; Jensen, Clayton, M.D.; Johnson, George, M.D.; Johnson, Tom, M.D.; Jordheim, Robert, M.D.; Kenyon, Doug; Ketterling, Rhonda, M.D.; Klakeg, Clay, M.D.; Klevay Les, Ph.D., M.D.; Knull, Harvey, PhD; Larson, Don, MS; Larson, Richard, M.D.; Leigh, Jack, M.D.; Leigh, Richard, M.D.; Litten, Warner; Luger, Joseph, M.D.; Mahoney, Jim, M.D.; McIntyre, Donald, M.D.; Moran, Walt, M.D.; Nelson, Eileen, MS; Newman, William, M.D.; Nielson, Forrest, PhD; Nordlie, Robert, PhD; Olafson, Richard, M.D.; Pedersen, Lila, MS; Ryan, Casey, M.D.; Sailer, Gerry, M.D.; Samuelson, Al, M.D.; Skjei, Donald, M.D.; Slotnick, Hank, PhD; Sommerness, Martin D., M.D.; Sopher, Roger, M.D.; Strinden, Dean, M.D.; Strinden, Earl, MS; Swenson,Wayne, M.D.; Theige, David, M.D.; Tingelstad, Jon, M.D.; Tscheider, Dick; Vanderwalle, Gerald, JD; Varberg B., M.D.; Wasdahl,Wally, M.D.; Wessman Bud, J.D.

Interviews: Pat McGuire

Brosseau, James, M.D.; Clark, Rodney, M.D.; Clifford, Tom; DeMers, Judy; Ebadi, Manuchair, PhD; Eelkema, Robert, M.D.; Eken, Randy; Fischer, Robert, PhD; Frank, Mary Margaret; Gilbertson, Roger, M.D.; Harwood, William, PhD; Hoeven, John, Gov.; Jensen, Clayton, M.D.; Johnson, George, M.D.;Johnson, Tom, M.D.; Knudson, Pam; Kupchella, Charles, PhD; Lutz, Dennis, M.D.; Miller, Brenda, M.D.; Mitchell, James, M.D.; Nordlie, Robert, PhD; Olafson, Richard, M.D.; Rothberg, Martin, M.D.; Saiki, Jack, M.D.; Samuelson, Al, M.D.; Smith, C. Milton, M.D.; Vennes, John, PhD; Wakefield, Mary, PhD; Wilsnack, Richard, PhD; Wilsnack, Sharon, PhD; Wilson, H. David, M.D.

APPENDIX II:

LISTING OF DEANS/CHAIRS/DIRECTORS 1905-2005
UNIVERSITY OF NORTH DAKOTA SCHOOL OF MEDICINE
AND HEALTH SCIENCES

Deans:

1905-1911	Melvin A. Brannon, M.S.
1911-1947	Harley E. French, M.D.
1947-1948	Alfred H. Lawton, M.D., Ph.D.
1948-1953	Wilbur F. Potter, M.D., Ph.D.
1953-1973	Theodore H. Harwood, M.D.
1973-1975	John W. Vennes, Ph.D. (Interim)
1975-1976	Richard E. Davis, M.D.
1976-1977	Neil J. Thomford, M.D. (Interim)
1977-1988	Tom M. Johnson, M.D.
1988-1993	Edwin C. James, M.D.
1993-1995	Clayton E. Jensen, M.D. (Interim)
1995-present	H. David Wilson, M.D.

Assistant / Associate Dean for Clinical Affairs:

	*A.F. Arnason
	William Goodall M.D.
	Clayton Jensen, M.D.
	David Theige, M.D. (Clinical Education)

Associate Dean for Academic Affairs:

1973-1977	John Vennes, Ph.D.
1977-1979	Vacant
1979-1989	Dwayne Ollerich, Ph.D.
1989-1992	John Vennes, Ph.D.
1992-1998	Thomas Norris, Ph.D.
1998-2002	Robert Rubeck, Ph.D.
2002-2004	Vacant
2004-present	Joshua Wynne, M.D.

Assistant / Associate Dean for Student Affairs:

1968-1977	*Wallace Nelson, M.D.
1977-1983	*Nancy Furstenburg, M.D.
1983-present	Judy DeMers, M.Ed.

Business Office - Director /
*Associate Dean for Fiscal Affairs:

	Donald Black
	Thomas Flanders
	John Reed
	Ray Peden
1983-1996	Randy Eken, MPA
1996-present	*Randy Eken, MPA

Campus Deans - Bismarck:

1973-1988	Keith Foster, M.D.
1988	Terry Dwelle, M.D. (Interim)
1988-1996	Paul Knudson, M.D.
1996-1999	Louise Murphy, M.D.
2000	Albert Samuelson, M.D. (Interim)
2000-present	Nicholas Neumann, M.D.

Campus Deans - Fargo:

1973-1975	Jack Harley, M.D.
1975-1978	Albert Liebman, M.D.
1978-1979	John Magness, M.D.
1979-1998	Richard Olafson, M.D.
1998-present	Bruce Pitts, M.D.

Bruce Pitts, M.D., Associate Dean and Director of
 Graduate Medical Education
William Newman, M.D., Assistant Dean for V.A. Affairs
Steffen Christensen, M.D., Assistant Dean for Students, S.E. Campus

Campus Deans - Grand Forks:

1973-1977	Ted Reiff, M.D.
1977-1979	Edmund Weis, M.D.
1979-1982	Robert Painter, M.D.
1982-1985	Garfield Pickell, M.D.
1985-1991	Lloyd Ralston, M.D.
1991-1997	Casey Ryan, M.D.
1997-2004	Eric Lunn, M.D.
2004-present	Jon Allen, M.D.

Campus Deans - Minot:

1973-1975	Charles Cargille, M.D.
1975-1976	David Holden, M.D.
1976-1982	W. B. Huntley, M.D.
1982-1987	Keith Folkert, M.D.
1987-1991	David Rinn, M.D.
1991-1992	Steven Eisenberg, M.D.
1992-1998	Warren Keene, M.D.
1998-present	Martin Rothberg, M.D.

Biochemistry & Molecular Biology Chairs:

1951-1983	Gene Cornatzer, M.D., Ph.D.
1983-2000	Robert Nordlie, Ph.D.
2000-2002	David Lambeth, Ph.D. (Interim)
2002-present	Gene Homandberg, Ph.D.

Anatomy & Cell Biology Chairs:

1907-1912	A. L. McDonald, M.D.
1912-1947	Harley French, M.D.
1947-1967	Chris Hamre, Ph.D.
1967-1972	Theodore Snook, Ph.D.
1972-1979	Dwayne Ollerich, Ph.D.
1979-1981	Jean Oberpriller, Ph.D. (Interim)
1981	Mark Olson, Ph.D.
1981-present	Edward Carlson, Ph.D.

Microbiology & Immunology Chairs:

1948-1962	Richard Marwin, Ph.D.
1962-1981	Robert Fischer, Ph.D.
1981-1989	John Vennes, Ph.D.
1989-1997	James Kelleher, Ph.D.
1997	Kevin Young, Ph.D. (Interim)
1997-present	Roger Melvold, Ph.D.

Pathology Chairs:

1936-1949	Arthur Saiki, M.D.
1949-1961	James Cardy, M.D.
1961-1984	Walter Wasdahl, M.D.
1984-1986	Patrick Ward, M.D.
1986-1988	Marvin Cooley, M.D. (Interim)
1988-2001	Roger Sopher, M.D.
2001-2002	Marvin Cooley, M.D. (Interim)
2002-present	Mary Ann Sens, M.D.

Community Medicine Chairs:

1968-2000	Robert Eelkema, M.D., DVM
2000-present	James Brosseau, M.D.

Pharmacology Chairs:

(Separate Department from 1977-1999)

1977-1985	James Boelkins, Ph.D.
1985-1986	John Belknap, Ph.D.
1986-1987	Ted Auyong, Ph.D.
1987-1988	Fathy Messiha, Ph.D.
1988-1989	John Vennes, Ph.D. (Interim)
1989-1997	David Hein, Ph.D.
1997-1999	Paul Epstein, Ph.D.
1999	Rejoined Physiology

Physiology Chairs:

(Now Pharmacology, Physiology & Therapeutics)

1924-1944	George Talbert, Ph.D.
1944-1946	Robert Brown, Ph.D.
1946-1947	Edward Ruud, M.D.
1947-1948	Alfred Lawton, M.D., Ph.D.
1948-1964	Wilbur Potter, M.D., Ph.D.
1964-1965	Stanley Brumleve, Ph.D.
1965-1972	Russell Wilson, M.D.
1972-1988	Stanley Brumleve, Ph.D.
1988-1990	Richard Rose, Ph.D.
1990-1992	Thomas Akers, Ph.D.
1992-1999	Willis Samson, Ph.D.
1999-2001	Manuchair Ebadi, Ph.D.
2001-2003	Edward Carlson, Ph.D. (Interim)
2003-present	Jonathon Geiger, Ph.D.

Medical Library Directors:

1949-1968	Loretta Swift
1968-1974	Melba Youngren
1974-1978	Charles Bandy
1978-1979	Lila Pedersen (Interim)
1979-1981	Edward D'Anna
1981-1982	Dwayne Ollerich (Acting)
1982-1991	David Biolard
1991-1992	Lila Pedersen (Interim
1992-present	Lila Pedersen

Physical Therapy Chairs:

1967-1993	Henry "Bud" Wessman, M.S., P.T., J.D.
1993-present	Thomas Mohr, Ph.D.

Occupational Therapy Chairs:

1976-Present	Sue McIntyre, M.S. (OTR)

Clinical Laboratory Science Directors:

1949-1978	Jean Saumur, M.S.
1978-2003	Wayne Bruce, Ph.D.
2003-present	Ruth Paur, M.S.

Athletic Training / Division of Sports Medicine:

1990-2003	James Rudd, LATC
2003-present	Steve Westereng, LATC

Division of Nursing (1947) /
College of Nursing (1959) Directors/Deans:

1949-1957	Breatrice Horsey
1958-1977	Margaret Heyse-Cory, M.S.
1977-1981	Elizabeth Zinser, Ph.D.
1981-1983	Judith Plawecki, Ph.D..
1983-1986	Inez Hinzverk, Ph.D.
1986-1995	Lois Merrill, Ph.D.
1995-2004	Elizabeth Nichols, Ph.D.
2004-present	Helen Melland, Ph.D. (Interim)

Medical Center Rehabilitation Hospital Director:

1965-1998	Donald Barcome, M.D.

Internal Medicine Chairs:

1973-1991	Reed Keller, M.D.
1991-1992	Robert Tight, M.D. (Interim)
1992-1995	Richard Gray, M.D.
1996	William Newman, M.D. (Interim)
1996-1998	Charles Foulks, M.D.
1998-2002	James Hanley, M.D.
2002-2003	Raymond Smego, M.D.
2003-present	William Newman, M.D.

Surgery Chairs:

1975-1979	Neil Thomford, M.D.
1980-1989	Edwin James, M.D.
1989-2005	David Antonenko, M.D.
2005-present	Robert P. Sticco, M.D.

Pediatrics Chairs:
1973-1976	Howard Joos, M.D.
1977-1982	Gerald Atwood, M.D.
1982-1987	William Rosen, M.D.
1987-2001	George Johnson, M.D.
2001-present	Stephen Tinguely, M.D.

Obstetrics & Gynecology Chairs:
1974-1975	Preston Dilts, M.D.
1976-1978	Michael Yannone, M.D.
1979-1983	Robert Carter, M.D.
1983-1986	Paul Bruns, M.D. (Interim)
1986-present	Dennis Lutz, M.D.

Neuroscience Chairs:
1973-1986	Lee Christoferson, Sr., M.D.
1986-1994	Richard Stadter, M.D.
1994-1996	Richard Olafson, M.D.
1996-present	James Mitchell, M.D.

Family Medicine Chairs:
1974-1979	Ed Donatelle, M.D.
1979-1980	Ralph Dunnigan, M.D.
1980-1986	Robin Staebler, M.D.
1986-1996	Clayton Jensen, M.D.
1996-2002	William Mann, M.D.
2002-present	Elizabeth Burns, M.D.

Radiology Chairs:
1978-1981	Richard Blank, M.D.
1981-1994	Norbert O'Keefe, M.D.
1994-1997	Mark Schneider, M.D.
1997	Department dissolved

Indians into Medicine (INMED) Directors:
1973-1974	Lois Steele
1974-1980	Bernard Kahrahrah
1980-1985	Lois Steele, M.D.
1986-1993	Gary Farris
1994-present	Eugene DeLorme, J.D.

Public Affairs Directors:
1975-1978	Mary Ann Meidinger
1978-1981	Judy Harris
1981-present	Pamela Knudson

Center for Rural Health Directors / *Associate Deans:
1980-1989	Kevin Fickenscher, M.D.
1989-1997	Jack Geller, Ph.D.
1997-2001	David Wilson, M.D. (Interim)
2001-2004	Mary Wakefield, Ph.D.
2004-present	*Mary Wakefield, Ph.D.

Biomedical Communications/
Information Resources Directors:
	Richard Winant
	Nancy Dunn
	Sue Caswell
1989-1998	Keith Stenehjem, Ed. D.
1998-present	Robert Rubeck, Ph.D.

Research and Program Development Associate Dean:
2001-present	Manuchair Ebadi, Ph.D.

Internal Medicine Residency Program Directors:
1975	Reed Keller, M.D.
1975-1979	Lawrence Pelletier, Jr., M.D.
1979-1980	Reed T. Keller, M.D.
1980-1981	Gary Lattimer, M.D. & Robert Tight, M.D.
1981-1982	Robert Tight, M.D.
1982-1991	Roland Nelson, M.D.
1991-1996	Anthony Gustafson, M.D.
1996-1997	Charles Foulks, M.D.
1997-2002	James Hanley, M.D.
2002-2003	Raymond Smego, Jr., M.D.
2003-2004	William Newman, M.D.
2004-present	David Theige, M.D.

Fargo Family Practice Residency Directors:
1975-1977	IngerLise Silbergleit, M.D.
1977-1987	Maurice Lindblom, M.D.
1987-1997	Richard Lenzmeier, M.D., Ronald Wiisanen, M.D.
1997-2002	John Baird, M.D.
2002	Program Closed

Grand Forks Family Practice Residency Directors:
1977-1980	James Hartley, M.D.
1980-1982	William Goodall, M.D.
1982	Jeffrey Mandel, M.D., Kevin Fickenscher, M.D.(Interim)
1982-1983	Garfield Pickell, M.D.
1983-1996	William Mann, M.D.
1996-2003	Larry Halvorson, M.D.
2003-present	Greg Greek, M.D.

Minot Family Practice Center Directors:
1975-1980	Robert Hankins, M.D.
1980-1981	Jim Ryan, M.D.
1981-1992	David Rinn, M.D.
1992-present	C. Milton Smith, M.D.

Bismarck Family Practice Center Directors:
1976-1984	William Buckingham, M.D.,
1984-1991	Ralph Dunnigan, M.D.
1991-1995	Russ Emery, M.D.
1995-present	Guy Tangedahl, M.D.

Center for Biomedical Research Director:
1981-present	Kap Lee, DVM

LEND/Distance Learning Directors:
1979-1989	John Vennes, Ph.D./ A. Wayne Bruce, Ph.D.
1989-present	A. Wayne Bruce, Ph.D.

Director (*Associate Dean), Office of Medical Education
1978-1980	Henry Slotnick, Ph.D.
1980-1988	*Dwayne Ollerich, Ph.D.
1988-2001	Henry Slotnick, Ph.D.
2001-present	*Richard Vari, Ph.D.

INDEX

A

Hoverson, Alyssa, 260*f*
Human Nutrition Research Laboratory, 100
Huntley, Duke, 179-180

I

Indians Into Medicine (INMED), 191-197, 194*f*
influenza epidemic, during World War I, 45-46
Innovis Health System, 176
internal medicine residency, 122, 179, 243
International Research Group on Gender and Alcohol
        (IRGGA), 219
Ireland, Guy and Bertha, 99
Ireland Research Laboratory, 99

J

Jackson, Andrew, 14
Jacobson, Bob, 202
James, Edwin, 182-183, 203-210, 203*f*, 215*f*
James, Frank, 22
James, Jesse, 22
Jayne, William, 15
Jensen, Clayton, 238*f*
    career of, 213-214
    on Cornatzer, 98
    on Ederstrom, 79-80
    on family practice, 135
    as interim dean, 214-215
    on James, 210
    on Johnson, Tom, 153
    and Minot AHEC, 182-183
    politics and, 241
    on Potter, 77
    on teaching, 169-170
    on Vennes, 147
Johnson, George
    on becoming a Dr., 178-179
    on Cornatzer, 98
    on Fargo opposition, 130
    Hamre and, 103-104
    on Harwood, 93
    on Keller, 210-211, 212-213
    liver studied by, 98-99
    medical school supported by, 176
    in third year repatriation, 158
Johnson, Lavonne, 203
Johnson, Robert, 212
Johnson, Tom, 150-163, 152*f*, 154*f*, 184*f*
    and Grand Forks physicians, 187-188
    on James, 203
    on Keller, 211, 212
    legacy of, 190-191
    politics and, 240-241
Johnson's Flub, 103
Joos, Howard, 148
Jordheim, Robert, 84, 176, 190

K

Karl Christian World Biomedical Information Research Center,
        198*f*-199*f*, 206
Keller, Reed, 148, 158, 210-213, 210*f*
Ketterling, Rhonda, 228, 250, 263

Kildahl, Johanna, 29, 29*f*
Kingman, Harry, 195-196
Klakeg, Clay, 52, 75, 123
Kling, Bob, 76
Kloster, Ron, 158
Knoppala, Lydia, 61
Knudson, Pamela, 150
Knull, Harvey, 214
Koch, Ken, 114
Koch, Robert, 15, 25
Kupchella, Charles, 235, 237, 238, 261, 265

L

Lakota Oglala Sioux, 194*f*
land, railroad sales of, 19
Landry, L. H., 14-15
Langer, William, 71, 72
Larson, Leonard, 171
Larson, Richard, 123, 179-180, 196-197, 267
Lawton, Alfred, 74*f*, 76
Lawton, Ben, 217
legislature, state
    dean of medical school and, 240-243, 259-261
    funds voted by, 156-163
    and medical school expansion, 83-86, 123-124, 127-128
    medical school opposed in, 259
Leigh, Jack, 147
Leigh, Jim, 95
Leigh, Ralph E., 73-74, 73*f*, 95
Leigh, Richard, 146-147
Leonard, Mrs. W. K., 17
Lewis, Merriwether, heroic medicine used by, 14
library, 83, 115*f*
Lindelow, Jill, 244*f*, 247*f*
Lipmann, Fritz, 99
Lister, Joseph, 15
Litten, C. Warner, 131, 175-176
Little Big Horn, 195
Lodmell, Lenier A., 57*f*
Longie, Kellie, 251*f*
Longie, Kevin, 251*f*
Lowe, Frank, 100, 106-107
Luger, Richard, 194
Lutz, Dennis, 179, 182*f*, 184-186, 224

M

Maginn, Richard J., 57*f*
Magness, John, 158
Magnin, George, 217
Mahoney, James, 53, 54, 86-87, 206, 254
Mandan tribe, smallpox epidemic among, 16
Manning, Anselm, 22
Marwin, Richard, 80-83
maternity home, 26-27
Mathys, Della, 57*f*
May, Dr., 19-20
Mayo Clinic, Fargo Clinic and, 175
McCann, LaVaun, 247*f*
McCann, Michelle, 247*f*
McCannel Hall, 112-113, 201
McCullen, Bill, 162

McDonald, Archie L., 29, 34
McGuire, Patrick, 6, 271
McIntyre, Donald, 77, 102, 104, 186
McVey, Frank, 44
Med Science North, 202
Med Science South, 202
MEDEX program, 125, 126
Medical Affairs Committee (MAC), 133
medical library, 83, 115*f*
medical licenses
    refusal of applications, 34-35
    standards for, 15, 23-24
medical park
    rehabilitation center at, 113-115
    United Hospital at, 202
Medical Practice Act, 24, 46
medical schools
    Carnegie Foundation survey of, 33
    Nineteenth century, 14-15
    standardization in, 27
    third-year transfers to, 138-139, 150, 155-156
    transfers to, 43, 71, 119-120, 122-123, 130-131
    two-year, 27
    collapse of, 122-123
Medical Science Building, 201
Medicare, four-year medical schools and, 111
medicine
    future of, 249, 267
    golden age of, 250
    in Nineteenth century, 13-14
    present state of, 251, 266-267
    as profession, 226-227
    Romanticism and, 13
    specialization of, 79, 121-122
    World War II advances in, 75
Menninger Clinic, 174
MeritCare Health System, 176, 243
Merrifield, Webster, 11, 26
Michigan State University, 136, 150
microPET, 237
military doctors, 16-19
mill levy, 3, 75-76, 84, 123-124
Miller, Brenda, 240, 246*f*, 263
Miller, Clel, 22
Miller, Jessica, 246*f*
Minnesota, third-year transfers to, 138-139, 150, 155-156, 167-168
Minot, AHEC center in, 179-186, 180*f*
Mitchell, James, 216-217, 237*f*, 238, 239-240
Moodie, Thomas, 71
Moran, Walter H., 57*f*

N

National Institutes of Health
    Fischer's work with, 82
    INMED and, 191-193
National Resource Center on Native American Aging, 257-258
Native Americans, 16, 184, 214, 257-258
    See also Indians Into Medicine
Nelson, Wallace, 109, 119-120, 121*f*, 133
neurology department, 83
Neuropsychiatric Research Institute (NRI), 135, 215-219

neuroscience department, 214, 216
New Science Building, 75, 83
Newman, William, 123, 189, 202, 211
Nineteenth century, 13-15
Nonpartisan League, 71
Nordlie, Robert, 96*f*, 97-98, 97*f*, 99, 160, 231
Norris, Tom, 214
North Dakota. *See also* Dakota Territory
    need for doctors in, 72-73, 84-85, 249-250
    physician standards of, 15, 23-24
    public support in, 6
    Vennes's return to, 6
North Dakota Department of Health, 46-47
"North Dakota Health Manpower" (Dunn), 131-132
North Dakota Medical Association
    approval of, 130, 132
    expansion analysis and, 126
    Vennes and, 149
"North Dakota Medicine" (Grassick), 17
North Dakota State Medical Center Rehabilitation Unit, 112-115
Northern Plains, epidemic on, 16
Northwest Area Foundation, 214
nursing program, 44-45
Nutzman, C. L., 57*f*

O

OB-GYN residency, 184-186, 190
Oberpriller, Jean, 160
Oberpriller, John, 160
Odegard, John, 127, 136
Oftedahl, Sverre, 28
Olafson, Richard, 176*f*
    Campos and, 61
    on Cardy, 160
    Fargo AHEC under, 176-179
    on Fargo opposition to expansion, 134
    on Hamre, 102
    on hospital relationships, 168
    on Johnson, 157-159
    on research, 240
    on Wilson, 224
"Old Practitioner" license, 24
Olson, Ole, 71
Olson, Stanley, 158, 162
Opheim, Bertha, 77
orthotics, 113

P

Page, John A., 74, 77, 82*f*
Painter, Robert, 188
Pap test, 59, 120-121
Papanicolaou, George, 59, 120
parent-teacher organization, 155
"Parkinson's Disease" (Ebadi and Pfeiffer), 237
Parnas, Laura, 225*f*
Pasteur, Louis, 15
pathology, 58-59, 62-63
pathology residency, 189
patients
    in medical school curriculum, 232-234
    in medicine, 251-253

Sinner, George, 129
Sisters of St. Joseph, 202
Skjei, Donald, 72, 83
Slotnick, Hank, 153, 191
smallpox, epidemic of, among Mandan tribe, 16
Smith, C. Milton, 182-184
Smith, Elizabeth, 57*f*
Snook, Ted, 101-102, 102*f*, 104-106
Snook Reticulum, 104
Snyder, Fred, 140*f*-141*f*
Sobolik, Bonnie, 207
Somji, Seema, 233*f*
Sommerness, Martin D., 83
Sopher, Roger, 206, 233, 234, 235
sources, 268-270
Starcher, George, 79, 106-107, 124
State Board of Medical Examiners, 24-25, 28, 34-35
state legislature
     dean of medical school and, 240-243, 259-261
     funds voted by, 156-163
     and medical school expansion, 83-86, 123-124, 127-128
     medical school opposed in, 259
State Medical Center, 75
State Public Health Department, 29-30
Steele, Lois, 191*f*, 194-195
Stiles, Bill, 22
Streibel, Bryce, 127-128, 130
Strinden, Dean
     on admission to medical school, 261
     in alumni fundraising, 207
     on being a doctor, 168
     on French, 53, 54
     on "golden age of medicine," 250
     medical school supported by, 134
     on transferring, 162-163
     on Williston clinic, 110
Strinden, Earl, 127*f*
     alumni fundraising by, 207
     on doctors' role in expansion, 139
     in expansion, 128
     on Johnson, Tom, 150
     medical school supported by, 161-162
     on Saiki, 65
Student Army Training Corps, 45, 56
Superintendent of Public Health, French as, 46
surgery residency, 203
Swenson, Wayne, 130-131, 172, 204, 217, 254
Swift, Loretta, 115*f*

T

Talbert, George, 56, 56*f*, 57*f*, 58
Taylor, John, 29-30
teaching, 169-170
telemedicine, 217
Theige, David, 155, 158, 168, 211, 213, 234
third year repatriation, 155-163
Thomford, Neil, 148, 149-150, 149*f*, 151-152
Thorsgaard, Enoch, 114
Thorson, Glenn, 158
Tinglestad, Jon, 126, 157, 211
tonsilitis, at Fort Totten, 18
Townsley, Mabel, 40-41. *See also* French, Mabel

Tribal Advisory Board, 195
Trinity Health Systems, 180-181, 183
Tscheider, Richard, 173, 242
tuberculosis
     in milk supplies, 25
     Saiki's treatment for, 64-65
Tuck (dog), 52
tuition, early rates of, 29
2-1-1 plan
     approval of, 138-139
     failure of, 167-168
     overturning, 150, 155-163
Two Bears, Lindsey, 192*f*
typhoid epidemic, in Grand Forks, 25

U

Unimed, 180
United Hospital, 188
     rehabilitation center at, 113-114
     in St. Michael's building, 201-202
University of North Dakota
     biology at, 26
     student military drills at, 18*f*
University of North Dakota School of Medical Technology, 83
University of North Dakota School of Medicine and
          Health Sciences
     accreditation of, 34, 76, 86
          withdrawn, 49, 72
     admissions committee of, 60
     anatomy curriculum of, 29
     chairs of, 272-274
     class of 1906, 30*f*-31*f*
     class of 1910, 42*f*-43*f*
     creation of, 26-27
     deans of, 272-274
     department chairs at, 148
     directors of, 272-274
     economic impact of, 264-265
     enrollment of
          under French, 47
          under Harwood, 108
     establishment of, and public health, 23
     first dean of, 23
     flood damage to, 266*f*
     as four-year institution
          French on, 69-71, 72-73, 74
          Harwood on, 106-111, 123
          Medical Association approval of, 130, 132
          opposition to, 130-131, 134-136
          residency programs and, 138
          state legislature and, 83-86, 123-124, 127-128
     under French, 41-56
     under Harwood, 87, 91-95
     under James, 203-210
     under Johnson, Tom, 150-163
     under Lawton, 76
     mission of, 1-4
     modernizing, 79-83
     opening of, 27
     under Potter, 76-87
     rehabilitation department of, 107-108, 113
     renaming of, 225-226

f denotes photo caption